PHILOSOPHY, SCIENCE, AND KNOWLEDGE

CHRISTIAN CULTURE AND PHILOSOPHY SERIES

GENERAL EDITORS
DONALD A. GALLAGHER, PH.D. AND
IDELLA J. GALLAGHER, PH.D.
BOSTON COLLEGE

OTHER BOOKS IN THE SERIES

The Scientific Art of Logic by Edward D. Simmons, Ph.D.
Natural Theology by James Anderson, Ph.D.
Cosmology: Philosophical & Scientific by Leo Foley, S.M.
An Elementary Christian Metaphysics by Joseph Owens, C.SS.R.
Aquinas' Search for Wisdom by Vernon J. Bourke, Ph.D.
God & the Permission of Evil by Jacques Maritain
The Logic of Scientific Inquiry by Paul Durbin, O.P. (forthcoming)

The colophon for the CHRISTIAN CULTURE AND PHILOSOPHY SERIES
consists of the Greek letters x and p, symbolizing Christianity, embraced
by C, a variant of Σ, representing the Greek word *sophia*.

PHILOSOPHY, SCIENCE, and KNOWLEDGE

WILLIAM E. CARLO
Professor of Philosophy, Boston College

THE BRUCE PUBLISHING COMPANY/MILWAUKEE

Also by William Carlo
The Ultimate Reducibility of Essence to Existence in Existential Metaphysics

Library of Congress Catalog Card Number: 67–19218

IN MEMORIAM
ERNST SCHARRER, M.D., PH.D.
PHYSICIAN, SCIENTIST, SCHOLAR

FOREWORD

THE sensitive problem of introducing college students to philosophy has been accomplished in a number of ways. The history of Greek philosohy has been one popular way, the thesis being that to relive the historical origins of the science of philosophy is a good way to introduce it to the individual.

Another popular way of introducing philosophy is through logic. In many institutions the first course in the philosophy department is logic. It sets the stage for philosophy as a rigorous discipline characterized by the patterns and laws of abstract thinking.

Both approaches have been successful in the hands of expert practitioners who manage to supply for the deficiencies of the methods with seasoned experience or youthful enthusiasm.

Professor Carlo has chosen to introduce philosophy by way of its relation to science and the other forms of knowledge. The high school student comes to college with a scientific sophistication unknown in previous generations, and it is against this background of science that the nature and integrative functions of philosophy in a university curriculum can be described and explained. This is the particular value of Part Two of the present work with its juxtaposition of scientific theory and the appropriate articulating philosophical doctrine. Both are explained by the mutual contrast.

Today, knowledge is not merely power. It is the very condition of freedom from the tyranny of nature and man. Compared to his fellows of past centuries, contemporary man is in an enviable position. He has reduced poverty, want, and fear to a level previously unknown in human history, a spotty story relieved by few idyllic interludes. He has more control over his economic, political, and cultural destiny — and greater participation in the instruments of its achievement than was possible in any other age. At no time has western man had more to eat and drink, been better clothed and housed, been able to travel fantastic distances at faster speeds; never have so many been so educated to such a point of refinement.

These superlative advantages of contemporary western man have been largely the fruits of technology, the application of the human knowledges and particularly the sciences. Mathematics, physics, chemistry, biology, economics, politics, psychology, sociology, education, engineering, law, medicine, and art have been the instruments that have transformed man from a beast of burden, a hewer of wood and drawer of water, from the slave of nature to the master of his environment. He now has the ability to plan, control, and transform an environment plastic and yielding to his touch.

Even those parts of the world which have not as yet shared so completely in this radical transformation and evolution of the very social fabric of human life, e.g., the underdeveloped countries, have made it clear that, although they have much to criticize about western culture, they are of one mind regarding its scientific and industrial capabilities and the material wealth and improved standard of living which flow from them.

Despite such largesse, however, within these self-same knowledges lie the seeds of the anxiety of contemporary man. The sciences can be loyal children or an unruly offspring turning on the society which nurtured them. The western nations are huddled in terror under the huge umbrella-like cloud of Hiroshima and Nagasaki. In similar ways the other sciences and knowledges can be misused. Physics and engineering have transported men farther and faster but have also contributed to the jamming of the city's streets and the pollution of its air and water. Sociological techniques are inadequate to brake the accelerating growth of crime. These abuses need not be catalogued here. Our author has done so in detail.

So imminent and serious are the consequences of the misuse of science that the situation is reflected in contemporary philosophy. Logical Positivism which spread the gospel of science as the ultimate human blessing has been supplanted by Existentialism which in its concern for the human person has expressed a hostile, and at times virulent, reaction to science. This fear of the consequences of scientific advances and their military and destructive potential has caused contemporary philosophers to question the beneficent nature of science as a knowledge and to substitute an irrational approach to the concrete individual of human experience.

Jean-Paul Sartre, for example, calls science "vicious" because scientific objectivity demands a certain detachment in order to know the object in a rational way. But since things are pure concrete existents, according to Sartre, with no essences or natures to know in theoretical fashion, the only approach to such a reality is to jump in and become involved — to do something by a practical confrontation. But scientific objectivity and centrality militates against such a commitment and involvement which is actually an irrational substitute for the rationality of scientific method and knowledge.

It is at precisely this point that philosophy can come to the aid of science. Science can remain mute in the face of such charges and let its works speak for itself — but the specter of the hydrogen bomb looms large on the horizon of the "everyman view" of science. Scientists in their professional capacities generally do not talk to each other about the nature of science as a knowledge. They discuss their scientific work. It is to philosophy that we must turn if we are to understand the nature of science, to evaluate its benefits, and mark its limitations. This has been one of the main concerns of our author.

Is science by itself enough for the "Good Life" and the "Good Society"? Until very recently, from the Logical Positivist and many other thinkers of our age, a simple affirmative answer would have been forthcoming. Nothing else, certainly not philosophy, was needed. To the Logical Positivist, philosophy is merely the discussion of problems science has not yet managed to solve. Once science turns its full attention to the formulation and solution of such problems, then philosophy vanishes. Philosophy is constantly retreating before the progressive advance of natural science which claims to be the only knowledge worthy of the name "science."

Philosophy, however, as Professor Carlo maintains, is a special discipline with a special method of its own. Even the question "What is Science?" is a philosophical question. The scientist to do his proper work needs not ask such a question.

Each of the sciences and human knowledges has its own object, method, and mode of procedure and no science can do the work of another. Most of the errors in the history of ideas comes from a kind of intellectual imperialism. A man of one knowledge tries to make it do the work of other knowledges. He uses it to deal with problems which are completely outside of its field of competency. The explanation and correction of such a situation forms the bulk of our author's work and I cannot do better than to refer you to it.

The Christian commitment can provide the necessary dynamism for the reconstruction of the social fabric but it needs a guide, a blueprint for the utilization of available accumulated knowledge, which it must receive from some theoretical knowledge, from theology directly and immediately, from philosophy indirectly. A Christian recognition

of the dignity of man, for example, cannot solve the delicate problems
of the freedom of the individual versus the civil or religious authority
of the society in which he finds his perfection and fulfillment. Philosophy, as our author demonstrates, can supply such guidance.

VERY REVEREND MICHAEL P. WALSH, S.J.
President, Boston College

PREFACE

We are interested in an *Introduction to Philosophy* which will be more than simply an introduction to the history of philosophy beginning with Greek thought. As an introduction to philosophy, Greek philosophy seems to be rather impoverished. The problems of Greek philosophy are much more comprehensible when seen in retrospect from the perspective of the mature philosophical doctrines into which they developed in medieval and modern philosophy. The doctrines of the one and the many or of the soul make more sense when we come to them after seeing theories in their maturity in the later medieval synthesis. On the other hand, we do not think that an *Introduction to Philosophy* should be simply a collection of problems, a problematic. These give the flavor of philosophical thinking without its over-all *scientific structure*.

We are primarily interested in a *synthetic* introduction which combines the virtues of the historical and systematic approaches by giving a taste of the logical rigor and argumentative strength as well as the all-encompassing scope and structure of philosophy.

In an age of science one of the most important problems for the philosopher is the relation of philosophy to science. The examination of this problem provides a stimulating channel of communication between these two branches of human knowledge. We have attempted to capitalize on the popular interest in science which at times amounts to awe.

The contemporary college student comes from high school with a scientific sophistication. He now studies in high school material which was college and even graduate school work a few decades ago. This knowledge can serve as a background for showing what philosophy is by distinguishing it precisely from science.

One of the unforgivable deficiencies in an introduction to philosophy is dullness. The style and treatment which is suitable for scholars who bring their own professional interest to philosophy is not the one to communicate the natural interest and excitement of philosophy to the neophyte.

In the teaching of undergraduate philosophy I think the pedagogical emphasis should be systematic. We do have a cohesive and consistent philosophy built up over the centuries and we should take advantage of this synthesis. An historical perspective showing how a doctrine developed and modified can be useful, but it is no substitute for the systematic approach on the undergraduate level. The historical approach is particularly suited for the graduate program in philosophy. The best way to become a philosopher is still by following a first-rate thinker through the windings of his thought, a learning by imitation or example. But a teacher should attempt to distill and crystallize certain recurrent themes in the history of philosophy and present them in an organized, systematic, digestible form, endeavoring to efface himself before his material but being aware at the same time that philosophy exists only in minds and not in books and it is through his rethinking that the student is meeting philosophy for the first time.

An introduction to philosophy should include logic and so we have added an appendix of a four to six week survey of the major elements of logic. It is very easy for students to conceive of philosophy as emotive thinking, the felicitous articulation of the first thing that comes into the mind. A study of logic shows that thinking has structure and order. There are necessary patterns to thinking. There are actual laws of thought. This experience can help a student to respect critical, rigorous scientific expression. The student should realize that thinking is not the expression of any chance thought or random whim. It is stiffened by the iron of an intellectual discipline. It has a necessity and order about it. Thinking is governed by certain laws. The philosopher is thinking both for himself and all mankind. This is not a vocation of airy speculation.

Also a kind of geography of knowledge mapping out the basic features of sensation, image, and concept and their relation to the intelligible structure of the thing, the principle of organization or form, would seem to be as adequate an introduction to logic and philosophy as the customary early Greek philosophy.

All parts of the volume are not of equal importance in a first reading or in an elementary introduction. Part I, Chapter III, sections 4–9 are meant for collateral reading rather than class discussion. They serve to point up the importance of such an effort and the extreme sophistication of the divisions discussed. But they are not strictly necessary to the development of the basic argumentation of Part I, Chapter III, the Classification of the Sciences. We may further suggest that the material of Part I, chapters II and III in conjunction with Part II, chapters I through VI is adaptable for use as a basic one-semester Philosophy of Science course.

This is an introduction to philosophy; it is not a survey of all the philosophical sciences and their problems. Our aims are more modest. We hope to outline the structure of philosophy and catch its flavor through some analyses of typical problems, e.g., politics, ethics, and esthetics. If the student does come to see what it is all about we shall be satisfied. He will still, we expect, have other courses of the philosophical program ahead of him. Philosophy cannot be learned in one course. It is the occupation of a lifetime and this is only to make a beginning.

ACKNOWLEDGMENTS

I am indebted for so much to so many that any list of acknowledgements must of necessity be incomplete. I would like, however, to express my gratitude to Dr. Ernst Scharrer, formerly chairman of the Department of Anatomy at the Albert Einstein College of Medicine of Yeshiva University, who in his wisdom and charity gave a philosopher the opportunity to learn biology and to participate in experimentation at the level of original research; to the United States Department of Health, Education and Welfare, for a Public Health Fellowship in the Interdisciplinary Program in the Basic Sciences; to Professor Gilbert Ryle and A. C. Crombie of Oxford University, for the opportunity to teach and tutor in the History and Philosophy of Science Program at Oxford; to my general editors, Drs. Donald and Idella Gallagher, for their warm encouragement and meticulous cooperation; to Mr. William May, of the Bruce Publishing Company for his thoroughly professional help and criticism which made this a better book than it would have been; to Francis Gendreau without whose capable help, technically and philosophically, this book could not have been completed as soon as it was; to Professor Don Traub of Anna Marie College and Rev. Charles Toomey, S.J. of Boston College who carefully read the entire manuscript and improved it by their suggestions and corrections. I would also like to thank Miss Jean McCarthy, secretary of the Department of Philosophy for her cheerful and capable help at all stages of the manuscript; and to Thomas Wall, Karin Waugh, George Collins, George Commenator, John McGinley and Frank Gammon for their aid in proofreading the galleys. My special gratitude goes to the Reverend John R. Willis, S.J., Dean of the School of Arts and Sciences, and to the Rev. Joseph Flanagan, S.J., chairman of the Department of Philosophy for their interest and encouragement of research in general and the help and special considerations on their part which made this volume possible. Finally I would like to thank the Very Reverend Michael P. Walsh, President of Boston College, and a prominent scientist in his own right, for his splendid Foreword.

In conclusion, we would like to express gratitude to the following for allowing us to reprint copyright material:

Cambridge University Press, for citations from William Dampier's *History of Science;*

Columbia University Press, for citations from George Gaylord Simpson's *The Major Features of Evolution;*

Curtis, Brown, Ltd., for citations from Morton White's *The Age of Analysis;*

Harcourt, Brace, and World, for citations from C. S. Lewis' *The World's Last Night;*

P. J. Kenedy and Sons, for citations from Charles Journet's *The Meaning of Evil;*

Oxford University Press, for citations from William Kneale's *Probability and Induction,* and from A. C. Crombie's *Grosseteste and Experimental Science;*

Prentice-Hall, Inc., for citations from Carl P. Swanson's *The Cell,* and from George Pitcher's *The Philosophy of Wittgenstein;*

Sheed & Ward, Inc., for citations from Charles Journet's *The Church of the Word Incarnate;*

Viking Press, for citations from George Gamow's *The Creation of the Universe.*

CONTENTS

PHILOSOPHY, SCIENCE, AND KNOWLEDGE

PART ONE

LOCATION OF PHILOSOPHY
AMONG THE KNOWLEDGES

THIS is an era of intense intellectual activity. Countless human beings are bringing all their mental energies to bear on the mysterious universe that confronts them. Before their insistent inquiry and persuasive art the universe is yielding its secrets. So richly rewarding have been the fruits of this investigation and of such mountainous proportions, that the mind seeking nourishment might well perish of indigestion. We have learned so much in so brief a period that we have been unable to appreciate its total significance. We have cut up an ordered and unified world into many little pieces, the better to examine each in scientific isolation, but we no longer are capable of putting it back together again. In a Humpty-Dumpty world, the modern thinker, like all the king's men, finds it easier to analyze than to synthesize.

As a result, the tremendous wealth of details accumulated by modern scientific techniques is in large measure useless because it lacks a synthesis in which it can be located and correlated, i.e., a philosophy. One would barely suspect that the different sciences are speaking of the same world, their languages are so different. This mutual unintelligibility and incommunicability must be dissolved if full use is to be made of our intellectual work, and if the significant achievements of one body of knowledge are to be made available for the profit of all the

1

others. The integration of all the human knowledges, both sciences and arts, is, as we shall see, one of the fundamental roles of philosophy.

Even a cursory examination will reveal that many of the current dangers to the community of nations arise from ideas dominant in the various knowledges. In fact, we might go so far as to say that the lack of self-awareness, the absence of self-recognition on the part of the sciences, has made them actually dangerous to human freedom, whereas they should be the guardians of our freedoms. For it is through knowledge that freedom is to be attained. "You shall know the truth and the truth shall make you free."[1]

By the use of their intelligence men have freed themselves in great measure from the first tyranny, the tyranny of brute nature and the despotism of their fellowmen. All the types of human knowledge have contributed to this advance from barbarism to culture. The recognized instruments of this transformation have been for the most part mathematics, physics, chemistry, biology, psychology, education, sociology, economics, and politics. Our debt to them is immeasurable. They have transformed the slave into the master and given him almost infinite aspirations and ambitions. But it is in precisely these instruments, the sciences, which have molded modern life, that we see a certain fundamental pattern, frightening but intelligible.

To recognize our vulnerability, we have only to visualize the future development of physics. In addition to bestowing benefits, it has inflicted certain evils. Man has not learned the secret of matter, but he has learned the secret of the destruction of matter. The day may come when the person who is able to wire the planet can explode it. Modern science is like the baby who, tugging at the tablecloth, is stunned and frightened to find his own strength pulling the world down upon his head.

This has been the era of mathematical physics. Tomorrow will be the era of biochemistry. Just as the union of mathematics and physics gave us the modern industrial age, so the union of chemistry and biology will result in a science that may utterly transform the social fabric as we know it. The silent assault of bacteriological warfare will be more terrifying than atomic blasts. What effect will the prediction and determination of the sexes before birth have on the existing social structure, for instance, of the family? Genetic mutation could supply the foundation for an occupational breeding. Human beings may be determined before birth to be hewers of wood and drawers of water, perfectly

---

[1] Cf. Mortimer Adler, *The Conditions of Philosophy* (New York: Athenaeum, 1965), pp. 20–49.

modified for their life's work. In fact, the production of life itself on the laboratory table is not inconceivable. What totalitarianism is so dangerous to human freedom as this type of regimentation?

The same dangers to freedom present in politics, economics, and science are also to be found in the fields of psychology, education, and sociology. One dangerous area is that of testing intelligence and aptitude. From a purely psychological standpoint, such tests do not do what they claim. A test, of course, tests only knowledge, not intelligence. Thus intelligence tests actually reduce themselves to some elementary knowledge common to all, elementary English and basic mathematics, in the attempt to eliminate the advantages of education and special training. The anomaly which the aptitude test presents is that it claims to test something which does not exist, but could exist, an aptitude. What it is actually testing is knowledge and experience. A real danger to freedom lurks here. Some ardent proponents of such tests seek to determine human lives on the basis of these devices. They would make auto mechanics of boys who could be surgeons. Human capacities are almost unlimited; the normal human being can become almost anything, given sufficient incentive. These tests may be handy ways of controlling large groups of people, the army for example, but they are not reliable enough for individual evaluation. Yet the layman and the uninitiated attribute to them an infallibility which professional psychologists do not disown, but rather foster. All too recently for many educators, the school was not an institution for the communication of knowledge, but for equipping the student for life, meaning a job. Any form of liberal education for the masses had to be subordinated to showing them how to make a living! Only the few aristocratic intellects should have the cultural courses that produce free men. There are some who would make the majority of the human race slaves to the economic needs of mankind.

A corollary of this notion of the school is its role as an *adjustatorium*. Its purpose is to adjust. Such educators may not be quite sure what they are adjusting, but, at any rate, they adjust. They train character. They develop personality — all without knowing, much less agreeing on, what character is, or what personality might be.

The head of the education department of a large university was recently quoted to the effect that his university was reducing its methods courses, and adding more liberal arts courses to the curriculum in order to achieve a better balance. He is even considering the advisability of lessening the hours of practice teaching demanded. Some professional educators look on this as an improvement. But who was responsible in the first place for a curriculum stretched and distended by methods courses?[2] They do not realize that they are returning to something most people were aware of long ago. To them it is a new conclusion scientifically established by the science of education!

The frightening thing about all this is that their every whim, sometimes with little actual scientific basis, can determine the indoctrination of tens of thousands of teachers — and then the experiment devolves upon millions of malleable human beings. What sort of freedom is compatible with the role of the guinea pig?

Another example is the infant science of psychoanalysis. Handled properly, it is a useful aid to medicine. But there are great dangers inherent in the way some practitioners use it, especially in the theory that underlies certain of its techniques. One of the needs of modern psychoanalysis is a shortened form of analysis, in order that it may be more universally applied. In fact, there is a large business organization which demands a certain type of psychoanalytic analysis, under the name of psychiatry, of course, and it is the aim of some to have every single individual tested for the good of the business, the country, and themselves as well. It seems logical, for are they not the scientists of the mind? Therefore, they are the ones to explain the laws of the mind and personality. Consider the dangers inherent in much of modern psychoanalytic theory. Imagine the day when the campaigner for public office must undergo a psychoanalytic evaluation![3]

The diabolical part of all this is that you are told you do the things you do without being aware of the real reason for doing them. Your action is really determined by the unconscious, or at least, the subconscious. You are told, for example, that you do something because of an unholy love for your mother. How do you answer such a charge? You are not supposed to know it. Only *they* know it. But who will analyze the analyst? If an analyst is obsessed by sex, then he is going to see a sex association in your every image, even the church spire. Is there any political tyranny as ghastly as this tyranny of the mind and heart?

We are not asserting that all these evils exist today. We are not asserting that they are pure evils unmixed with any good. What we are asserting is that if the various knowledges are left to go their own way without any sort of theological and philosophical guidance, then the day may come when the human being, trapped Frankenstein-like by the monstrous offspring of his own intelligence, will look up at the

---

[2] Cf. Arthur E. Bestor, *Educational Wastelands* (Urbana: The University of Illinois Press, 1953), pp. 137–147.

[3] Cf. T. Reik, *Listening With the Third Ear* (New York: Grove Press, 1948).

stars from out of his physical, mental, and moral cage, and curse the day he was born. Is this the legacy of the human race? It may well be. It is almost a fact in some parts of the globe. Why should such dangers exist? What do we know about the structure of the human mind and its knowledges which would free us from the tyranny that they can exert over us? An analysis of the nature of knowledge, the nature of science, and the limitations of the specific knowledges is absolutely necessary if man is to use them for his good rather than for his destruction. Will men be masters or slaves? In order to answer some of these eminently vital problems facing the human race, we undertake this analysis of the nature of knowledge and the function of the different types of knowledges, not only to understand what science is, but most important of all, to preserve our human freedom.

Before we attempt to construct a philosophy we should be clear on the place it occupies relative to the other sciences, arts, and human knowledges. Such a perspective enables us to trace the ramifications of general philosophical principles through the concrete instances which embody them.

Likewise, some review of the general geography of knowledge, at least the distinction between imagination and conceptualization, is necessary. Images are only of secondary importance in philosophy and we should recognize that only conceptual thinking is proper to philosophy. Philosophical conceptions are rooted in sensory knowledge, but by the time they are crystallized and formulated in an artificial scientific fashion, they seem to have broken the umbilical cord and bear little trace of their humble origin. This latter will be our starting point.

CHAPTER I. / THE GEOGRAPHY
OF KNOWLEDGE

AT THE ROOT of any discussion of human knowing lies one very basic fact which can be verified by an inward glance at our own knowing operations. We have within ourselves a whole universe of knowledge. As I mention the Empire State Building, something rises to the forefront of your consciousness. You give birth, in a strict biological sense, to something within your mind. The Empire State Building is in some way within you, is part of you. You contain it with ease. That huge mass of concrete and steel seems to fit easily within the narrow circumference of the human cranium, a bone structure which materially could not contain a good-sized lamp. Yet the Empire State Building, as known, does not take up any more "room" than your knowledge of a fly. These mental entities are very real things. You grow them within you the way you grow teeth in your jaw, nails on your fingers, and hair on your head. This is the question to ask of the mystery of knowledge: How do we get things inside us and make them part of ourselves? How do we explain the transformation of huge masses of bulk and weight over tremendous distances? You have within you, as I remind you, the entire country in which we live, the whole of the planet on which we walk, the fantastic reaches of the solar system. What goes on behind your eyes as you read these words? How explain that psychic explosion which we call consciousness, passed in speech from human to human like fire from a torch?

§ 1. THE SENSATION

We begin with the Common Sense knowledge from which all science must start and to which it must return, reflectively, in order to *perfect* knowledge. At this point it is not necessary to explore the reasons for affirming that all knowledge begins with being or that the "thing" is first in the process of knowing. Restricting ourselves to Common Sense knowledge, a knowledge of effects, results, and conclusions, as opposed to scientific knowledge which is characterized by a more basic penetration of reality to the level of causal wellsprings of activity, how do we get something, a rose, for example, into our own substance? No single passageway of bodily consciousness can receive the rose as a whole. The five basic corridors of sensory knowledge have their own proper aspect of the thing known. We cannot taste the red, nor hear the sweet. We cannot see the loud, nor touch the sour. It is impossible to hear dimensions. Each sense is occupied with its own proper object, although there may be some secondary concern with the object of another sense. Sight, for instance, is interested primarily in color, but color spread out in space involves a knowledge of dimension. Hence, although dimension is properly the concern of the sense of touch, it is in some way related to sight. The eye, however, can easily

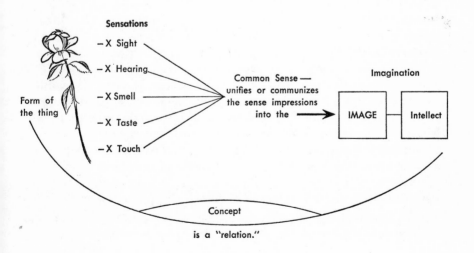

be deceived where distances and dimensions are involved. Distant objects seem smaller; the stick half-submerged appears bent. Touch, on the other hand, is not so easily deceived and quickly tells us whether a very lifelike statue is alive or not.

Of course, particular sensations will vary in their importance in knowing the thing and therefore in the dominant influence they exert within the process of knowledge. Taste, for example, is a negligible factor in knowing a rose, but important in knowing a pickle. In knowing a rose we obviously do not depend to any great extent on sensations of sound, but these are of vital importance in our perception of violin music. We need not bring all the senses into play in our knowledge of each thing. Some senses will be more appropriate to some sensible things than others. But, as a rule, the more senses utilized, the deeper the knowledge. A more vivid impression can be made by a crudely quantitative approach, by piling sensation upon sensation, instead of attempting to communicate some particular sensation in an intensified form. Good novelists take advantage of this principle by weaving a scene which brings every sense into play within the reader's imagination.

If, then, no sense organ can receive the whole of the rose which is known, but only some proper aspect of it, then the rose must be broken down into proper sensibles in order to get within us. We must somehow atomize the rose or rock we perceive. We break it down into a color, a taste, a softness, an odor, and so on.[1]

§ 2. THE IMAGE

Thus the first element of consciousness is the sensation. We experience this sensation in the scalding pleasure of hot coffee and the tingling chill of a snowball. Next in the psychological process comes the image. You can think of drinking coffee now, and even though you are not drinking it, you have within you in some way the taste and aroma of coffee. Direct experience of things through *sensations* and a relationship to them through *images* show us, in our analysis of knowledge up to this point, two distinct types of entities. Think of the tune to *Yankee Doodle*. The music is running through your head right now. But you do not *hear* a sound. You can likewise think of a red tie or dress hanging in your closet. You do not *see* red as you do in the sensation. You are not using your eyes at all. In the image you *know* red in some other way. Although you are not tasting coffee now, you know what coffee

---

[1] For a further discussion of the epistemological validity of separation rather than the psychological function we are emphasizing here, cf. below, pp. 91–92.

tastes like. There is no rose here at present, but you know what a rose smells like.

All of these experiences can be summed up by saying that there is a difference between sensation and image. In sensation we experience directly; in the image we *know* in some other way. Sight is, of course, a type of knowledge, but it differs from imagination and is inferior to it. You "see" red without sight. You "hear" music without using your ears. You "savor" a cigarette without smoking it. That, of course, is why the Greeks used different names to designate two basically different mental entities, the sensation and the image. Imagination, of course, does not eliminate sensation. You could not imagine a tree if you had not first had sensations of it. All knowledge begins with the senses, but it need not stay there. You can even have intellectual knowledge of things, and perhaps knowledge of intellectual things.

To obtain a real understanding of the imagination, it is important to distinguish it from the sense of sight, the highest of the senses. The danger of confusing a higher mental power with a lower because of a superficial likeness is one that the psychologist must always guard against. This was precisely David Hume's error. He absorbed all higher forms of knowledge into sensation as the basic coin of intellectual exchange and thus eliminated many puzzling problems.[2] Although it may not occur to us until we turn our whole attention to the matter, the image is something very different from the perception which vision gives us. For example, when you imagine your mother's face, you can see her features in detail, her coloring and hair styling, but do you actually see anything? Are your eyes serving any purpose at all? If you close your eyes and try to bring the image of your mother's face to the forefront of consciousness and to localize it in the region of the eyes, all that is present to the retina is, of course, the so-called after-image left on the eye by the light just perceived — red, purple, and so forth. The significant point is that in the image, you do not, strictly speaking, *see* anything. This seeing is the sensation. The image is not seen, it is *known* in some other way. The image is a very different *mental entity* from the sensation.

In the plan of the geography of knowledge which we are constructing and within which we expect to locate the basic units of properly intellectual knowledge, I am using the term *entity* to stress the reality of these facts of experience. However, I do not mean to describe them as the ultimate irreducible data of consciousness, or as the terms of an

[2] David Hume, *Enquiry Concerning Human Understanding*, sec. II, 12, 13 (Selby-Bigge ed.), p. 18.

artistic production. Subsequent metaphysical analysis will, I am confident, demonstrate their operational and relational character. However, I am prescinding from just such an analysis at this point in order to concentrate on the particular properties of these mental realities in which we are most interested. For that reason I characterize them, not without hesitation, as *entities* or beings.

§ 3. THE CONCEPT

At this point, then, we have seen at least two distinct kinds of entities involved in knowledge. This second type, the image, can be delineated to the "nth" degree and described in the greatest detail in terms of matter. For instance, if you wished to draw it, you could even describe details which you probably did not think you knew. If you were asked to describe the house in which you live, you could do so with a wealth of detail — wood or brick construction, one-family or multiple dwelling, large or small, flat-roofed or gabled — the whole tremendous universe of imaginative knowledge you carry within you. But if you are asked to describe "house," you give birth to something within your consciousness which seems to be lacking in concrete details. This abstract "house" is a very different kind of thing from the image of "your house." The image can be described with a plethora of detail; it is always of some particular material object; it is constantly changing. This other type of mental entity, on the contrary, seems to be a pure meaning; it is abstract and includes within itself the intelligibility of a whole species, nor can it have one of its intelligible notes changed without changing the meaning itself.

For example, I could describe my father to you and there would be as many different images of my father as there are readers. But as soon as I say "father" an intelligible entity is brought to birth in the consciousness of everyone. You all know exactly what I mean. The image is, strictly speaking, incommunicable. It can be depicted with a wealth of concrete detail, but it is not directly communicable. But another type of entity, the so-called generality or concept or idea, can be immediately communicated in speech; it has no details; it is not concrete but abstract. If, as Hume teaches, images and concepts are only degrees of indetermination of sensation,[3] how explain the obvious correlation of the image with individuals or the precision of definition and exactitude of meaning present in the concept?

It is not possible for a man to have a concept without forming some sort of image, more or less adequate. But even though the concept always

---

[3] *Ibid.*

evokes a concomitant image, there should be little danger of confusing the one with the other, because they are so different in kind.[4]

§ 4. THE IMMATERIALITY OF KNOWLEDGE

As capable a thinker as David Hume saw in the concept only a weakened, indistinct sense impression. But experimental analysis of the conceptual cognitive apparatus has disclosed certain baffling evidences which receive short shrift from Hume. Plato, Plotinus, Augustine, Avicenna, Averroës, Aquinas, Descartes, Berkeley, and countless others, all first-rate thinkers, saw something in our intellectual processes which led them to label these processes as spiritual or immaterial. And it was from an analysis of these same mental operations that Plato first posited immaterial realities as the result of a philosophical discourse. It was in one aspect of this same conception that Augustine found an understanding of God in the notion of the immaterial he discovered in the neo-Platonists. Aristotle's agent intellect and the development of this notion at the hands of his commentators into a separate agent intellect was an attempt to explain the immaterial aspects of conceptual knowledge despite a soul which had to be material because it was the principle of organization of matter. Avicenna's "suspended man," Averroës' "separate intellect" and Descartes's *Cogito* — all these doctrines have as prime motivation the attempt to explain the immaterial aspects of intellectual cognition.

Certain operations of the mind seemed to them to contradict the fundamental behavior of bodies. They violated the laws of matter, as they conceived of these laws.

Historically, matter has meant everything from pure potentiality to the concrete being with all its characteristics. For the purposes of our discussion I should like to identify *the material* with those qualities usually associated with material substance or identified totally with matter. The characteristics of quantity, weight, bulk, dimensions, perhaps the locus of color, and so forth are what I have in mind. These form a common denominator of the theories of matter and provide a workable definition for it. Even Aristotle's notion of matter as pure potentiality, the constancy that underlies change, the principle of limitation of form, can be encompassed within this practical descriptive definition.[5]

---

[4] For the epistemological implications of the concept, especially in its articulations with the idea, cf. below, pp. 88–92. Our purpose here is primarily psychological.

[5] According to Whitehead, matter is conceived as anything that has the property of simple location in space and time. Cf. A. N. Whitehead, *Science and the Modern World* (New York: Mentor, 1948), p. 50.

In actual fact the uniformity or continuity that underlies change may be reduced to these characteristics. When a log is burned in a bell jar — a closed system — there are certain characteristics that endure. If no gas is permitted to escape, the weight will be the same; there will also be some bulk or dimension present, proportionate to the temperature, pressure, and the physical phase of the system.

I would like to examine the basic characteristics of conceptual knowledge which enabled men to call it immaterial and upon this model to postulate the possibility and at times the reality of the immaterial structure of being. Such thinkers were convinced that they perceived intellectually what they could not see, hear, smell, taste, or touch.

As fascinating an occupation as it is to reconstruct in detail the thought of the great philosophers — and perhaps it is even true that that is the only way to learn how to philosophize — nevertheless I would like to organize these evidences according to my own model.

I think we can say that there are, among others, four basic evidences for affirming the reality of the immaterial in knowledge. The concept is immaterial because it:

1) is inexhaustible in terms of matter.
2) is inexpressible in terms of matter.
3) violates the law of the irreversibility of space.
4) violates the law of the irreversibility of time.

§ 5. THE CONCEPT AS INEXHAUSTIBLE IN TERMS OF MATTER

What do we mean when we say that the concept is inexhaustible in terms of matter? An example is the best explanation. If I were to give you a sheet of paper and ask you to put down on that sheet whatever came to your mind when I spoke the word "tree," what sequence of mental events would take place? As I mention the word "tree," something happens in your mind. Something rises to the forefront of your consciousness which was not there before. You have given birth to something in your mind, a concept.[6] No tree which you drew on paper would be exactly what you have in mind, because you could draw another one which would also be included in "tree." How would you draw it? Would it be a pine, a maple; would it be tall, stunted, full, thin? You could draw a series of trees. In fact you could draw trees until the day you died, yet you could still draw one more. The significant point here is that you cannot completely express in terms of line and dimen-

---

[6] Thomas Aquinas, *De Potentia*, VIII, 1, resp.

sion what you have in your mind. You cannot exhaust the intelligibility of a concept by any number of images.

You could draw the image of the tree in your garden with all the detail of which you are artistically capable. You could capture, as it were, that tree. You could say with exactness, "There is the tree in my garden." But this cannot be done with what rises in your mind when I speak the word "tree." At what point in your drawings can you say, "That is what I have in my mind when you say 'tree'"? You cannot even point to the complete sheaf of drawings you have made and, taking them as a whole, make the same assertion. No matter how many drawings or models you make, you cannot exhaust the intelligibility of the concept. There is a certain disproportion between what you have in your mind and what you can translate into matter. There is always more in your mind than you can interpret in terms of matter, in terms of pencil and paper. That is what we mean when we say that the concept is inexhaustible in terms of matter. You cannot exhaust its meaning in line, form, color, etc.

Following the same line of reasoning, can you make any drawing and point to it saying, "That is 'house'"? Of course not. You could make a drawing of *your* mother. You can do that with images. But can you execute a drawing of "mother"? Is the concept "mother" tall or short, stout or thin, dark or fair, old or young? There is something which you have in your mind which can never be adequately interpreted in terms of matter. It is not exhaustible in terms of matter. Although you can capture the image under the conditions of matter, at no point can you completely capture the concept in terms of matter.

§ 6. THE CONCEPT AS INEXPRESSIBLE IN TERMS OF MATTER

The concept is not only inexhaustible in terms of matter, some concepts are actually inexpressible in terms of matter. There are some mental entities which seem to be more profoundly divorced from matter. In fact, they are actually immaterial because they cannot be understood in terms of matter at all. For example, what is honor? You cannot express it in terms of matter. It has no height, weight or bulk — no dimension at all. As a consequence, we say that it is inexpressible in terms of matter. All material things, all bodies, have certain characteristics which we commonly call material characteristics, namely weight, bulk, dimension, color. All bodies have these attributes. But none of these attributes can be found in the mental entity that a man produces in thought. Examine the concept as you would any body, any bodily thing. How tall is honor? How much does love weigh? What color is beauty? You have something in your mind of which it is impossible to predicate the attributes which, as we know from physics, all material things have. The conclusion is that certain mental entities which we call concepts are not only inexhaustible in terms of matter but are actually inexpressible in terms of matter. This is what philosophers meant when they said that concepts are immaterial. They do not have the properties that all material things, all bodies, must have.

Excellent examples of mental entities inexpressible in terms of matter are mathematical figures. Although we are constantly seeing sketches of such figures, they cannot actually be drawn. The best you can do is an imaginative representation of the circle, the triangle, the line, and the point. A triangle is supposed to be a three-sided figure, a closed plane, the sum of whose angles equals 180 degrees. It is in fact simply a two-dimensional figure, with only length and width. But is it possible to draw a two-dimensional figure? You can think it, but you cannot draw it. The same is true of the line. The line is the shortest distance between two points; it has only one dimension, length. But as soon as you put pen or pencil to paper, a three-dimensional being, a body, results. The drawn line actually has a length, width, and thickness, the thickness of the ink or lead used to draw it.

The circle, likewise, is a line equidistant from the center at every point. Since the line cannot be drawn, it logically follows that neither can the circle. Our sketches are imaginative representations that obey the laws of images. But mathematical figures are simply definitions, concepts in the mind, which are nonetheless real. You can think them, but you cannot express them in terms of matter and its conditions. If they were not real, this building could not have been built. These mental entities in our minds cannot be represented in terms of matter at all. We cannot imagine them, but we can think them. If they are inexpressible in terms of matter, then they are immaterial. Calling concepts symbolic forms, for instance, does not solve this problem, nor does it dispense with it. It simply uses another vocabulary. The problem still remains.[7]

§ 7. THE LAW OF IRREVERSIBILITY OF SPACE

Third, human knowledge violates the law of the irreversibility of space and time. This law might be formulated as follows: "Every prior

---

[7] William E. Carlo, "Matter as a Mode of *Esse*," *Proceedings of the American Catholic Philosophical Association*, XXXVIII (1964), pp. 142–154.

cause immediately precedes its posterior cause, and every posterior cause immediately follows upon its prior cause." The property of dimension is one of the basic characteristics of bodies. Bodies always exist in place or, to put it abstractly, in space. By space is meant abstract dimension, the abstract receptacle of bodies. In speaking of space and time I shall follow the same method that I employed with the term entity as applied to our contents of knowledge. I shall take space and time as proximate data of reality, mindful however of their reducibility to the changing principles of matter.

The law of the irreversibility of space means, for example, that it is impossible for you to get from one side of the room to the other without passing through every spot, every inch, every millimeter of the space between. You cannot get from here to the door without passing through every inch of the intervening distance. You must pass through every point in sequential linear order between your position and your destination.

When you take a trip from Grand Central Station in New York to Chicago, what are the mental requisites for such an operation? You have to be in Chicago mentally, first, before you can get there. How could you go anyplace if, somehow or other, you were not there first mentally? Otherwise you would meander or wander the way a dog or a brook travels. You could never get anyplace unless, somehow or other, you were at your destination before you started. You are not there bodily, of course, so you can only be there through knowledge. But that is precisely the point. Before you start anywhere, you must know where you are going, otherwise you would never get anyplace.

There were, however, many people in the last war who did not know where they were going. They were not taking a trip; they were being taken on a trip the way you would take a suitcase. Animals have powers of locomotion far superior to those of human beings, yet they never take trips because they have no intellectual powers.[8]

---

[8] We know this much about homing pigeons and migratory birds as well as spawning salmon, etc.: a human being *by knowledge* could not duplicate their behavior. If a man were transported to the wilds of the Maine woods blindfolded and then left alone, he could not circle two or three times and then head straight for home. He would need knowledge. He would have to know where he is and where he is to go. A map and directions would be necessary for knowledge to function. Animals do by instinct what a man does by knowledge. A young bird which has never been to the winter feeding grounds of his migratory species can find his way. How does the bird which has never had young before know enough to build a nest? A human being in the same situation could not know! The animal does by a built-in physical tendency what a human being can do only by a psychical tendency — by knowledge. The human being would be lost in the woods of Maine while the homing pigeon flies unerringly

Right now you can be in Buffalo, now Albany, now Chicago, San Francisco, Boston, St. Louis. You are actually violating the law which no physical body can violate. You cannot move bodily one foot from the position in space where you are located without passing through the twelve inches of intervening space. This implies the freedom with which you are ranging over space, which no material body can do. And yet, you are doing it. We do it day in and day out, and therefore we come to be so accustomed to it that we overlook its significance. You are doing something with space that no physical body can do. Of course, you are doing it mentally. That is just the point. What is being done here can only be done by an intellect.

There must be the realization of a final destination, but not necessarily of a proximate destination or the intervening distance. Even if you simply know direction and distance, you know something. When you read a map, although you have never been there before, you are following the knowledge of another mind. You are making his knowledge of a place yours. If you wanted to go to Paris from New York City, even though you have never been to Paris, you would not go to a railroad station, because you have made another man's knowledge your own. You must have that knowledge before you even start. You cannot take one step without it.

You have a complete freedom of space. Only one type of thing in the whole universe of things we know can violate this basic law of physics. Therefore, the conclusion is that human knowledge is immaterial. A projection of this kind is impossible for bodies. Only the human mind has such a capability.

§ 8. THE LAW OF IRREVERSIBILITY OF TIME

Just as with space you cannot go from one point to another without passing through the intervening points, so with time. There is no way you can get bodily from Monday to Thursday without going through Tuesday and Wednesday. You cannot be thirty years old before you are twenty-nine. The attractiveness of the boast, "I'll knock you into the middle of next week," lies in its extravagance, in the warm satisfaction that here is one threat that cannot be topped.

---

to his coop. There has been a variety of attempts to explain such phenomena as migratory flights by the postulation of electromagnetic fields, the direction of the sun, gravitation, etc., but all seem still inconclusive. However this point is clear. Animals do not take trips by knowledge. A human being could not duplicate such behavior under the same conditions.

But what happens when you make a date for Saturday? Monday you have your shoes mended, Tuesday you pick up the tickets, Wednesday you have the car washed. Something that has not happened yet, Saturday night, is determining what you are doing all week. You actually are pulling yourself out of the moment of time in which you are located and moving into the future, just as you can move into the past. You can go back in time to the day you graduated from grammar school, high school, or college, and in precisely the same way you can penetrate into the future. Your body cannot even get half-a-minute ahead of itself but *mentally* you can. In some way you actually *span the present and the future.* Somehow or other you have your toe in the door of the future. You are the master of time; otherwise how could you ever start an action which is to terminate in the future? The human intellect violates the laws of the irreversibility of space and time, two of the basic laws of matter. Therefore, in a way, it is immaterial. A physical body is locked in the moment of time in which it exists and cannot get out of it except by following a proper sequence of causes. But intellectual knowledge proves the exception. Mentally you can rise above that. You can go back into the past and ahead into the future. Every time you make a date or set a schedule you are in some way violating the law of the irreversibility of time and testifying to the immaterial character of your mental operations.

Finally human art demonstrates the same freedom in respect to time. In order to make a chair, can you lock yourself in a room with wood and nails, and suddenly realize a Chippendale has been produced? You cannot possibly make things unless you know from the beginning what you are going to make. You have to decide whether you are going to use wood or metal. Before you produce something, it must exist in your mind. In some incipient, abortive way you are *spanning the present and the future.* You have to know what is going to exist, a chair, for example, before you can even start to make that chair; you have to be able to span the present and the future, not that you actually exist in the future. You are merely thinking of it — *but that is the whole point,* that the intellect can do that. Something has not actually happened, yet it can influence what you are doing now. Art flows directly from the immaterial intellect.

Going over the law of the irreversibility of time, then, a body is locked in the moment of time in which it is located. Your body cannot possibly get two minutes from now without enduring every intervening second. Yet mentally it can. When you ask a question, for instance, you are expecting an answer. Your actions can be determined by something that has not happened yet. The only way that can be is that somehow or other you can get a foothold in the future. Could these operations of the mind be of constructural nature, like the atomic theory, for instance? But the fact remains that you know that there is going to be a future and you are somehow planning for it. The human mind is not subject to the laws of the irreversibility of time the way the body is. In human art when you make a thing, the future is determining the present and the future exists in some way in the present. What is going to happen is determining what you are doing now. You are somehow mentally spanning the present and the future in a way that your body cannot.

§ 9. THE IMMATERIAL AND MATERIALISM

Of course an understanding of the immaterial demands a correlative knowledge of matter and its properties. Materialism, as an intellectual doctrine, arose historically with the development of a quantitative physics.[9] It is a comparatively modern phenomenon, and differs considerably from the naïve materialism of Democritus and Lucretius.

The fundamental motivation of Descartes's mechanism was his desire to establish physics as a science, to give it its scientific charter. To that end Descartes set apart an area of reality completely and exhaustively interpretable in terms of mathematical physics. As an immediate consequence he was forced to strip things of their qualities, their fundamental organizational patterns, and push them back into the mind.[10] There they become the direct objects of intellection. Thus, idealism and materialism are two aspects of the same intellectual achievement. But idealism did preserve some recognition of the immaterial aspects of human knowledge. Empiricism on the other hand is a methodical elimination of what is properly intellectual. It is a reduction of the concept to a weakened sense impression so that images and concepts are diminished modes or poor imitations, residual impressions of the vivid sensation.[11]

Matter could be a principle to which the operations and characteristics of physical things are analytically reducible. Matter could be the constituent of material reality, but it might also mean a particular level of perfection. The immaterial and the material might be equated with

[9] Cf. Chap. IV, 7 for a discussion of this point.
[10] René Descartes, *Meditationes*, II; Adam-Tannery, t. VII, p. 34, 11. 5–9.
[11] David Hume, *Treatise on Human Nature*, Bk. I, Pt. I, sec. II (Selby-Bigge ed), pp. 7–8.

the more or the less in an order of what is basically qualitative perfection, in the hierarchy of being.[12]

However, we have not been interested here in attacking materialism directly, but we have been definitely interested in knowing more about the unique phenomenon of human knowledge which historically has provided the basis for the theory of the immaterial.

This analysis has given us two things. It has afforded us an understanding of what is meant by conceptual thinking or intellection, the proper tool of metaphysics. Also it has introduced us to the notion of the *immaterial,* a notion that must grow to familiarity if we are to understand what is meant by being, the structure of reality more basic than matter and indifferent to matter.[13]

---

[12] "Another advantage enjoyed by metaphysics in our time is that the concept of mere matter, which haunted not only Greek and medieval but also Indian thought, has been shown, far more clearly than ever before, by the development from Leibniz to Bergson, Peirce, and Whitehead, to be superfluous. It was always a term for intellectual embarrassment, as anyone who has read the history of the concept must, I should think, know. Today we have leading scientists who hold that 'matter' has no ultimate content distinguishing it from that of 'mind' or 'experience,' from examples of which alone it can be abstracted. Our only problem here, we are now, as never before, free to say, is to find the adequately generalized or non-anthropomorphic versions of such 'physical' ideas as 'experience,' 'feeling,' 'sign,' 'sympathy,' and the like, in order to cover all conceivable scientific facts about the experienced world" (C. Hartshorne, "Present Prospects for Metaphysics," *The Monist,* XLVII, 2 [Winter, 1963], pp. 196–197). "This 'dematerialization' of the elementary particles is an extremely important feature of present-day physics, which aims at eliminating inert matter from its picture of the world and replacing it by a lively interplay of forms. The theory of relativity had already taken a first step in this direction by recognizing that mass is equivalent to energy. To be sure, this did not amount to a final rejection of the idea of substance, since the conversion of mass into energy does not rule out the possibility that the energy of a body may demand a substance as its carrier" (Arthur March and Ira M. Freeman, *The New World of Physics* [New York: Vintage Books, 1963], pp. 178–179).

[13] The immaterial and the universe as a *body* make sense only within a theory of the attenuation of the material — embedded ultimately in an immaterial matrix.

CHAPTER II. / THE KINDS OF KNOWLEDGE

IN ANALYZING any part of reality, we must consider not only the thing we are investigating, but also our proper mode of inquiry.[1] If there were but one, single homogeneous knowledge which differs only by reason of the object it investigates, then the difficulties of human knowing would be simplified immeasurably. If all the limitations of human knowledge are ignored, as has been the case since Descartes, then a homogeneous knowledge is distinguishable only by its application. Mathematics differs from grammar because one deals with numbers, and the other with speech; chemistry deals with the elements and their compounds, whereas spelling deals with words. If this were the case, then

---

[1] "As the Philosopher says in the beginning of the *Metaphysics,* it *belongs to the wise man to order.* This is because wisdom is the highest perfection of reason, whose business it is to know order. For although the sensitive powers know some things absolutely, it belongs to the intellect or reason alone to know the order of one thing to another.

"Now there is a twofold order in things. One is the order of the parts of some whole or some multitude to each other, as for example the parts of a house are ordered among themselves. The other is the order of things to an end. And this order is more primary than the first; for as the Philosopher says in the *Metaphysics,* the order of the parts of an army among themselves exists by virtue of the order of the whole army to its leader.

"Furthermore, order is related to reason in a fourfold way. For there is a certain order which reason does not make but simply contemplates, as for example the order of things in nature" (St. Thomas Aquinas, *In I Ethica,* lect. 1, nn. 1–2, ed. Pirotta; trans. Armand Maurer, p. 79).

any human mind, no matter what the method of its proper discipline, would be free to analyze with equal prerogative. Since knowledge, however, is not homogeneous, since knowledges do differ *as* knowledges, and not only by reason of their subject matter, certain complications arise. The professional mathematician can study a book on diving all winter long, but, when he first steps out on the board in the middle of June, the results are rather disastrous. Experience is witness to the fact that no matter what the mental development in one area of human knowledge, it can never be adequately transferred to a different area of knowledge. *Knowledges differ by an inner, intrinsic differentiation, and it is due to this fact that one knowledge cannot be used as a substitute for another, because it is incapable of doing the work of another.* Descartes was only being consistent, when he attempted to instruct Harvey in the workings of the circulatory system, by substituting the deductive method proper to mathematics in an area where, by its very nature, the inductive method must be primary. If there is only one homogeneous knowledge distinguishable by reason of the object to which it is applied, then there is no reason why Descartes could not do so, even though the results were catastrophic.[2]

To understand further the fundamentally different structures of the various knowledges, we need only point to the fact that many knowledges deal with man, but their definitions of man as defined within the scope and methods of their own fundamental movements will vary. In physics man is an articulating system of stresses and strains. In chemistry man is a complexus of elements and their compounds. In mathematics man is a quantity. In biology man is a mammal of the order of primates. In economic theory he is a producer and consumer. Whatever else we may say about these knowledges, we must recognize their structural differences, since they deal with the same thing and yet ignore so completely aspects of this thing rich in intelligibility for other knowledges.

The conclusion is evident, then, that the human intellect, when it comes to investigate reality, must be aware of the natures and limitations of the different kinds of knowledges if it would escape a multiplicity of diverse and contradictory answers. We must understand something about the basic exigencies of the various knowledges if we are to evaluate and profit by what they have to contribute to the total understanding of reality. We can make disastrous errors by substituting the results of one knowledge for another. If, for instance, physics has matter

---

[2] Descartes, *Discourse on Method*, Pt. II, Adam-Tannery, V, VI, p. 19, cf. also E. Gilson, *The Unity of Philosophical Experience* (New York: Scribner's, 1939), chaps. 5–8.

in its motions as its object, then the physicist, as physicist, working completely within his own method, must be immersed in the procedures of measurement, an immersion which is absolutely necessary if he is to do original work in his field. However, in attempting to understand a particular thing completely, he will be in danger of analyzing it exclusively within the proper method and according to the techniques which have become the habitual mode of operation of his scientific life. But since this method and these techniques were constructed to know matter and to know it exhaustively, then whatever does not fall within the laws of matter must be *either* materialized *or* denied. Thus a physicist completely immersed in a method made to know matter and matter alone, blind to the nature of his own knowledge, and unaware of the existence of other knowledges with objects proper to themselves, must of necessity answer in terms of atheism and materialism when he attempts to answer the question of the existence of God and the spirituality of the soul. Every man must be the master of some knowledge. *But he cannot afford to be ignorant of all other knowledges, or he will find himself attempting to answer questions that confront him as a man in terms of the only material he has, the methods and techniques of his own knowledge.* Most of the great philosophical errors of history have been due precisely to such a mistake. It is the tendency of every man to exalt *his* knowledge as the answer to the ultimate questions of reality. If he has no other knowledge, and is nevertheless seeking ultimate answers, what else can he do? So Descartes tried to interpret all reality in terms of mathematics, Kant in terms of physics, Comte in terms of sociology, Marx in terms of economics, and Freud in terms of psychology. They tried to interpret all reality in terms of the law of their own particular area of reality.[3]

---

3 "Traditional preoccupation with finding a criterion of certainty and identifying it with a given discipline, whether it be mathematics or the empirical sciences, has gone hand in hand with the notion that such a solid criterion could provide a philosopher's stone. In the medieval age of belief, and the seventeenth century's age of reason we see classic examples of this effort to single out one faculty or one science as key to the universe or the intellectual globe. One kind of knowing is set up as a model whose method the others are asked to follow whether it be theology or mathematics. In the eighteenth century the triumph of Newton's physics made mechanics king; in the nineteenth, Hegel's history and Darwin's biology took on a similar importance, and toward the close of that century psychology made a strong bid to dominate philosophical studies. In place of this disciplinary imperialism the twentieth century tends to be more democratic and pluralistic. Not only does it avoid setting up one kind of knowledge as central, but it even denies the centrality of knowing as a form of human activity. This is evident not only in the extreme vitalism of Bergson, but also in Wittgenstein's effort to show that language has many uses, which are all of interest to a philosopher. It is reflected in the pluralistic metaphysics of James and even in Dewey's denial of what he calls the ubiquity of the knowing

In constructing a classification of human knowledges we may, at times, appear to be rather far away from our principal preoccupation, the analysis of the nature and applications of philosophy and science. But this is not a digression, it is a geography. In order to locate the precise role that philosophy plays in relation to the different knowledges we must first understand something of the natures of these different knowledges. Our task is, then, to examine knowledge in its intrinsic dynamics in order to discover its proper movements and the laws under which it operates.

A good way to initiate an investigation into knowledge is with the genius of Aristotle, as Thomas Aquinas does. Aristotle begins his *Metaphysics* with the words: *All men by nature desire to know.* We can see what this means, he tells us, by an examination of the sense of sight, which is the highest of all the sensory powers and the most akin to intellectual knowledge.[4] It is certainly true that we desire to see, even when we have no care to match shirt and tie or to transfer food from plate to mouth, but just for the pure joy of seeing. The same is true of intellectual knowledge, Aristotle tells us. Man wants to know even when no practical end is in sight, even when there is nothing to make or do. Knowledge is its own delight. The value that a human being confers upon knowledge becomes evident when we examine that most powerful of all human drives, the instinct of self-preservation — an instinct so strong that it is capable of turning mother love into cannibalism. This fundamental instinct is not a drive for life itself in a human being, but for a certain type of life, human life. Man seeks awareness or knowledge, not the unthinking processes of nutrition, growth, and reproduction by which life is often characterized. If a man had to choose, in a hypothetical case, between dying immediately, or contracting a form of sleeping sickness, being unconscious for the remainder

experience. It is illustrated by the later tendency of logical positivists to avoid what has been called the reductive fallacy. Once it becomes clear that there are no sharp lines of demarcation between disciplines and that no one of them can claim to a fundamental position in the scheme of knowing, and once it becomes clear that there are forms of human experience which are just as important as knowing, the way is open to a philosophical study of man in the broadest sense" (Morton White, *The Age of Analysis* [New York: New American Library, 1958], pp. 240–241).

4 "All men by nature desire to know. An indication of this is the delight we take in our senses; for even apart from their usefulness they are loved for themselves; and above all others the sense of sight. For not only with a view to action, but even when we are not going to do anything, we prefer seeing (one might say) to everything else. The reason is that this, most of all the senses, makes us know and brings to light many differences between things." Aristotle, *Metaphysics*, I, 1, 980b 23–28, ed. R. McKeon, *The Basic Works of Aristotle* (New York: Random House, 1941), p. 689.

of his life, and then dying — the hypothesis being that there is no possible cure or regaining of consciousness — we venture to say that the average man would prefer to die immediately. Man does not place primary value on the aspects of existence that he has in common with the vegetable. When he wants to live, he wants to be aware of things. He wants to know for the sheer joy of knowing! The life of the cauliflower has no attractions for a human being.[5]

§ 1. THEORETICAL AND PRACTICAL KNOWLEDGES

Thus in knowledge itself we find the basis for the first distinction among knowledges, a distinction without which all order in knowledge is impossible. This is the distinction between theoretical or speculative, and practical knowledge. By speculative knowledge, knowledge for its own sake, we mean the supreme natural good of human existence. Imagine the wonder of it, if a man could be produced in the full possession of his faculties, but who had never before experienced this relation to things which we call knowledge. Just the colors of a room would fascinate him, the shape of things, the various ways that man has organized matter, as well as the works of nature in its infinitely greater productions. Imagine the thrill with which he would see another human being, walking, talking, and moving! It would be like a million moving pictures wrapped up into one in its dramatic impact. This is the natural movement of the intellect, even before it cares to make or do anything. By a natural, almost gravitational inclination, it seeks its object, and in knowing things, it in a way possesses them. For it is certainly true that the beauty of the peacock and the sunset, the strength of the lion, the dancing fleetness of the antelope, and the soaring flight of the eagle do exist for the knowing being in a way that they do not exist for the stone or the tree. When you know things, they, in a way, become yours. That is why a man will turn to look at a beautiful thing. It explains also the fascination of spectator sports — for the grace of the infielder, the skill of the pitcher, and the power of the batter become yours, in a way, when you know them, with the consequent delight that follows on the possession of any perfection and the satisfaction of any appetite.

Practical knowledge, on the other hand, is not the natural movement

---

[5] "To try to see more and better is not a matter of whim or curiosity or self-indulgence. *To see or to perish* is the very condition laid upon everything that makes up the universe . . . it is so vital and so blessed to *know*" (Pierre Teilhard de Chardin, *The Phenomenon of Man*, trans. Bernard Wall [New York: Harper & Row, 1959], p. 31).

of the mind seeking its object and resting in the delight of its possession. In practical knowledge man uses his intellect for a purpose outside its own inner, intrinsic constitution, which is a *speculum* or a mirroring of the thing. Practical knowing uses the intellect in order to make or do something. Something which a human being wants becomes the object of his movement. His intellect does not move in accordance with its natural momentum. Another faculty or desire calls it into movement, sustains it at every step, and only permits it to rest when the car has been bought, the steak consumed, or the girl wed. The intellect is operating at the command of some appetite or desire, and the object of this appetite becomes the object of the intellect. This is the evidence, sketchy and in part, upon which scholastic thinkers, historically, have based their assertion of the primacy of speculative knowledge.

Scholastic thinkers by this assertion do not intend to demean practical knowledge in any way. One has to be a man to be an artist, for art and work manifest a rational intellect. They flow from the dignity of humankind. The brute cannot make things, not because he lacks a thumb or a hand, but because he is not rational, notwithstanding certain similarities to rational behavior which instinct possesses. But if a man had the body of a dog, he would still make things, although under certain difficulties. Practical knowledge is most important to human existence. We call it practical simply because in it knowledge has as its object not that of its own natural movement but the object of another appetite which is using knowledge to gain its own end. This is true, even though the artist does a great deal of intellectual work. If a man wants to make a statue, he has to think this wood would be best for a large statue, this for a small one. This type of wood, due to its grain, is better for curves, this type for angles. This kind would be better for outdoors, this for indoors — a tremondous amount of technical knowledge which takes the best years of a lifetime to accumulate. The knowledge involved is inexhaustible. All knowledge is specifically human and worthy of the dignity of the intellectual being, but practical knowledge is not for the sake of knowledge itself, but for the sake of something else, some artifact like a chair or an automobile.

The distinction between speculative and practical knowledge, this inner differentiation within the knowledge itself by reason of its end, is not the result of whim. It has its roots in the very nature of the knowledge under investigation. By speculative knowledge we do not mean that we study medicine for the sake of merely knowing it, never intending to practice. Nor do we mean that, by the simple expedient of studying medicine with the intention of practicing it, we thereby make it a practical knowledge. We know how to do something. We know how to restore the harmony of a physical organism. Even when we never practice, we still learn how to do something, to cure the sick, even though we do not intend to do it. The distinction of speculative and practical is thus not based on the intention of the knower, but on the direction of the knowledge itself. Despite certain inadequacies, speculative knowledge is the highest type of knowledge because it is the fulfillment of man's highest faculty, the intellect, and its most basic appetite, the desire to know.

Ours is an age of practice, of action, of doing things. Why? Because we can do so much more than ever before! The power of Atlas is ready to our hand and the seven league boots wait for us to step in. With such tremendously effective tools so close at hand, who can resist or want to resist the temptation to use them — and to use them consistently? Imagine contemporary men like the child in a carpenter's shop. There are hammers, gleaming saws, and smooth glittering screw drivers. The palms itch and the fingers stretch to them. If men were not in so brilliant a technological society the effort needed to use more primitive and less fascinating tools might make action less appealing. The severities of plowing with a wooden share might make the green of the trees, the blue of the skies much more attractive. Contemplating the beauties of nature from a reclining posture beneath the shade of a tree becomes more personally satisfying.

These comments are of course generalities, but the point I wish to make, is, I am sure, a very valid one, namely, that man's particular environment can make him more interested in practical or speculative knowledge at different historical periods. This does not mean that the primacy of the practical or of the theoretical is shifting in value from generation to generation, but only that contingent circumstances can determine preoccupation of particular thinkers at particular times — for example, contemporary thinkers trying to understand our pragmatic, technological age are tempted to place overemphasis and to impose an implicit, hardly conscious, value judgment on the general philosophy of the day.[6]

But the only way to actually decide the question of the primacy of theoretical or practical knowledge is by an objective analysis of the economy of human thought — the ontology of knowledge, the role which knowledge plays in the universe and in the human pursuit of human perfection.

---

6 John Dewey, *Reconstruction in Philosophy* (New York: Holt, Rinehart and Winston, 1926), chap. 5.

§ 2. THE KNOWLEDGE OF COMMON SENSE

In addition to the distinction between speculative and practical knowledge, there are further divisions of knowledge. Speculative knowledge itself is of two types: *science* and the *knowledge of common sense*. *Science* is distinguished from the knowledge of common sense, the knowledge of the man in the street, inasmuch as it deals with causes or explanations, whereas the *knowledge of common sense* is concerned with conclusions. When you observe a stale apple you see that it is wrinkled and dry; it has lost color and taste. You have real knowledge and certainty of the fact that it is stale, but you do not have scientific knowledge. You do not know the *causes* of this phenomenon. You do not know scientifically what you mean when you say that the apple is stale unless you know that the sugars have become starches, a process which is best expressed in a formula of organic chemistry.

When you boil an egg, you know that in three minutes it will be soft-boiled, in five, hard-boiled. You have real knowledge and certainty of the fact, but you do not have scientific knowledge. You do not know the causes of this operation going on before your eyes. Unless you know the laws of heat in relation to water and protoplasm, you do not know, scientifically, what you mean when you say something is cooked. Cooked? What does this mean? Is it the application of heat? What then is heat? What is the difference between a hot piece of metal and that same piece when cold? Many are puzzled when confronted by such questions. We must know the scientific laws of chemical reactions. We have to know the causes of a thing or the reasons why it is what it is. No one in his right senses would step in front of a speeding car. But why not? It hurts, bones would be broken, the result might be death. But just what happens when a car strikes a man or a dog? Why should a moving body have such an effect on another? We know that it does — from experience. We know the results of such an accident. We know conclusions, but we do not know the causes of the event. We avoid a speeding car, not because we know the physical, chemical, and biological reactions which would take place at the impact of car and body, but because we know that, failing to do so, the result would be most disastrous. Unless we know the physical laws of matter in motion, we cannot *explain* what happens when a car strikes us. Another example: if a bomb were set in the center of an assembled group, the place would be vacated instantly. But why? Do we know just what happens when a bomb explodes? We know the results, the effects of a thing. (We know that the air turns into a stone wall before our faces!) But unless, again, we know the laws of matter in motion, of the expansion of gases, for example, the causes of an event, we have not scientific knowledge. By common sense, of course, we do not mean a hard-headed business sense or a practical, prudential judgment. Even though many elements of practical knowledge are interwoven, the knowledge of common sense is not a practical knowledge. We need not learn it by doing. We need not fall from a ten-story building in order to discover what happens. We know the results.

Common sense knowledge provides us with the basic conclusions needed for the direction of practical knowledges. The psychiatrist, the lawyer, the artist, the moralist, even the psychologist need not have scientific knowledge. They do not have to know definitions in order to attain their end. Their common sense experience from effects is sufficient. They begin with the fact as an ultimate datum of reality, and from that starting point pursue effectively their separate ends.

Scientific knowledge becomes necessary only if there is confusion or substitution of this fundamental knowledge by a science such as physics, which has no business to be analyzing the nature of anything because natures do not fall within its proper sphere.[7] Then one must go to the scientific examination in order to counteract such an error. But, ordinarily, common human experience and the control over the effects of our human actions are sufficient for the starting point of the practical knowledges.

§ 3. COMMON SENSE KNOWLEDGES: HISTORY AND LITERATURE

Although common sense knowledge of effects, results, and conclusions is naturally spontaneous and flows from the primitive depths of knowledge as a physical tendency springing untutored from the primal patterns of intelligibility, the traces of an intellectual causal principle, it can to some extent be susceptible of an initial structuring and organizing. This is not sufficient to make it science, but sufficient to allow it a certain autonomy as a knowledge. By this we mean particularly the disciplines of history and literature.

Since they do not penetrate to the level of causes, they do not offer explanations in a scientific sense but remain properly within the periphery of common sense knowledge. Their proper structuring and organization, like all structuring and organization of method, result from the object of the science, which in turn derives from the common subject

---

[7] On this point, cf. below, Chap. III, 1 and 2.

matter as it confronts the intellectual potentialities of the human knower.

These knowledges do partake of a certain generality, even a universality. This universality is based on their objects, which give us perspectives or insights into the "vague" being which is the proper object of the intellect, the *ens primum cognitum*. Nonetheless, they lack that radical vision which cuts to the root causes of things, and consequently they do not penetrate to a scientific level. They are of special value, however, because they do give man a knowledge of all things in the area of concrete individual experience, and human experience as stretched and distended within the added dimension of time. Stretched out on the rollers of time, only thus can certain larger factors of human experience be understood. The spiritual, quasi-immortal lives of institutions, for example, their size comprehended in the duration of movement, become intelligible in the larger patterns of the tapestry of human individual and institutional affairs.

By reason of their universality, history and literature approach philosophy, and metaphysics in particular, in their overall generality and integrative function. This is why history and literature are so valuable at the core of a curriculum. They give it breadth, perspective, and balance. If one had to choose only one subject for an education, there would be a particular danger in choosing a science. Certainly one penetrates deeply into the structure of reality to the level of causes, but the deep shaft is narrow. A thinker can lose poise and judgment when he moves outside of the narrow area of professional scientific competency. Certain notorious examples are all too familiar. History and literature give that breadth of knowledge so necessary for the liberally educated man. They share in the universality of being as being even though they do not perceive it as the cause of causes, the explanation of causality.

§ 4. SCIENTIFIC KNOWLEDGE

The other type of speculative knowledge is science, which has been defined as a *certain knowledge through causes*. There has been a great deal of human energy expended in an analysis of the nature of science, and we do not intend to try to give a definitive and exhaustive treatment to a subject on which such great philosophers as Descartes and Kant have blunted their genius. On the other hand, there are certain fundamental intelligible patterns evident in this complex mental operation. There are certain basic laws that have stood the test of time since Aristotle, and, what is just as important, they have served to illumine whatever deviations have occurred. When we assert the certainty and necessity of the character of scientific knowledge, we are merely reiterating a common intellectual experience. The status of science has been attached invariably to those knowledges that demonstrate an invariable power of prediction. Historically, the precise knowledges to which the dignity of science was assigned have varied, but the reason for the conferring of such a title has always remained the same. Science is a necessary type of knowledge.

There was a time in the history of man's intellectual endeavors when the title of science, with all its dignities and privileges, was given to metaphysics. Today, metaphysics is considered the transcendental illusion, and it is physics which comes to mind when we hear the word science. This does not mean that the criteria of scientific knowledge have changed, but merely that man has become accustomed to certitude of another type. Yesteryear and today, there is no quarrel about the scientific status of mathematics. It is science par excellence, the ideal type of human knowledge. Why has its dignity rarely been challenged? Precisely because of the certainty of its laws. Mathematicians do not dispute the Pythagorean theorem, that the square of the hypotenuse of a right triangle equals the sum of the squares of the other two sides. Thinkers do not quarrel over whether two plus two equals four. It is this certitude that Descartes had in mind when he chose mathematics as the archetype of all scientific knowledge. And it is this same characteristic that even today causes men to model economics, sociology, psychology, and education upon mathematics, in order that they may, through the copious sprinkling of numbers and quasi-mathematical formulas, share in the scientific value of mathematics itself. This would be the proper procedure if the mere presence of numbers was the cause of certainty. But the certitude of mathematical science comes from a source other than the physical fact of numbers. This we shall explain at its proper place in our discussion.[8]

There is no doubt, however, that at every period of history, it has been because of its certainty and necessity that the title of science, a scientific charter, has been bestowed upon any knowledge. Certainty is a characteristic of scientific knowledge because science is concerned with the necessary regularities in its objects. The certainty of science flows from a necessity, a uniformity of operation in the thing. In turn, the necessity of physical operation depends on the causes involved, the necessity of effects following invariably on their causes. For example,

---

[8] Cf. below, Chap. III, 1 and 2, pp. 36–50.

water always boils at one hundred degrees centigrade under standard conditions. All horned animals have cloven hooves. All ruminants have double or triple stomachs. There is something in matter by reason of which solids always expand under heat and contract when cooled.

§ 5. THE CAUSES OF THINGS

If science is concerned with causes, if it is a *cognitio certa per causas* (certain knowledge of causes), then sciences will be distinguished by reason of the kinds of causes or levels of explanation with which they are concerned.[9] Our first task, then, is to clarify just what we mean by a cause. When a principle, i.e., something first, has a positive influx on its consequent, that is, when it leaves something of itself in its consequent, it is called a cause. For example, a father leaves an imprint of himself on his child, a poet on his poem, fire on the wood it burns. If one came upon a chair in the middle of a desert island, one would know immediately that a man had been there. A chair embodies in itself something of the spiritual intellect that conceived and produced it. Every effect resembles its cause, since something of the cause itself is clearly present in the effect.

Therefore, you can reason back from effect to cause and ahead, from cause to effect, in prediction. Thus, you can know something when you know it according to its causes. According to Aristotle, in order to really know a substance in any basic fashion, we must know the four causes that explain it. He lists these as: the efficient cause, the maker; the final cause, the end for which the thing is made and the reason why the maker acts; the formal cause, that which makes a thing the kind of thing it is; and finally the material cause, that out of which the thing is made.

In regard to existence, the efficient cause of a thing is, of course,

---

9 "Homo autem, secundum diversa cognita habet diversas cognitiones: nam secundum quod cognoscit principia, dicitur habere intelligentiam; scientiam vero, secundum quod cognoscit conclusiones; sapientiam, secundum quod cognoscit causam altissimam; consilium vel prudentiam, secundum quod cognoscit agibilia" (St. Thomas, *Summa Theologica*, I, 14, 1, ad 2). Cf. St. Thomas, *In Meta.*, Proemium, "Now we can understand 'the most intelligible things' in three ways. First, from the order of understanding; for that seems to be more intelligible from which the intellect derives its certitude. Whence, since the intellect acquires certitude of science from causes, the knowledge of causes seems to be most intellectual. It also follows that the science which considers first causes seems to be the supreme director of the others" (Armand Maurer, *The Divisions and Methods of the Sciences* [Toronto, Canada: The Pontifical Institute of Mediaeval Studies, 1953], p. 81). ". . . dicendum est quod scientia est secundum modum cognoscentis: scitum enim est in sciente secundum modum scientis" (*S.T.*, I, 14, 1, ad 3).

the most important; but the formal cause, nature or essence, is the primary object in knowledge. For once the formal cause is known, you can work back to the efficient cause, and ahead to the final cause. Knowledge of the formal cause gives the knowing being a power over things, a control of their intelligible aspects.[10]

To locate this *formal cause* in reality, to understand just what it is that we mean when we speak of form or essence, or nature, an analogy may prove useful. Analogies have a certain importance in philosophy. Not that they provide, in themselves, an illumination of those intelligibilities which are so immersed in concrete, individual reality, that they cannot be intelligently disengaged, but must be experientially communicated, as in practical, poetic knowledge; not in this direct fashion is the analogy of value to the philosopher as it is to the poet. But it does serve to rivet the attention of the mind on the precise aspect of reality to be investigated; it provides the rich imagery and emotional resonances psychologically necessary to rational activity to keep it revolving about its exact object, and thus it makes possible the eventual intellectual penetration of a problem to intelligible depths very difficult to arrive at otherwise. It is only in this fashion that we make use of images, metaphors, and similes, and not for the intelligibilities they occasion more directly in their proper role in a practical knowledge such as poetry.

If by way of analogy we consider the dissolution of three representative life forms, a man, a dog, and a rose bush, we find that they may be reduced to the same kind of synthesis in organic chemistry, carbon and its compounds, and to exactly the same materials in inorganic compounds. If the material to which these things may be reduced in their dissolution is the same, and if the elements out of which they are constructed are similar, then how do we account for the differences among a man, a dog, and a rose bush? The differences of things demand some basic principle of explanation. There must be something different in a man and a dog, if the same meat and cheese when eaten is woven in one case into a hand, in the other, a paw. Matter alone cannot account for the differences of things. There must be some principle of organization which makes a man a man, a dog a dog, and a rose bush a rose bush. There must be some principle of organization that takes the zygote or primary living cell of a human being and molds it, shapes it, organizes it into a man. And the same for the dog and the rose bush. This is what the scholastics meant by *form, that by which a thing is what it is,* that by which a man is a man, a dog a dog, and a rose bush

---

[10] Cf. *infra,* Part IV, Chap. XI, 4, p. 179 f.

a rose bush. And this is what we mean by the *soul* of things. *A soul is simply a certain kind of form, the form of a living body,* a form from which flow the immanent operations that characterize living beings, i.e., such operations as nutrition, growth, reproduction, sensation, locomotion, intellection, and volition.

If this is what it means to be a soul, then the canard, "I never found a soul under my scalpel," becomes ridiculous. Where does the heart come from? What organizes lungs out of the bread and butter we eat? What systematizes protoplasm into the awesome complexity of the human brain tissue? Every time you shake hands with a man, you touch his soul. In his five fingers with their protective nails, we see the stamp of the soul on the body, the principle of organization that makes a thing to be what it is.

This, of course, is not a proof for the existence of forms in things. We simply mean to point out the intellectual absurdity of a speculative materialism. We do not mean practical materialism. That is very understandable. Man has always been attracted and torn asunder within himself by the compelling beauties and delights of the material things that beckon to the hungers of his own nature. All of us well know the fascination of this type of materialism, but we do find absurd a speculative materialism. We reject an intellect that can reduce all the complexities of reality into one basic homogeneous stuff, matter, that can ignore the obvious differences in things, so that a man, an automobile, the sun blazing out of the sky, and the rose bush it warms and vivifies, are all made of but one homogeneous, basic stuff. The differences of things are more important than what they have in common, and it is their differences by which they are specified when they are known to us as a man, a dog, or a rose bush. We shall have more to say about this later.[11]

---

[11] Cf. *infra,* Part I, Chap. III, 4, p. 54.

CHAPTER III. / THE CLASSIFICATION OF THE SCIENCES

SINCE science is properly a knowledge of causes, then the different sciences will vary by reason of the kind of causes they seek.[1] In the philosophical sciences we are concerned with the ultimate causes of all things. We are looking for the most basic principles which make things what they are, and, consequently, explain them. The philosophical sciences deal with what a thing is in its last analysis. Because they are concerned with ultimate causes, the philosophical sciences study essences directly. And since they know essences, the method of procedure must be deductive. From the application of general principles, these sciences arrive at knowledge in particular cases. For example, once we know that in essence man is body and soul, if we know that Reginald is a man, we know that he is composed of body and soul. If we see the essential relation of speech to man's essence, then the same type of deduction follows. Man has a body and, more specifically, lungs and vocal chords by reason of which he can produce sound. He is also possessed of an intellect which produces concepts which in turn find their verbal expression in these sounds. Once we see the essential connection of man's fundamental constitution and the power of speech,

---

[1] Cf. chart on p. 35.

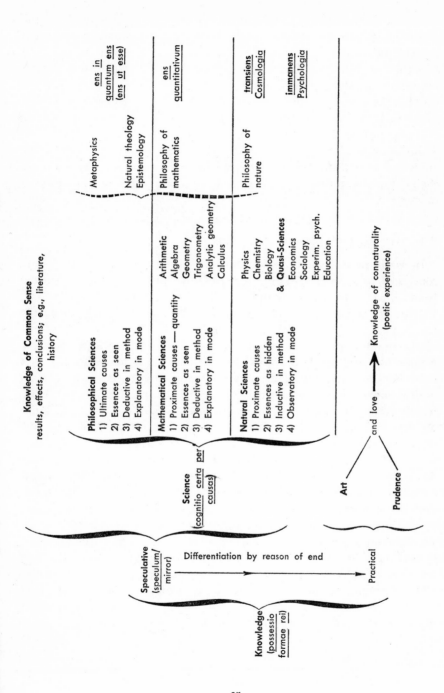

we know that wherever we encounter a human being, he will have the power of speech. By the power of speech we do not mean the actual exercise of speech as in conversation, so that the dumb man would lack the power of speech; rather we mean the inner structure or faculty by reason of which man can speak. A doctor who is skillful enough could make a dumb man speak. But no doctor, no matter how skillful, could make a tree speak. Man has the power of speech even when he is silent, just as the swimming champion has the ability to swim even while sunning himself on the sands. Also, since these philosophical sciences tell what things are and attempt to explain the essences of things, their ultimate causes or explanations, they are called explanatory in mode.[2]

§ 1. THE MATHEMATICAL SCIENCES

In mathematical sciences, as compared with the philosophical, we are concerned with proximate causes, i.e., the quantities of things abstracted from concrete things. Quantity is the accident from which flow size, weight, dimension, measurability, and divisibility. Although abstracted from concrete things, the objects of mathematics exist, nevertheless, only in the mind. We abstract roundness from an apple or squareness from a table top, and mentally construct a circle and a square which do not exist outside the mind. *Only the roundness and squareness exist in reality as real accidental characteristics of real things.* Like the point, which takes on height, width, and thickness when drawn, the circle and square can only exist in their simplicity and perfection in the mind. They are intellectual constructs, as Poincaré recognized.[3] And this is precisely the reason for the celebrated certitude of mathematical thought. Since the objects of mathematics exist in the mind, since they are produced by the mind, since they are cut of the same cloth as the mind, we can know them exhaustively. And since we know them exhaustively we can deduce from them with absolute certitude. *We know the essences of these accidents which we have constructed mentally* — mental constructs. We can know the essence of a *square,* though not the essence of a *square thing.* We can see the precarious position of those knowledges like education, sociology, and economics which, in order to become sciences, model themselves upon mathematics. In order to attain a share of the certainty of mathematical knowledge, some are of the

---

[2] Cf. *infra*, Part II, Chap. X.

[3] Henri Poincaré, *Science and Hypothesis*, trans. G. B. Halstead (New York: The Science Press, 1905), introduction and Chap. 1; cf. also Chaps. 3–4.

opinion that all they have to do is to sprinkle their work with numbers, graphs, and technical definitions, the nearest thing in words to mathematical formulas. They do not realize that *the source of mathematical certitude is not the mere presence of numbers nor the rigor of deductive procedure, but the simplicity of the objects involved.* Mathematical entities, since we make them, are known exhaustively. When we know that the triangle is a three-sided figure, the sum of whose angles equals 180 degrees, then we have captured a triangle; everything else can be deduced from the first principles of geometry. But real things are much more complex than abstract quantity.[4] There is a whole wealth of intelligibility that we ignore when we designate a thing as two, or circular.

We cannot know the essences of real things so exhaustively because the human intellect cannot possess, absolutely, all that is knowable in things. However, the fact that education and sociology cannot arrive at the same degree of certitude as mathematics does not mean that they are unimportant by comparison, as some pseudoscientists today seem to think. When Aristotle said that a little knowledge about the highest things is more valuable than a great deal of knowledge of the lowest things, he put his finger on the point at issue.

Since man is of such importance, anything that we can know about his development, relationships, and well-being is by that fact very valuable. Even the little that is known becomes of much more importance than a mountain of mathematical facts about lower things. This realization should give the social scientist a conception of his own dignity independent of a slavish humility to mathematics and physics, a sense of the worth of his own knowledge. Because his insights are incapable of exhausting the richness of human nature, must he reduce this richness to the barrenness of quantitative relations?

§ 2. THE NATURAL SCIENCES

The natural sciences also deal with proximate causes, the accidents of things. However they do not care what things are. They do not know essences or natures immediately. If we ask of the various sciences: what is man? — we receive the answers we saw earlier. In physics man is an articulating system of stresses and strains; in chemistry man is a com-

---

[4] We can measure precisely the volume of an abstract cylinder, but we cannot measure with the same precision a concrete wastebasket. Its sides are not uniform. Even a calculus cannot smooth them out completely. The best way to measure *accurately* the volume of an individual wastebasket is to fill it with a liquid and then measure the liquid. Only in mathematics do we have this precision of measurement, never in the real world. It is too complex.

The Aristotelian-Boethian
Classification of the Sciences:*

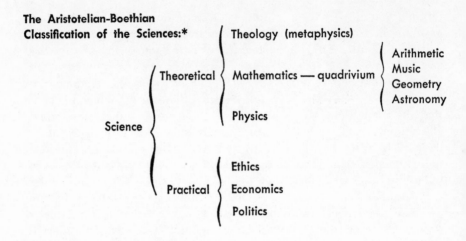

Theology (metaphysics)

Science
- Theoretical
  - Theology (metaphysics)
  - Mathematics — quadrivium
    - Arithmetic
    - Music
    - Geometry
    - Astronomy
  - Physics
- Practical
  - Ethics
  - Economics
  - Politics

The Platonic Classification /*

Science
- Physics
- Ethics
- Logic

(used by stoics, academics, and epicureans and passed to the Latin West by Augustine and Isidore of Seville):

plexus of elements and compounds; in biology he is a mammal of the order of primates, that is, he has a vertebra so constructed that he walks upright, and a mammary gland to suckle his young; in economics he is a producer and a consumer; in philosophy, however, he is a rational animal. All the *sciences* define the things they deal with in terms of accidents, whether of quantity, quality, or otherwise. When, however, *philosophy* defines man as a rational animal, whether right or wrong, it is at least attempting to tell us *what* things are, something that not one of the other sciences alone, or all of them together, attempt to do.

* Used by Cassiodorus, *Institutiones,* ii, 3, R. A. B. Mynors, ed., p. 110.
** For an account of this subject see L. Baur's edition of Dominicus Gundissalinus, *De Div. Philos.,* p. 349 ff.; M. Grabmann, *Geschichte der scholastischen Methods;* R. W. Hunt, "The introductions to the 'Artes' in the twelfth century," in *Studia Mediaevalia R. J. Martin,* p. 85 sqq.
Quoted by A. C. Crombie, *Grosseteste and Experimental Science* (Oxford, 1943), pp. 21–22.

When the physicist, in illustration of the law of acceleration, drops objects from the Empire State Building, the results will be the same as long as the objects have the same weight and dimensions. The physicist is interested in how fast they fall; how long they will take to reach the ground; what is the rate of acceleration per second per second. It makes no difference whether these articles are men, sacks of potatoes, or barrels of flour. The job of the physicist *as* physicist is not to tell what things are but only how they operate. He is concerned only with matter in motion.

Some scientists, or rather some philosophers of science, particularly logical positivists, hold that physics and chemistry do explain the nature of things by the atomic theory. They claim that a shifting of position of many electrical particles, the same in both substances, explains, for example, how the combination of two poisonous substances, sodium and chlorine, produces the food sodium chloride, or common table salt. In other words, quantitative addition or subtraction accounts for qualitative change. They would have us believe, too, that the piling up of billions of microcosms of tiny particles and space (for so they describe atoms and molecules) produces what we feel as solids when, for example, we pound a fist on a desk. The natural sciences cannot explain what things are, but only how they act. In this sphere, operations, the atomic theory is certainly valid. It is certainly fruitful, too, to draw imaginative representations of atoms, models, in order to work more easily with operations, but this theory does not explain the essences of things.

A. Induction and Essence

Although we do not know, through the natural sciences, natures or essential definitions in the way that we do in the philosophical and mathematical sciences, essences cannot be completely eliminated from the natural sciences. Our contention is that if there are no essences in things, then the inductive method is reduced to a raw enumeration which in no way carries with it the principle of its own necessity.[5] If we deny the existence of essences or natures, some sort of structure, then

---

[5] "It will be obvious that Popper has abandoned the 'inductive' analysis of scientific method, according to which science begins from 'pure observations' which it gradually builds up by induction into generalizations. Scientists gradually come to believe in the existence of regularities, on this vein, as a result of their having repeated experiences of similar patterns of events. But in fact, Popper objects, we are all of us born with expectations, inborn reactions, of which the expectation of regularity is the most important. What we have gradually to develop is a *critical attitude* — not a propensity to generalize, but a willingness to subject our generalizations to testing" (J. Passmore, *A Hundred Years of Philosophy* [London: Duckworth, 1957], p. 410).

the certainty and necessity so necessary to scientific method has no basis. Simply because a given number of instances have been examined, as in examining ten men we see that they have the power of speech, are we then justified in formulating the general law that all men have the power of speech?[6] If we find that in each case water boils at one hundred degrees centigrade under standard conditions, are we justified in stating that in all cases water boils at one hundred degrees centigrade under standard conditions? Does this simple enumeration carry any more weight than the hypothetical fact that since we have found in every case that broomsticks have red bands, the next time we come across a broomstick it is going to have a red band? Why cannot the next man we meet not have the power of speech?

Unless there is some essential connection between the thing and its characteristic property, then there is no foundation for the certainty of scientific knowledge.[7] Only if there is something about man by reason of which he has the power of speech, if there is some center of stability, some principle of regularity, some inner structure from which this characteristic flows, can we preserve the scientific character of induction.[8]

---

6 "Since the time of Bacon it has been thought one of the principal tasks of philosophy to justify induction. But philosophers have not made sufficiently clear to themselves what sort of justification is required, and most of the attempts to solve the problems have been misconceived. At one time it was held necessary to establish some truth of high generality about causation which would serve as a premiss for an argument by elimination. The underlying assumption of this approach was that induction could be justified only if it was presented as a variety of deduction. We have seen, however, that induction is not always concerned with causes and that it is not an argument by elimination" (William Kneale, *Probability and Induction* [Oxford: Oxford University Press, 1952], p. 223).

7 "Although the old way of thinking still has some defenders even among those who do not make the mistake of supposing that all induction is concerned with causes, it is now generally realized that we cannot hope to find any method of arguing with certainty from facts to laws. No self-conscious, reflective scientist wishes to claim that the induction he practices is infallible, and no philosopher who understands his job wishes to suggest that he can provide the scientists with a guarantee that if they follow a method purified by him they will always reach true conclusions. It has therefore become customary to say that the conclusions of induction are only probable, and various attempts have been made in recent times to justify induction by showing when and why its conclusions attain high probability in the sense of the theory of chances. Some of these attempts are adaptations of the argument by elimination, while others are supposed to be free from all association with the old doctrine, but we have seen that they are all alike open to the objection that the notion of probability appropriate to the theory of chances has no application to the results of induction" (*ibid.*, p. 221).

8 "I have based my arguments on the assumption that there may be truths of principle which we cannot know *a priori.* . . . The doctrine that there are truths of principle which we cannot know *a priori* is presupposed by the activity of natural scientists" (*ibid.*, p. 254). ". . . but we do restore the reason for practicing induction. So long as we believe that there are or may be principles of necessity or impossibility,

Therefore, although the natural scientist does not deal with essences immediately, he cannot deny their existence, otherwise he cuts away the scientific character of knowledge.[9] Certain modern scientists have seen the problem in just this way and have suicidally followed out the consequences of their denial of essences. The result has been that they have actually denied the certainty of their own knowledge and reduced scientific law to mere probability, a conclusion that contradicts both science and experience.

Consequently, the basic problem in any explanation of induction is an assessment of the role of essence, whether we call this the "truths of principle" as William Kneale does, or the "family resemblances" as Wittgenstein does.

No matter how abstract essences may seem they are always justified by the attempt to explain the intelligible aspects of things. As "transcendent hypotheses"[10] they are no more abstract than many accepted

we have good reason for conjecturing probability rules, whereas without that belief we should have no reason. The fact that we cannot at present make any profitable conjectures about the form of the principles presupposed by probability rules about transcendent objects is no obstacle to the attempt to formulate such rules, for we are often in a similar situation when we practice primary induction. Nor should it make us give up the hope that by a further refinement of our transcendent object terminology we may someday get an explanatory hypothesis which satisfies us better. No doubt, we are farther from the ideal of secondary induction than we once thought, but the only insurmountable obstacle to scientific progress is defeatism" (*ibid.*, p. 256).

[9] "To put the matter more fully and more precisely, if I say that a perceptual object belongs to a certain natural kind, I think of it as having a nature which is not, and cannot be, manifested in any single perception nor yet in any sequence of perceptions, however long. Our difficulty in describing ampliative induction arises from our failure to realize this strange feature of perceptual object terminology" (*ibid.*, p. 257).

[10] "The essential point is rather that the physical world as described in such theories cannot, from the nature of the case, be observed as sticks and stones are observed. I can see a wave passing over the surface of a pond, but it is merely senseless to speak of seeing or observing in any other way an electromagnetic wave. It is even impossible to imagine these things, for if we try to imagine them we must attribute to them qualities such as colour or perceptible hardness which they cannot possess. I propose to call hypotheses about things of this kind *transcendent*, because I think it is necessary to indicate quite clearly that they are concerned with things which are not observable even in principle. This is a difficult doctrine, and two questions about it come to mind immediately.

"In the first place, if all our ideas are derived from experience, as it seems plausible to say with Locke and the empirical school of philosophers, how can we even suppose the existence of things which are in principle unobservable? The answer is that in these hypotheses we suppose only the existence of a set of things having a certain structure which can be expressed in the language of mathematics. The sense in which the word 'structure' is used here can best be understood from an example. A tune which is heard and a musical score which is seen may be said to have the same logical structure although they are sensibly very different. That structure might conceivably be expounded to a person who had neither hearing nor sight but only

scientific theories and concepts basic to the social sciences. Essences are always rooted in the world of nature, at least minimally, by their explanatory power. This can be regarded as an inescapable truth of

touch. Structure cannot, of course, exist without content, and, when I say that in transcendent hypotheses we suppose only the existence of a set of things having a certain structure, I do not mean that we suppose the existence of a set of things having only a certain structure, for that would be absurd. What I mean is that, although we cannot even conjecture what the content is that embodies the structure, we can reasonably suppose that there is a set of things of that structure, just as a man deaf from birth can suppose that there are complex objects called tunes which embody the structures about which he reads in books of music. That transcendent hypotheses are concerned only with structure has often been overlooked in the past, because scientists and philosophers have mistakenly allowed themselves to slip some imaginative elements, such as perceptible hardness, into their conceptions of the objects mentioned in the hypotheses. Berkeley pointed out quite correctly that hypothetical entities of the physicists were unimaginable, but he concluded wrongly that because they were unimaginable they were inconceivable" (ibid., pp. 93–94).

"Hypotheses are already prior knowledge. As regards essences, we know from common sense that things are of different kinds — then we attempt to give this insight of common sense knowledge an explanatory foundation — to make it in other words explanatory and scientific.

"Secondly, how can hypotheses of this kind explain laws about observable things? If the hypotheses contained no reference to the world of common sense, it would, of course, be impossible to explain laws about observables by their help. These hypotheses are, however, doubly general propositions (universal and existential) of such forms as: 'Wherever light of such-and-such a colour (i.e. a perceptual object) occurs, there is a wave process of such-and-such a wavelength, and vice versa.' They are introduced for the purpose of explaining laws, and, however abstruse they may become in the course of development, they must always remain attached in this way to the world of perceptual objects if they are to achieve their purpose" (ibid., p. 94).

"Natural laws which have been formulated originally in the perceptual object terminology can therefore be translated into the transcendent object terminology. When so translated they naturally appear more complex, because the new terminology is, so to say, of finer grain. Instead of a comparatively simple statement about the melting point of a chemical substance we have a statement about the average velocity of molecules of such-and-such internal constitution at the time when the attractive forces between them no longer suffice to keep them in a rigid formation. But the greater complexity of the expressions for laws in the new terminology is intended to exhibit the necessity of the laws, and the price paid is small if the new terminology does indeed make it possible to explain the laws within a comprehensive theory" (ibid., p. 95).

"In the earlier stages of its development a transcendent hypothesis may contain assumptions about unobservable objects which are similar to the laws of nature we formulate about observable objects in that they cannot be seen to be necessary" (ibid., p. 97).

Leibniz and Huyghens' scientific procedure serves as the model for "transcendent hypotheses": "There is to be found here a kind of demonstration which does not produce a certainty as great as that of geometry and is, indeed, very different from that used by geometers, since they prove their propositions by certain and incontestable principles, whereas here principles are tested by the consequences derived from them. The nature of the subject permits no other treatment. It is possible nevertheless to attain in this way a degree of probability which is little short of complete certainty.

philosophic inquiry. It has forced itself on the most diverse thinkers in the history of philosophy from the time of the Pre-Socratics to the present. Here we should not be mislead by semantics. The compelling

---

This happens when the consequences of our assumed principles agree perfectly with the observed phenomena, and especially when such verifications are numerous, but above all when we conceive in advance new phenomena which should follow from the hypotheses we employ and then find our expectations fulfilled. If in the following treatise all these evidences of probability are to be found together, as I think they are, the success of my inquiry is strongly confirmed and it is scarcely possible that things should not be almost exactly as I have represented them. I venture to hope, therefore, that those who enjoy finding out causes and can appreciate the wonders of light will be interested in these varied speculations about it" (Huyghens, *Treatise on Light, Preface*, 1960).

"Newton's doctrine in this passage [General Scholium] and in other places where he talks of scientific method is very puzzling, because it does not square with his own practice. . . . But more remarkable still, his establishment of the theory of motion and of the principle of universal gravitation, which he cites as an example of direct induction from phenomena, is in truth a very notable achievement of the hypothetical method. The so-called law of gravitation is that every body attracts every other body with a force which is proportional to its own mass but varying inversely as the square of its distance from that other. This is indeed a universal proposition, but not one which could conceivably be established by the discovery in experience of instances falling under it. We do not perceive forces of attraction between the bodies we can observe, and we never shall, because forces are objects of a sort we cannot hope to perceive. What we do observe are movements of perceptual objects such as stones, but these give no direct confirmation of the law of gravitation. My chair and my table, for example, are not, so far as I can see, moving towards each other at present; indeed, the law of gravitation does not require that they should, for it deals only with forces, not with actual movements. Even the famous apple did not furnish an instance which directly confirmed the law. For, as Newton himself would insist, the movement of the apple was not determined solely by the attraction of the earth; the resistance of the air and the attraction of the distant heavenly bodies all had some part in determining the course of events. Newton's law of gravitation was, of course, established by an argument from experience, but not by ordinary induction" (Kneale, *Probability and Induction*, pp. 99–100).

"If he were alive to-day, Newton would probably admit without hesitation that hypotheses like that which Huyghens put forward have been amply justified, and that it is inconceivable that physical science should now try to dispense with them" (*ibid.*, pp. 100–101). "Newton, despite his famous 'hypotheses non fingo' certainly used 'transcendent hypotheses' in the formulation of the law of gravitation — forces are not *perceivable* between the bodies we observe" (*ibid.*, pp. 99–100).

"The aim of phenomenalists in our time is, therefore, rather to explain away the appearance of transcendence which they find in physical theories. Some of them content themselves with saying that any statement which appears to be about transcendent objects can be replaced in principle by a series of hypothetical statements about sensa. I have never seen any detailed attempt to carry out this programme, but I am quite confident that any such attempt would fail. Since, as we have seen, statements about perceptual objects cannot be replaced by statements about sensa, there is no reason at all to suppose that statements about atoms and electrons can be eliminated in this way. On the contrary, a direct transition from the terminology of physical theory to the sensum terminology is clearly impossible" (*ibid.*, pp. 101–102).

"The observation of X-ray shadows or of vapour trails in Wilson chambers may perhaps seem to bring us nearer to the transcendent objects of which the physicist

force of this truth is such that it cannot be denied, whether we call
the reality signified "essences" as Aristotle and the scholastics held,
or "family resemblances" a la Wittgenstein.[11] The same reality has

speaks than any experiment with familiar perceptual objects, but this is mere illusion.
The physical theories were formulated before these particular techniques were developed and do not stand or fall by the results obtained from them rather than by
the results of any other physical experiments" (ibid., pp. 101–102).

"The transcendent aspects of physical theories cannot be substituted for by hypothetical propositions verified by sense. The terminology of physical theory is irreducible to the terminology of sense data. It always demands perceptual objects
rather than pure sense data. What takes place within the nucleus of the atom is
not the object of direct sensory observation.

"The philosophers to whom I have just referred argue that all the novelty of those
physical theories which appear to be transcendent lies in their terminology. According
to their view the physicist is mistaken if he thinks that he has introduced new
existential hypotheses in talking of atoms and electrons. He has merely found a
new and more convenient way of talking about observables. The new way is more
convenient because it makes for what Mach called economy of thought.

"For expressions of the perceptual object terminology, which are comparatively
simple but yield only mutually independent propositions, there are substituted more
complex expressions which enable us to present natural laws as consequences of
some small number of postulates. This is just a matter of definition. Nothing is
asserted about the world in the new terminology which was not asserted in the
perceptual object terminology, but what is said is given in a form more convenient
for calculation" (ibid., pp. 102–103).

Scientific theories cannot be mere linguistic devices or idealistic constructions because scientific hypotheses do actually explain something about the structure of
material reality on the basis of which laws are formulable otherwise only as such
hypotheses, as a matter of cause, fruitful of innovatory consequences:

"I conclude, then, that the statements made by physical scientists in the formulation
of transcendent hypotheses are to be taken at their face value, namely, as assertions
of the existence of imperceptible objects with certain specified structures. No other
account seems to me to do justice to the facts; and I think that, when philosophers
and scientists feel difficulty in admitting that transcendent hypotheses are what they
seem to be, that is only because, like Berkeley, they have adopted an unduly narrow
view of the possibilities of thinking" (ibid., p. 103).

The hypothetical method is a form of "secondary" or "indirect" induction with
provocative relations to deduction.

11 Wittgenstein states very definitely that there is no common thing, no community
which is called essence. "Our passion for unity is not, of course, confined to the field
of language alone. We tend to assume that there is something in common to all
horses, to all tables, to all men, to all games, to all religions, and so on. And this is
a natural assumption. The class of horses, for example, cannot be a merely random
one. Its members, the individual horses, no matter how different they may be in other
respects must have some characteristics in common — or so we think — for otherwise
they would not be named or nameable by the single general term 'horse.' These
shared characteristics constitute the essence of that kind of thing, constitute 'horseness.'
And, since everything is of some kind — it is either a man, a table, a piece of silver,
or whatever — everything has an essence. There can be no gainsaying the powerful
influence this idea has exerted on man's thought from the time of Plato down to
the present.

"One form of the craving for unity, then, is a craving for essence, and it is so
strong that we tend to assume that everything actually has an essence — that it is

been, we must note, variously designated throughout the history of philosophy. Today, in addition to Wittgenstein's notion of "family

---

the essence of all nouns to name some entity, or kind of entity, in the way that 'John Jones' or 'tree' do, that it is the essence of all declarative sentences to state some fact in the way that 'The cat is on the mat' does, and so on" (Pitcher, *The Philosophy of Wittgenstein* [Englewood Cliffs, N. J.: Prentice-Hall, 1965], pp. 216–217).

"Wittgenstein sets out to show that the belief in essences, although widespread and entirely natural, is mistaken. Whereas philosophers have traditionally looked for sameness and unity, Wittgenstein looks for difference and multiplicity; indeed, he once remarked to a friend that he had considered using as a motto for the *Investigations* a line from *King Lear* — 'I'll teach you differences.' According to Wittgenstein, one has only to examine, for example, the various individuals to which a given general term applied, to see that there is nothing which they all have in common. As a plain matter of fact, they do not share a common essence. Wittgenstein cites the examples of games: If we look at all the things called 'games,' we will not find some characteristic (s) that they all have, in virtue of which we call them by that name. Wittgenstein's own account there is so lucid and pungent that I cannot do better than simply quote it:

> Consider for example the proceedings that we call 'games.' I mean board-games, card-games, Olympic games, and so on. What is common to them all? — Don't say: 'There *must* be something common, or they would not be called "games."' — but *look and see* whether there is anything common to all. — For if you look at them you will not see something that is common to *all*, but similarities, relationships, and a whole series of them at that. To repeat: don't think, but look! — Look for example at board-games, with their multifarious relationships. Now pass to card-games; here you find many correspondences with the first group, but many common features drop out, and others appear. When we pass next to ball games, much that is common is retained, but much is lost. — Are they all 'amusing'? Compare chess with noughts and crosses. Or is there always winning and losing, or competition between players? Think of patience. In ball games there is winning and losing; but when a child throws his ball at the wall and catches it again, this feature has disappeared. Look at the parts played by skill and luck; and at the difference between skill in chess and skill in tennis. Think now of games like ring-a-ring-a-roses; here is the element of amusement, but how many other characteristic features have disappeared! And we can go through the many, many other groups of games in the same way; can see how similarities crop up and disappear [PI, sec. 66].

"These words can come as a revelation. Whereas one had always quite uncritically, and most likely also unconsciously, taken it for granted that all things called by a general term had something — an essence — in common, he sees now that it is not necessarily so. At one stroke, that assumption has been revealed and destroyed. As it falls away, one's entire view of language, and indeed of the world, is quite altered" (*ibid.*, pp. 217–218).

"Rather we tend to assume that there is some community, something common in all horses which causes us to call them by the name 'horse.' Actually there are only 'family resemblances' and overall 'similarities.'

"We must not, however, rush from one extreme to the other; we must not infer from the fact that there is no essence of games or religions, that each is nothing more than a motley, disconnected group of things which are arbitrarily called by the same name. There is no warrant for thinking that the denial of essence leaves no reason whatever why a range of different things are all named by a single general term. Although they have no common essence, they have certain 'family resemblances.' Suppose we consider the many different activities called 'games':

resemblances" we might also take notice of the "Types" mentioned

---

And the result of this examination is: we see a complicated network of similarities overlapping and criss-crossing; sometimes overall similarities, sometimes similarities of detail.

I can think of no better expression to characterize these similarities than 'family resemblances'; for the various resemblances between members of a family: build, features, colour of eyes, gait, temperament, etc., etc. overlap and criss-cross in the same way. — And I shall say: 'games' form a family.

And for instance the kinds of number form a family in the same way. Why do we call something a 'number'? Well, perhaps because it has a direct-relationship with several things that have hitherto been called number; and this can be said to give it an indirect relationship to other things we call [by] the same name. And we extend our concept of number as in spinning a thread we twist fibre on fibre. And the strength of the thread does not reside in the fact that some one fibre runs through its whole length, but in the overlapping of many fibres [PI, secs. 66–67].

"So there is a good reason for applying a single general term to a range of different things, only it is not what believers in essence have thought it was" (ibid., p. 219).

"The word 'game' might be called a genus term, and the concept 'game' a genus concept; there are several species of games falling under it (board-games, ball games, card games, dice games, and so on); and individual games (e.g., chess, tennis, bridge), in turn, belong to one or more species. But not all general terms are genus terms or even species terms. Perhaps, then, it is only because of their special kind of generality that genus and species terms have no unitary meaning. But this is not so. Consider the term 'lemon,' for example. Lemons normally have certain characteristics: a yellow color when ripe, skin of a certain thickness with a waxy texture, ovoid shape, acid taste, a size and hardness that falls within a certain range, and so on. If an object has all these properties, it is definitely a lemon. It might happen that in a particular region of the world, due to atomic fallout, lemon trees started producing fruit of a pinkish color, and with a sweet taste, but having all the other characteristics of ordinary lemons. These fruits would doubtless still be lemons: pink lemons, or sweet pink lemons. A thing cannot lack all, or even very many, of the typical lemon properties, and still be a lemon; but there is no one property, or group of two or three properties, which an object must have to be properly called a lemon. It must simply have some combination of the cluster of properties which lemons typically have. Thus lemons, like games, have no essence; and 'lemon,' like 'game,' has no unitary meaning" (ibid., p. 221).

According to Wittgenstein, one has only to examine various individuals to which a term is applied to see that there is nothing which they have in common. But how does he distinguish this "community" which he identifies with the traditional "essence" and thus denies, from the "family resemblances" and "overall similarities" which he affirms? His difficulty seems to be that he considers "essence" or "community" as *univocal predication* while "family resemblances" and "overall similarities" seem to be predicated analogously.

"Wittgenstein's thesis, although highly plausible for terms like 'horse,' 'lemon,' and 'game,' is not at all plausible for terms like 'brother' and 'vixen'; for to be a brother, it is essential that one be male, and to be a vixen, it is essential that a fox be female. There is, then, an important distinction between those terms that do and those that do not fall under Wittgenstein's thesis. I am not sure how to characterize this distinction in any more fundamental way, but somehow or other it is one that must be made" (ibid., p. 221).

For an interesting discussion of this perplexing subject, see Hilary Putnam's "The

by Bertrand Russell,[12] the "Truths of Principle" favored by W. Kneale,[13]

Analytic and the Synthetic," *Minnesota Studies in the Philosophy of Science*, III, H. Feigl and B. Maxell, eds. (Minneapolis: University of Minnesota Press, 1962). For an article that opposes the claim asserted in this footnote, see J. R. Bambrough's "Universals and Family Resemblances," *Proceedings of the Aristotelian Society*, LXI (1960–1961), especially pp. 212–214.

"To whatever extent Wittgenstein's doctrine is true, to that extent he has dealt a powerful blow against the traditional view of essentialism. According to that view, the characteristics of any class C to whose members a common term T is applicable — the class of horses or games or trees, for example — can be divided into two distinct groups: (a) a relatively small group of essential characteristics — the qualities a thing *must* have in order to be a member of the class C, and which only members of class C have, and (b) a larger group of nonessential, or accidental, characteristics — the qualities that members of class C may or may not typically have, but in either case do not need to have in order to qualify as members of C. The essential characteristics were each supposed to be necessary, and the group of them together sufficient, for membership in the class C. Wittgenstein has attempted to break down this distinction between essential and accidental characteristics; he claims that there are not two radically distinct groups of characteristics of a class C whose members are denoted by a common term T — there is only a single cluster of characteristics, some sub-set of which, and not the *same* sub-set in every case, a thing must have in order to be a member of C, in order for the term T to be (properly) applicable to it" (*ibid.*, pp. 221–222).

But Aristotle, for example, is very clear in his attribution of analogous predication to essences or essential determinations.

It would seem that Wittgenstein after denying the traditional notion of essence because of some Wolffian or Hegelian "straw man" of a prototype, then proceeds to reintroduce the self-same phenomenon which necessarily has to be explained under a different name. But Aristotle would find these essences easily recognizable despite their masquerade.

12 B. Russell, "Mathematical Logic as Based on the Theory of Types," *American Journal of Mathematics*, Vol. 30 (1908), pp. 222–262. Cf. W. Quine, *Methods of Logic* (New York: Holt, Rinehart, and Winston, 1961), pp. 236, 248 ff.

13 "It is evident from the nature of the case that no one can produce an unquestionable example of a truth of principle which he does not know *a priori*. For, although we may suggest that some hypotheses of natural science are such truths, the inductive method on which we rely when we accept these hypotheses does not allow us to claim knowledge of them. But it should not be supposed that this consideration is a strong objection to the theory put forward here. In order to show that ampliative induction, whether primary or secondary, is a rational policy it is not necessary to prove that there *are* truths of principle. It is sufficient to establish that there *may be*, i.e. that the suggestion is not absurd. When they are engaged in their ordinary concerns, inductive scientists usually assume the existence of such truths with natural faith. If this assumption could be *disproved*, there would, indeed, be no reason why they should continue their efforts. But I have argued that the common attempts to disprove it rest on a misconception; and this is all that is required, at least until someone produces an objection which is more difficult to meet. For we want to make true conjectures about the boundaries of possibility, and induction is the only systematic way of trying to do what we want to do. A traveller in the desert who is dying of thirst will struggle towards the place where he thinks he sees an oasis. If presently he is satisfied that what he saw is only a mirage, he may as well lie down and die. But, for a man who understands his situation, even the thought that he may reach water by going in that direction is enough to justify further efforts" (W. Kneale, *Probability and Induction*, pp. 258–259).

or the "Projects" described by Sartre.[14] All these formulations point to similarities in structure which are generalizable and conceptually manipulatable. "Regularities of nature," "Uniformities of operations," "Realms of essence,"[15] all these philosophical formulas indicate some common philosophical experience to which all these thinkers are subject and which they attempt to communicate and explain within the limitations of their ultimate metaphysical positions.

B. The Problematic of Natural Science

What sort of an enterprise is science? Is it a knowledge like poetry and painting? Is it primarily concerned with making or doing something so that its term is a product? In other words is it something practical, an art perhaps? Then is its quintessential form or type to be found in engineering?

What is so-called science of observation? Does the scientist have extraordinarily keen powers of observation? Does he possess super-senses or perhaps specially educated senses? But an eagle or a dog has sharper organs of sight than a man, whereas a half-blind scientist can do brilliant work. The answer seems to lie deeper than that, on a profounder level of mental operation than simple sensation.

Is there some further technique which must be added to observation to enable it to transcend a naïve empirical investigation — one, moreover, that seems to be common to all the knowledges? Does the experiment provide this frame of reference and judicial check on fundamental powers of observation enabling them to work on an experimental level? But is experiment as a technique insufficient? Does it imply more basic suppositions within which the experiment may be constructed in the light of a preconceived hypothesis to be confirmed by the results of the experiment? Or is it the way the results are stated? In other words, must physical propositions, for example, be crystallized in a mathematical equation to achieve real scientific expression? Must a knowledge be mathematicized to gain scientific stature, as Descartes's visionary conviction held?

Is science characterized by hypothesis, or must all knowledge in its incipient moments be hypothetical? Is the construction of the hypothesis an assumption or more than assumption? Is the hypothetical insight the result of a causal chain which the mind follows swiftly, and often surely,

---

[14] J. Wild, *The Challenge of Existentialism* (Indiana University Press, 1959), pp. 88–89; J.-P. Sartre, *Being and Nothingness*, tr. A. Barnes (New York: Philosophical Library, 1956), pp. 95–101.

[15] G. Santayana, *Scepticism and Animal Faith* (New York: Dover, 1955), Chap. 14.

but with the cautious deliberation and elimination of obstacles which are demanded for knowledge to achieve public status? The hypothesis in its framing is the result of a previous knowledge which looks toward verification by confirmatory evidence, stronger than that on which it was originally built. But the hypothesis demands knowledge and insight. Perhaps it is the most creative step in the whole process of scientific knowledge.

Is science characterized by theory? Is it a *theoria* as opposed to a *practice* or *praxis?* Philosophy and science have been distinguished in one traditional way according to the logical method involved. Science is inductive in method while philosophy is deductive in method. Granted, this is an oversimplification, but can this distinction be validly applied if we reduce it to a matter of emphasis? Can we say, for example, that natural science is primarily inductive in method while philosophy is primarily deductive?

Such statements seem to differentiate between the two disciplines, but do they refer to the simple quantitative employment of the specific methods? Namely, is there simply more induction in natural science while philosophy more often employs deduction to reach its conclusions? If these two knowledges are distinct they must be distinguished by the intrinsic mechanics of a method chosen because it fits the particular end and object which the discipline has in mind. The choice of method reaches right down to the very roots of the specification of the knowledge involved.

C. Mode of Observation

Science moves at a very deliberate, measured pace in its movement from sense data which are not quite precise enough to satisfy its exigencies. A refining and measuring process must transform the raw facts of sensation into the finished product glistening in its intelligibility. The brute sensory data must be fixed in some frame of reference, located within some individual organization, so arranged in an integral series that the mind is enabled to grasp at least some partial arc of the indefinite span of causes.

The induction of philosophy called abstraction need not be so precise and measured. The concepts it wants to reach are more general — pure organizations. It can in some cases prefer an induction from a single instance in a formal way, although this is certainly a rather precarious performance.

If the natural sciences do not know natures, then their method cannot be deductive, i.e., they cannot work from the essential definition to the properties which flow from it. Rather, the method they use must be inductive and proceed from the particular to some general conclusion, a progressive approximation of the essence which can be used as a substitute for the essential definition. In this way water is an odorless, colorless, tasteless liquid which boils at one hundred degrees centigrade and freezes at zero degrees centigrade, etc. The sum of the observations of accidental qualities or proximate causes is taken as a substitute for the nature, a "descriptive definition" in place of an essential definition to function in a *science of observation* instead of the explanatory mode characteristic of mathematics, for example.

§ 3. THE INEXACT OR QUASI-SCIENCES

Economics, psychology, sociology, and education are not sciences but rather knowledges which apply the methods of the natural sciences to realities and areas of investigation which lie in great part outside the scope of the natural sciences. The great scandal of our day has been that these knowledges have modeled themselves on mathematical physics in order to partake of its scientific stature. But, as we have seen, it is not possible to make sciences out of these knowledges by the mere insertion of numbers.

In order that economics might become a science it would have to operate in an absolute, planned society. The sociologist would have to disrupt families deliberately under artificial conditions to be able to predict the outcome of social forces as they operate, for instance, in divorce. Psychology must reduce man to a determined effect of determinable causes in order to arrive at any satisfactory so-called scientific knowledge of his behavior.

Freedom enters into the subject matter of economics, for instance, as a variable constituent and it is for this reason that economics can never achieve scientific stature. As long as human beings have the power, despite coercive advertising and propaganda, to say yes or no, to buy or to refuse to buy, then the so-called laws of economics can never become necessary or certain. Free human acts can never become predictable in any absolute fashion, no matter how eager ardent proponents are to make a science out of such a body of knowledge. Here a real danger exists. For the attempt to make a science of economics usually follows one of two roads, each entailing the elimination of human freedom. One would absorb individual free actions into an almost mystical mathematicism, a corruption of the proper role of statistical knowledge. This is very dangerous when the statistics are used as directives of action without sufficient corroboration. The indiscriminate use of polls is an example.

The second or alternative method of removing the frustrating inadequacy of modern economics is by a direct attack on freedom itself. In the completely planned economy, for example, economics would possess an absolute value. In a society where the economist possessed an exact index of production because the worker was told where to work, what to produce and how much, and he also had at his command the precise consumption because each worker was given just so many tickets and so could consume just so much and no more — in this type of planned economy there is a real temptation for the professional economist. He may possess an exhaustive index of necessary economic facts. He may predict in absolute fashion like the mathematical physicist, that paragon of scientific knowledge. He may become a scientist. There is a terrible temptation to power and a very real fascination in the planned economy which we must keep in mind when consulting the economist on the proper direction of economic progress and achievement.

Economics, although it is not concerned with the nature of freedom, is interested in the precise structures for attaining freedom in the economic order. Both phases of freedom, both choice and autonomy, are necessarily represented. Freedom of choice finds its natural expression in the self-determination of the worker to choose his work and his employer, while autonomy is found in the obligation of the entire society to bring about those material conditions consonant with the highest development of the specifically human powers of man. Consumption implies need and thus is an instrument for freeing man from slavery to his material wants. Thus advertising, although beneficial and even necessary in a mass society, in its effects on consumption should not enslave man by an excitation of desire and emotion to a point where he can never free himself from these artificial needs, terrible in their obsession. Production, likewise, is bound up with competition, price policies, and regulations, saturated with the stuff of freedom. Monetary economics, finance, profits, investment, taxation, interest, all of these have a profound bearing on human freedom, and since money is the standard means of acquiring economic goods, it must be handled so as to free all, not only the favored few.

It is here that the economist and kindred thinkers such as the sociologist and the political scientist make their contribution to human freedom; for example, the labor relations expert is almost completely dedicated to preserving freedom in employment. Labor problems, wages, and unions are all devices to gain and preserve the liberty of human beings.

Since psychology has attempted to model itself upon the methods and techniques of physics, it has, to the extent of its success in doing so, been deprived of the ability to analyze reality as a proper object; in fact it has cut itself off from the interpretation of any immaterial reality. Evidence of this is the disproportionate amount of space in contemporary psychology texts devoted to the treatment of sensation as compared to the pitifully inadequate treatment of what is called "imageless thought." What is so tragic is not only that immaterial operations do not fall within the proper scope of psychology thus conceived, but also that many psychologists believe this ignorance to be all that our knowledge can attain to in understanding itself. Contemporary existential psychology makes clear the validity of this introspective method, controlled and reflective, in obtaining legitimate probable knowledge about man. Such discussion is not as crucial a point of departure for a philosophical psychology as it was before phenomenology and existentialism made such inroads on the scientific ideal, modeled on the natural sciences, of psychology and sociology. This country, however, is still the stronghold of such a scientific ideal in psychology and sociology, aping the methods of mathematical physics, and it is important to make this point to the American student who may or may not have been introduced to such a work as the late M. Merleau-Ponty's *The Structure of Behavior*.[16] They do not realize that there is a scientific knowledge of man's intellectual processes about which volumes have been written and to which men of genius have dedicated their entire lives. That is the price that a man of one knowledge must pay. But the shame of it is that society must subsidize his intellectual bankruptcy.

Contemporary psychology is not one science; it is a hybrid knowledge. It is composed of many techniques and methods drawn from several knowledges, possessing only the artificial unity of a common subject matter. Physiological psychology is the most scientific of all the divisions of psychology because it is really part of biology. Part of psychology falls under the natural sciences along with sociology, economics, and education, especially experimental psychology. Adolescent psychology, child psychology, and much of the study of personality actually belong to the knowledge of common sense and, at times to practical knowledge. Thus the dicta of the child psychologist should not be given the au-

---

[16] M. Merleau-Ponty, *The Structure of Behavior*, tr. A. Fisher (Boston: Beacon Press, 1963), Chaps. I and II.

thority of the scientist. When we are told that we should not spank our children, this is not a certain conclusion of the science of psychology, but the considered judgment of a prudent, experienced mind. Although we owe these judgments respect, we should not accord to them a necessity even when they confirm common sense.

Sociologists, psychologists, and educators are not scientists in the strict sense. They do not have a method on which they can rely completely. But they do valuable and necessary work which we could not do without. Their contribution, however, is in a different order. They are not scientists, they are sages. An educator of experience, his iconoclasm and academic dogmatism mellowed by time — a man of great intelligence who has centered his intellectual powers constantly upon the problems of this field, whose life has revolved around the difficulties of the classroom — should be able to see more deeply and with clearer insight into the confusion of human relations. He is not a scientist. He is a sage. And his opinion should have a high value and carry great weight. If anyone is to know the answers, he should; and so his advice should be sought and should play a part in every major decision. He is a sage, a wise man, he has prudential wisdom, but he is not a scientist and his judgments do not carry the necessity of physical law. They are not always right. They may be half wrong. They may be completely wrong. Therefore, such judgments should not rigorously determine the actions of men. We should not be controlled and determined by the latest fad of educators. Often they themselves do see their mistakes but it may take a long period of time to rectify them.

Since psychology, like economics, models itself on physics, problems will present themselves in the same way. One of the reasons for the success of the Freudian interpretation of psychological phenomena lies in its reducing all human operations to some determined, albeit unknown, concatenation of causes. The superego, the ego, and the id are concepts more abstract than metaphysical notions. Freud has transliterated the very facts of which ancient and medieval philosophers were very much aware into a denial of human freedom.[17] This reconciliation of the conclusions of psychology with its own materialistic methods and techniques is in good part responsible for the fame of Freud. Every trace of the immaterial has been eliminated from fundamental human behavior.

Education, likewise, is not a science, and its conclusions do not carry the authority that scientific conclusions do. Yet such is the confusion sometimes evident in the behavior of professional educationists that they

17 Cf. *infra*, Part II, Chap. IX.

seek to impress on millions of malleable human beings as absolute fact what may have only the certitude of opinion. Drastic and revolutionary changes in these fields should be undertaken very cautiously and deliberately in conformity with the type of knowledge that we have of these areas. For our knowledge here does not possess the certainty that it does in science and therefore is not as reliable a guide. Thus, the relatively contemporary innovation of public education should proceed cautiously and be very loathe to discard the lessons learned from the history of that education which has been private and religious. I am holding no brief against public education, of course, but it is amazing to find some of its advocates who do not realize the comparative inexperience and apprenticeship of the state in education. The inability to locate religion in its proper place in our school systems is merely one example. We must proceed slowly and be willing to learn from the past.

It is in a recognition of the fundamental freedom of the human being and an attempt to preserve its dignity that so-called progressive education has found so much of its strength and appeal. But the spontaneity of progressive education must be restricted and channeled by the rules of discipline. A progressive education with its loose curriculum and a traditional education with its planned curriculum, based on the development of the whole man, are but one phase of the relations of initial freedom and freedom of autonomy.

§ 4. THE PLATONIC CLASSIFICATION OF THE SCIENCES

There have been a number of major efforts to classify the sciences. The oldest is perhaps that of Plato. The background for Plato's classification of the sciences is the division he draws between the two worlds of sense and of intelligibility. In this world of sensibles only opinion is possible, merely guesswork or conjecture in knowing the images or likenesses of sensible things. From sensible experience and induction from it, we reach belief which is knowledge of sensible realities. Genuine knowledge is only of the forms. Philosophy, the all-embracing science extending to all reality, is attained by a process of preparation, of education. First will be music (poetry, history, rhetoric), and gymnastic. This is followed by the more abstract science of mathematics, placed between opinion (*doxa*) and knowledge (*epistēmē*) and utilizing a discursive process. The reasoning of mathematics is called understanding (*dianoia*) and deals with arithmetic, geometry, solid geometry, also astronomy and harmony among numbers. Philosophy, the highest kind

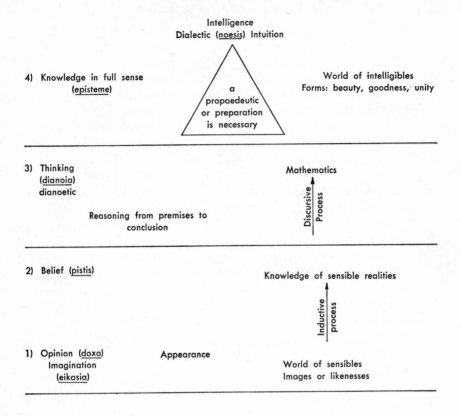

of knowledge, attains forms or ideas. It is knowledge in the highest sense of the word, pure reason or dialectic.

§ 5. BACON'S CLASSIFICATION OF THE SCIENCES

Bacon's classification of the sciences is a universal plan made to order for his method and the conception of the universe upon which it is based. The foundations of his plan are history and experience, the cornerstones of his monumental classification. He divides science into two sweeping categories: theology, which is concerned with divine revelation, and philosophy, which is dependent upon external sense. First philosophy *(Philosophia Prima)* is a general science whose purpose is the reception of axioms not peculiar to any science but common to all. Philosophy is divided into natural, divine, and human science: the doctrine of God, of nature, and of man. This *Philosophia Prima* is a first branch of philosophy as it is opposed to theology.

BACON'S CLASSIFICATION OF THE SCIENCES
Inductive Method: The New Logic

First Philosophy
An enumeration of the
general principles of the
introductory structure of
all knowledge.

Material causes

Physics — Mathematics

Accidental forms

Efficient causes

Natural Philosophy

(Theoretical philosophy)

Metaphysics

Formal causes

Final causes

Laws of individual operation

Natural philosophy is divided into speculative and practical with mathematics as an appendix, divided in turn into pure and mixed or applied mathematics. Speculative philosophy is divided into physics and metaphysics with an appendix called speculative physics treating of natural problems and the opinions of ancient philosophers. Physics, which is concerned with things wholly immersed in matter and movable also, may be resolved into the science of the principles of things, the science of the structure of things, and the science of the variety of things. This last named division may be subdivided into abstract physics, or physics of nature dealing with material forms or schemas in matter, and motion, both simple and compound, and into concrete physics of creatures dealing with the distribution of the parts of natural history and including beneath it both astronomy and astrology.

Metaphysics is taken in quite a different sense from the Aristotelian.[18]

---

[18] Cf. *infra*, Chap. IV, 3–5, pp. 67–78.

It deals with abstracted and fixed objects and is concerned with a knowledge of forms and final causes. Practical knowledge, as opposed to speculative, treats of the sciences of mechanics and of magic. Magic too has lost its accepted meaning and is considered by Bacon as experimental philosophy testing the hidden forces producing great effects. An appendix to practical knowledge is an inventory of human helps and a catalog of experiments.

The third great division of the sciences, following the science of God and natural science, is the science of man. Its major divisions are human philosophy and civil philosophy. Civil philosophy deals with the arts of conversation, human relations, or negotiation or business, and finally state policy or government. Human philosophy treats man as a composite and has a subdivision flowing from body and soul. Under body we have medicine, cosmetics, and athletics, while under soul we treat of logic, ethics, and the arts of logic, judgment, invention, memory, and tradition. This is certainly a comprehensive and detailed, if not wholly consistent, classification of knowledge.

§ 6. LOCKE'S CLASSIFICATION OF THE SCIENCES

All things that man can know fall into three general categories. These three classes of science are *Physica, Practica,* and *Logica* or the "Doctrine of Signs."

Physics deals with the natures of things as they are in themselves, their relation, and their modes of operation. It is also termed natural philosophy due to its concern with proper beings in their constitution, properties, and operations. Spiritual as well as material things fall within the scope of this science, for instance, God and the angels. The specifying end of *Physica* is pure speculative truth, and it is this that formally distinguishes it from *Practica*.

Practica is the science of the correct applications of our powers and actions in pursuit of the good and the useful. The most important subdivision of *Practica* is ethics, which is concerned with formulating the rules and measures of human action in pursuit of happiness and the best methods of applying them to practice. Thus, the distinctive end of *Practica* is not pure speculation and the knowledge of truth, as it is in the *Physica*, but the "Right" and the conduct conforming to it.

The third division of science is *Logica* or the "Doctrine of Signs." Its office is an examination of the signs necessary in knowledge and its communication, the most important of which are words — for words are the best means of expressing ideas, which are in turn the proper vehicle of knowledge and its necessary instrument.

Physica, Practica, and *Logica* are thus the natural categories into which our understanding of things falls, and they embrace in their distinctive classifications all things as known to us.

§ 7. COMTE'S CLASSIFICATION OF THE SCIENCES

The background for Comte's classification of the sciences is provided by the three phases of intellectual development applicable to the individual as well as society. The theological or supernatural phase treats of the causes and essences of things as dependent directly upon supernatural agents. In the metaphysical phase essences are merely the observable constancies of phenomena and the result of natural forces. The third and final phase is positivism, where the uselessness of inquiry into causes and essences having become obvious, the interest lies only in observation and classification of phenomena in their relations and resemblances — the discovery of the laws of phenomena.

The theological phase passes successively through the stages of fetichism, which is the endowment of inanimate things with life and intelligence, polytheism, and ultimately monotheism. This in time is superseded by metaphysics, which substitutes an entity inseparable from phenomena for a supernatural agent. Note the transition from the supernatural to phenomena themselves.

In the positive stage he explains phenomena by considering only those consistencies and relations inductively achieved and formulated as the laws of nature. The purpose of positivism thus is to generalize science and by so systematizing reality a philosophy of the sciences is presented as a foundation for a social order. In order to accomplish this we must take from science the matter and method of philosophy. All the sciences, physical and social, thus become bases of one science to be investigated by one method alone — the positive method. Thus, positive philosophy is divided into six fundamental sciences: mathematics, astronomy, physics, chemistry, physiology, and finally the crowning science of sociology.

§ 8. SPENCER'S CLASSIFICATION OF THE SCIENCES

Spencer begins his essay "The Classification of the Sciences," with a criticism of Comte's classification that serves as a point of departure for the fundamental rationale behind his own system. He asserts that the general sciences do not develop in the order of their decreasing generality, nor is the progress, within each science, from the general to the special. Spencer's own organization is achieved on the basis of characteristics possessed in common. He classifies by grouping together like attributes and separating the unlike.

Science is divided into three all-inclusive categories. Abstract science treats of the abstract relations under which phenomena are presented to us. Its principal division is mathematics based on the conception of space as the abstract of all relations of coexistence, and logic based upon time as the abstract of all relations of sequence. Logic as dealing with the essentially qualitative relations is opposed to mathematics which treats of quantitative relations. Mathematics can be eventually subdivided into a geometry of position, calculus, arithmetic, algebra, calculus of operations, geometry, kinematics, and finally a geometry of motion.

Passing now from the sciences which are concerned only with the blank forms of relations under which being is manifested to us, we come to those which treat of phenomena themselves, existents in their own right. We can further distinguish between those sciences which treat of phenomena in their elements, abstract-concrete sciences, and those which treat of phenomena in their totalities as we really find them in nature, concrete sciences. The abstract-concrete sciences, in which being under its universal mode and its several nonuniversal modes are regarded as independent, treat the terms of its relations as simple and homogeneous, which they never are in nature. All abstract-concrete sciences have for their object, analytical interpretation. It is their aim to decompose the phenomena and to formulate their components apart from one another; synthesis is employed only for the verification of analysis. Abstract-concrete sciences are divided into two basic categories based upon Spencer's conception of the constitution of matter. For him every phenomenon is more or less composite — a manifestation of force under several distinct modes. Hence result two objects of inquiry. We may study the component modes of force separately, or we may study them as cooperating to generate in this composite phenomenon. Our second classification is divided into the general divisions of mechanics and molecular mechanics and their particular subdivisions, physics, chemistry, etc.

The third and last division is that which treats of phenomena themselves in their totalities, concrete sciences. These sciences, taking the modes of being as they are habitually connected with one another, have for the terms of their relations those heterogeneous combinations of forces that constitute actual phenomena. The subject matter of these concrete sciences is the real as contrasted with the whole or partially ideal. It is not their aim to separate and "generalize apart" the components of all phenomena, but to explain each phenomenon as a product of these components; the purpose is not now to formulate the factors (the elements) of phenomena, but to formulate the phenomena resulting from these factors under the various conditions which the universe presents. The sciences corresponding, as they are, to phenomena are thus: astronomy, geology, biology, psychology, sociology, etc.

CHAPTER IV. / THE
PHILOSOPHICAL SCIENCES

JUST as there are different types of knowledges, science being the highest, and different kinds of science, among which philosophy holds a prominent place, so there is more than one philosophical science.[1] These divisions of philosophy may be distinguished by the degrees of materiality consonant with their mode of operation. If a thing is intelligible in proportion to its immateriality,[2] then the more immaterial the knowledge, the more perfect it is. The degree to which the mind departs from the materiality of things is the basis of distinguishing the different philosophical sciences.[3] The philosophy of nature deals with things that cannot exist without matter nor be thought of without matter. That is why the object of this science is moving or changing being, matter in motion, because matter is the principle of change in things.

One of the doctrines of Aristotle, which must be understood if we are to follow his thought, is the theory of matter and form. This theory found in the Aristotelian physics takes its origin from the analysis of change. Change is a baffling monstrosity of nature; something which

[1] Cf. chart, p. 35. More primitive illustrations of this same classification may be seen in the Aristotelian-Boethian classification on p. 38 and the classification under the form it possessed in the later Greek schools. Cf. these classifications on p. 38.

[2] Cf. *supra,* Chap. I, 4–9, pp. 11–19.

[3] On the degrees of abstraction, cf. J. Maritain, *The Degrees of Knowledge* (New York: Scribners, 1959), pp. 35–38.

was not, is, and something which was, is not. "Where did it come from? Where did it go?" are questions that men still ask of the changing substance. Like Aristotle, Thomas Aquinas finds three fundamentals in change which must be explained if change is to be intelligible. When anything changes — whether it be the apple that is eaten, the pair of shoes that wears out, the oak tree that is shattered — in every such case these three fundamental aspects must be realized:

1) something goes out of existence,
2) something comes into existence,
3) something remains constant.

When we eat an apple something goes out of existence; the roundness, the sweetness, the redness, the pulp, the core, the pits — all that which we know as apple is gone. Something new takes its place — something that has all the characteristics proper to human flesh.

The particular addition to human flesh which comes to us in nourishment did not exist before. Yet obviously something had to remain constant — something had to endure through the change. If there were no such continuity, then of course change becomes impossible. If every time we ate an apple we consumed it totally, having nothing to pass over into our own flesh and bones, then there is no change, but an annihilation and creation. The apple would have to be totally annihilated and the additional quantity of human flesh created out of nothingness: a twofold operation which our experience of change daily denies. This is the origin of the theory of matter and form. There must be something in an apple which makes it be an apple — some *principle of organization* which makes an apple to be an apple, from which flow the characteristics of such a thing — its sweetness, its redness, its roundness, and so on. When we eat an apple, the entire apple is not annihilated, it simply loses the organization of apple. The form of apple passes out of existence. Whatever made it to be an apple is now gone. That is an evident fact of existence. Whatever the characteristics of human flesh may be, they are certainly not those of an apple. With human flesh a new form has taken over that material formerly organized into apple. Here arises that notion of matter which has had so important a role in the history of ideas. Matter for Aristotle is that principle which underlies the substitution of forms, and those qualities are called material which endure and persevere throughout a change. For instance, the total weight before a chemical change is equal to the total weight of the resulting constituents after the change. It is this equivalence in weight which makes possible the scientific structure of chemistry based as it is on the possibility of balancing the elements and compounds entering into a chemical change and those that result from it. In the last analysis chemical formulas are based on the matter of corporeal substance. If a log is burnt in a bell jar the weight of the jar will be the same even when the log has been reduced to a handful of ashes — as long as no gases have been permitted to escape. It is interesting to note that those characteristics that endure throughout change are exactly those characteristics which we term material — weight, bulk, dimension; those characteristics which go out of existence and come into existence we call formal characteristics because they take their origin from the principle of organization of matter — the form of the thing.[4]

The philosophy of mathematics is concerned with things that cannot exist without matter but can be thought of without matter, for example the circle abstracted and constructed from an apple. But metaphysics, the highest of the philosophical sciences, has as its proper object things that can both exist and be thought of without matter, such as God, angels, honor, and love.

§ 1. THE PHILOSOPHY OF NATURE

As we have seen, the natural sciences do work with essences as hidden. Although not directly concerned with essences, the natural sciences nonetheless presuppose that there *are* essences. Otherwise they would not be characterized by certainty and necessity. Some scientists might scoff at this idea, but if they are logical they must admit the presence of essences to give certainty to their laws. The method of the natural sciences is to examine a number of particular cases and draw conclusions based on probability. This is the inductive method, reasoning from particular cases to general principles. Now, scientists could not possibly try every single case, yet their laws show certainty and necessity. This comes from the essences hidden under the accidents they consider. For example, to induce from the observation of ten brooms with green bands that the eleventh, or all brooms, will have green bands, is ridiculous. However, the scientific law, induced from the observation of particular cases, that water always boils at one hundred degrees centigrade is valid because it is part of the very nature of water to do this. Since these sciences do not attempt to explain the essences of the objects with which they deal, we say they are observatory rather than explanatory in nature. Ask the physicist, for example, why the object dropped from the building falls down rather than up. He will answer, "Because of the laws

---

[4] On form, cf. *supra,* Chap. II, 4, p. 29 ff.

of gravitation." In other words, it falls down because objects fall down.

From this discussion, it can be seen that the philosophical sciences occupy an important place, because they tell *what* things are. Moreover, philosophy is the only science which deals with all beings, that is, with all reality. Its crown is metaphysics, the study of being as being. We can see this when we divide philosophy according to the kinds of abstraction.

In everyday language, when we say that a thing is abstract we mean that it is vague and hard to understand. In philosophical language, abstract means just the opposite. When the mind knows, it sheers off the matter of an object, so to speak, and grasps its form. Therefore, that which is most understandable is that which is least concerned with matter. Abstraction is the process by which the mind concentrates on the immateriality of a thing.

Since man gets his knowledge through the senses, his mind is attracted first by changing things, *ens mobile,* things which can be thought of and exist only with matter, e.g., a man, for a man is not a man unless he is soul and body united. Here the mind is on what Jacques Maritain calls the first degree of abstraction, where he directs his attention to the natural sciences and to the philosophy of nature. This *philosophy of nature* deals with the same things as does natural science, but emphasizes the *ens* — what is this changing being?

There are two types of motion. The first is called *transient,* from the Latin *transeo,* "go over." This movement begins with the agent but ends outside the agent. For example, when someone throws a piece of chalk, the movement begins with him but ends across the room somewhere. The movement is lost to the agent. Cosmology is the science of transient action. The second type is called *immanent,* from the Latin *maneo,* "remain." This begins and remains in the agent for its own perfection, and is only found in living things. Examples of immanent actions are accidents in living things. These are the results of the soul's forming matter. Thus, the hand is the result of the soul's shaping prime matter into living flesh. Psychology is the science of immanent action.

The relationships between the philosophy of nature and natural science are precise ones. The philosopher of nature cannot afford to ignore the discoveries and achievements of the natural science of his day. He must be steeped in it. For example, the periodic chart is a much better illustration of the theory of matter and form than the famous four elements of antiquity: earth, air, fire, and water; on the other hand, the natural sciences cannot ignore the philosophy of nature. One of the most critical problems that faces the modern scientist is the question of the unity of the sciences. How can the various natural sciences be unified and their mountainous collections of data be coordinated? One way of achieving such a unity entails the choice of one science as the principle of unity of the others. But there is no one natural science that includes within its object the proper objects of the other sciences in order to serve as a unifying instrument. The search is frustrating when it seeks, on the level of the methods and techniques of the natural sciences, a principle of unification, a kind of universal natural science. But the philosophy of nature can be a principle of unification for the natural sciences. Being outside of them, it can provide direction and order! For example, the alchemists, in their reputed search for the philosopher's stone, maintained that a base metal could be transmuted into a precious metal. At a time when the chemists and natural scientists of the day generally ridiculed their efforts in view of the theory that the elements were supposed to be the ultimate indivisible units of reality, the alchemists knew that it could be done because they had learned from Aristotle the structure of material substance. The natural scientist was not aware of this until the actual transmutation of certain periodic elements was accomplished in the 1930's, and most convincing of all, the production of new substances as an accompaniment of atomic fission. The philosophy of nature in this way is capable of giving direction and order to the natural sciences and thus of acting as the principle of unity for all.

This does not mean that we would have just one science, the philosophy of nature, with all the so-called natural sciences as mere applications of this universal knowledge, more artistic than scientific. It is certainly true that art plays an important role in the natural sciences. It takes the skill of an engineer to perform many experiments, even in biology, the least organized of the sciences. The natural sciences, however, possess an autonomous scientific character, and this must be maintained against those who would attack the natural sciences and categorically deny their proper autonomy. For these thinkers the philosophy of nature and the natural sciences deal with one and the same set of principles, for instance, that it is the soul from which flows life itself and also the local motion that the physicist studies. Therefore, should we have only one science, the *physica* of the ancients and medievals? This is not a position to be lightly dismissed, for it dominated men's minds for centuries.

But ontological principles are not necessarily the principles of a particular science. The intellect makes precisions in the things it studies; that is precisely what we mean by the formal object of a science. The natural sciences have their own type of formal object, the proximate causes of things, and this object is a legitimate area of investigation. They are capable of a unified treatment of their proper object, self-sufficient and independent of philosophical procedure. The law of acceleration and Boyle's law are evidence that it is possible scientifically to delimit one's field of operation. The possibilities of such phenomena as the atomic theory or the theory of evolution suggest the autonomous nature of these knowledges. They find principles of unity within their own proper spheres. We do not mean that the atomic theory and the theory of evolution are philosophical substitutes. They are not, though many scientists do not seem to be aware of that fact. But they do show how, on the level of the natural sciences, they can provide the unification of their own knowledge so necessary for scientific progress. The fact that so many advances have been made by scientists wholly unaware of even the possibility of philosophical thought argues a certain autonomy of procedure. If they needed essences as a constituent of their proper object while they denied essences, how could they have accomplished any genuine scientific work?

Of recent years there has been such a glorification of the natural and mathematical sciences, and the empirical method, as the only sources and method of obtaining knowledge that it is of prime importance for us to get a clear idea of what this thing called metaphysics really is. Are we, as thinkers, being naïve when we claim that metaphysics is concerned with the highest knowledge of the natural order; that it is the supreme regulative science because its proper office is to classify and relate all knowledge; that the basis of Thomistic metaphysics is being? Are we blindly following a philosophy outmoded by the recent developments in science and closing our eyes to progress?

The Body-Soul Relationship

The body-soul problem finds its significance as the perfect expression of a deeper philosophic viewpoint. Much of the confusion resultant upon an analysis of the relations of soul and body, is due either to the defection or the complete lack of metaphysical structure within which the mysterious unity of the human composite in the face of its disparate components makes sense. We shall trace this problem through several philosophers, attempting to discover a common intuition, or denominator, at the source of their diverse difficulties.

Like most of philosophy, this problem begins with Plato. His emphasis on the spirituality and immortality of the soul leads to the radical cleavage of soul and body. Man is essentially a soul. The soul merely lives in a body like a dweller in his house. It is related to the body as rider to horse or the pilot to his ship. The soul, so absolutely unlike the body, does not really belong in it; in fact the reason for its presence there seems to be the result of a fall, an accident. The normal and natural state of the soul is to be free of its prison and to exist without the body in the freedom of pure contemplation of the ideas. This, although it accounts for the psychological conflict of soul and body, does not explain the obvious unity of the human composite. Even the neo-Platonists, perhaps Plato's best interpreters, saw this difficulty and hastened to give the soul a natural home in the body in order to perfect matter and lead it back to the "One."

Aristotle saw the difficulty and attempted to correct it; however, he did not come through quite unscathed. For him, the soul is the first act or form of the body — an organized, physical body having life in potency. The soul is to the body as form is to matter. And as matter and form are to substance, so soul and body are to man. They are essential principles forming an inseparable unity.

This view gives a satisfying interpretation of the unity of the human composite, but neglects, in its consideration of soul and body in terms of matter and form, the peculiar character of the components found in man. If soul is form, what becomes of its immortality? If immortal it has to subsist *per se,* to be a substance. But if it is a substance how is it possible for it to inform the body, to be the first act of the body, giving existence to it and organizing it in the one act of information? This is how the problem has been posed historically and the difficulties raised are due to a defective metaphysical structure.

The fundamental fact vitiating Plato's stand is the being he gives to matter as over against Aristotelian pure potency. When you start from a prime matter that has reality, that is already formed, you cannot have form as the first act of the body in the precise Aristotelian sense. We necessarily have a theory of two substances with the consequent impossibility of achieving a substantial unity in the human composite. This conception of the substantiality of matter has had a long history. In the thirteenth century we have St. Bonaventure attempting to bridge these two substances by a doctrine of the plurality of forms progressively actualizing a matter possessing an almost insatiable craving for form.

Descartes too has this notion of two substances. For him the essence of man is to be an unextended thinking thing (a substance whose whole nature or essence is merely thinking). Body, due to his clear and distinct ideas of it, is an extended and unthinking thing. The mind is entirely and truly distinct from the body and may exist without it. The fact of pain, the sensations of hunger and thirst for instance, is the means of my knowing that I have a body. This pain also shows me that I am not only lodged in my body as a pilot in a vessel, but that I am so intimately conjoined, and as it were, intermixed with it, that mind and body compose a certain unity. It is in sensation that we become aware of the union and apparent fusion of mind and body. How this unity is accomplished between a mind whose office alone it is, and not of the composite whole of mind and body, to discern the truth, and a body fashioned of bones, nerves, muscles, etc., a real machine that would still exhibit involuntary actions even if there were no soul in it, Descartes does not tell us. The pineal gland cannot span the infinite distance between two substances.

For Malebranche, too, knowledge belongs to the soul alone and not to the whole man. Bodies cannot act on minds. There is no relation between soul and body. Soul as thought and body as extension are substances. Spinoza and Leibniz continue this radical separation of soul and body in knowledge, allowing no role or duties to the body in knowing.

The Aristotelian theory of matter and form, by refusing existence to prime matter, does preserve the unity of the composite and saves us from the fundamental error of those who attribute a form to it. However there is some insufficiency in Aristotle's handling of a substantial immortal soul as an element of the human composite. This difficulty is naturally of the utmost importance to the Christian philosophers and it is one that St. Thomas disposes of quite satisfactorily even though his solution entails a revolutionary revision of metaphysics.

St. Thomas agrees with Plato and Descartes that the soul is a spiritual substance and as such is made for truth. What necessity has it for a body? Here is where St. Thomas first differs with them and this initial change gapes wider and wider as we trace his doctrine. Despite its spiritual nature the soul is not an angel. It is an intellectual being but the least of that order. The soul needs the body in order to know. He follows Aristotle in his "nothing is in the intellect which was not first in the senses." Unlike the soul of Plato and Descartes, in the natural order, the separated soul is blind and dumb even after a period of union with the body. The phantasm is necessarily present even in present knowledge and the intellect has constant recourse to it. Thus the body perfects the soul in its operations. It perfects it also in its nature for it is the proper matter to its form. On the question of the reality of prime matter, St. Thomas, with Aristotle, considers it as pure potency. Whatever existence the body has is due to soul as its form. The only substance it has is that of the human composite, man. Thus the division of the component principles of man is not correctly soul and body, but rather soul and matter. Body presupposes form. Thus it is truer to say that the body is in the soul than that the soul is in the body.

So far St. Thomas follows Aristotle who approaches the body-soul problem from the point of view of soul as a form of the body rather than as a spiritual substance possessing a nature of its own. Aristotle could not quite achieve this reconciliation. (The Averroistic doctrine of the unity of the possible intellect in man bears witness to this.) St. Thomas undertakes to consider the soul as form of the body and still preserve its spirituality and substantiality. His solution is simply this. If the soul as form is the principle of existence of the composite there is no real reason for an incompatibility with its being the principle of its own existence. These few words imply a radical revision of metaphysics from the point of view of existence, a task which we cannot attempt to describe here. But in simple fashion the substance is this. If, in an essentialistic philosophy, "to be" is to be a form or an essence, and "to exist" is to be an individual or a substance, then the principle of existence has to be that which limits or receives form, call it matter or potency as you will. Then if the principle of existence flows from matter or its equivalent, form cannot exist *per se* and still function as a form in the Aristotelian sense. But in a metaphysic where "to be" is to exist and the form is the principle of existence of the substance, there need be no incompatibility in the fact of the principle of existence of the composite possessing its own existence.

§ 2. PHILOSOPHY OF MATHEMATICS

After changing things, the mind concentrates on quantitative being, *ens quantitativum*, things which can be thought of without matter but cannot exist without matter, e.g., the square, the circle, numbers. This is the second degree of abstraction, and includes mathematics and the *philosophy of mathematics*. Here again, philosophy emphasizes the *ens* — what is this quantity which we measure and number?

The mathematician cannot afford to wait until philosophers construct a starting point for him — or until philosophers agree on what is a legitimate starting point. He must be about his proper work, which is to *do* mathematics, not philosophize about mathematics. This is why the notion of mathematics as a game with arbitrary starting points has a value of expediency. The mathematician can get on with his mathematical work without having to solve philosophical problems first. He can define numbers within his own system very satisfactorily without having to root it in the quantity of material bodies.

§ 3. METAPHYSICS

Finally the mind reaches knowledge of the highest order, grasping things which can both exist and be thought of without matter, as God, angels, and being as such. This is the third degree of abstraction, the study of *ens inquantum ens,* being as being, the proper object of metaphysics.

Thus, we have seen that speculative knowledge is higher than practical, science higher than common sense, philosophy the crown of the sciences, and metaphysics the crown of philosophy.

Of all the human knowledges there is none more abstract and more difficult of comprehension than metaphysics. It is from its exalted position as the supreme achievement of the human intellect in the natural order that its difficulties flow. The more profound a science, the more difficult of comprehension. And it is precisely because of these difficulties that metaphysics has fallen into such disfavor today. I am certain that, if a survey were made of philosophy courses throughout the country, we would find less time and effort spent on metaphysics than on any other branch of philosophy. And yet metaphysics is the most important branch of philosophy. Can we teach the other philosophical sciences without metaphysics? How can certain parts of psychology like the immortality of the soul be intelligible without metaphysics, or the nature of philosophy itself be discussed? How can ethics be taught without a thorough grounding in the notions of essence and nature?

There is a real need then to make metaphysics comprehensible, and to make it intelligible without doing violence to its nature. This book is an experiment in the satisfaction of this need, not so much by an adequate treatment of the principles and structure of metaphysics, as by indicating the framework of its application. Our purpose is not to show what metaphysics is (a difficult enough question) but rather what metaphysics does, which explains in a way what it is.

Metaphysics is not merely a collection of insights on the level of the deepest penetration into reality. It is a science, and as such, it begins someplace and goes somewhere. There is an initial natural starting point and a necessary direction. The scientific sequence of problems is not an arbitrary one. When the speculative mind enters within the structure of being there is a dynamic pattern or geography that it must follow. The movement of metaphysics is as rigorous as that of geometry or logic. The science of being is very far from being a fanciful production of the creative imagination, fluid and amorphous. It is stiffened with the iron of a mental discipline, the certainty and necessity of the scientific character it eminently possesses.

§ 4. DIALECTIC IN PLATO, ARISTOTLE, AND HEGEL

Metaphysics for Plato is dialectic, a science of being which deals with the real in a hierarchy of forms. We define a thing by locating it in its proper form, by locating it in relation to the "Good." An important text for the understanding of dialectic in Plato is *Republic*, VII, 532–534. He calls dialectic a hymn flowing from the intellect only, and not from sense. It is a vision whose best parallel is found in sight. Dialectic is a progress, an intellectual movement from the lower sciences and grades of reality through the higher, until it rests in the highest and first principle, the good. All knowledge below this is but a search and a preparation for dialectic which Plato calls the coping stone of the sciences, differentiated methodically from them by the fact that it uses hypothesis only as a scaffolding until it arrives at truth, the form. A noteworthy characteristic of Platonic dialectic is the fact that it is a way of being, a metaphysic, not a logic — something brought out most clearly by Plotinus and other neo-Platonists, perhaps Plato's most accurate interpreters.

Aristotle conceived dialectic quite differently than did Plato. It is not science at its highest level but merely a specious type of reasoning. Science is reserved by Aristotle for demonstration alone. The *Topics* is an entire treatise on dialectic in which he says that reasoning is dialectical if it proceeds from *opinions* that are generally accepted by either all or a majority of philosophers. The function of dialectic in Aristotle is also quite different from its role in Platonic science. For Aristotle it does not grasp reality or essences, it does not reduce things to their principles or forms and locate them in relation to the good, it has only an auxiliary or preparatory usefulness in science, and it serves only for intellectual training, casual arguments, and the approach to the philosophical sciences. It is of use to the study of the philosophical sciences, for while the demonstrative premise is the assertion of one of two contradictory statements, the dialectical premise is given the choice between two contradictories and will defend or attack either with equal facility. Thus, it is useful

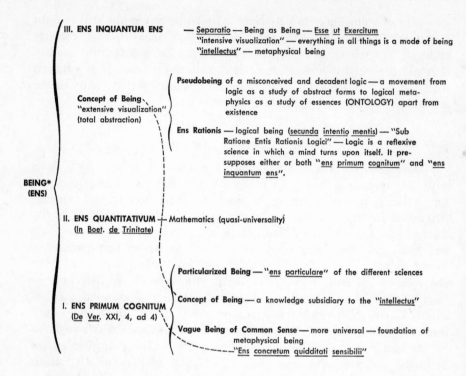

BEING*
(ENS)

III. ENS INQUANTUM ENS — Separatio — Being as Being — Esse ut Exercitum
"intensive visualization" — everything in all things is a mode of being
"intellectus" — metaphysical being

Concept of Being,
"extensive visualization"
(total abstraction)

Pseudobeing of a misconceived and decadent logic — a movement from logic as a study of abstract forms to logical metaphysics as a study of essences (ONTOLOGY) apart from existence

Ens Rationis — logical being (secunda intentio mentis) — "Sub Ratione Entis Rationis Logici" — Logic is a reflexive science in which a mind turns upon itself. It presupposes either or both "ens primum cognitum" and "ens inquantum ens".

II. ENS QUANTITATIVUM — Mathematics (quasi-universality)
(In Boet. de Trinitate)

I. ENS PRIMUM COGNITUM
(De Ver. XXI, 4, ad 4)

Particularized Being — "ens particulare" of the different sciences

Concept of Being — a knowledge subsidiary to the "intellectus"

Vague Being of Common Sense — more universal — foundation of metaphysical being
"Ens concretum quidditati sensibilii"

---

* In the first article of the first question of *De Veritate,* St. Thomas has given us a brief summary of what may constitute a course in metaphysics.

"In matters which are open to proof," he says, "the demonstration must lead back to some principles which are known to the intellect by themselves. So too when we investigate what a thing is. Otherwise in both cases we should go on to infinity, and thus all science and knowledge would perish.

"Now that which the intellect first conceives as what is best known and to which it reduces all of its conceptions, is *BEING,* as Avicenna says in the beginning of his Metaphysics, I, 9. Whence it is necessary that all other conceptions of the intellect be obtained by adding to being.

"But nothing can be added to being which is, as it were, of an extraneous nature, after the manner in which a difference is added to a genus or an accident to a subject because every nature whatsoever is essentially being. Whence also the Philosopher in the third book of the Metaphysics says that being cannot be a genus. But certain things are said to be additions to being in the sense that they express a manner of being which is not expressed by the name being itself. This may happen in two ways.

"One way is that in which the manner expressed is a certain special manner of being. For there are diverse grades of entity according to which diverse manners of being are obtained, and according to these manners of being the diverse classes of things are obtained. For substance does not add over and above being a certain difference which signifies some nature superadded to being, but by the name substance is expressed a special manner of being, namely, being in itself, and so it is for the other genera.

for science because the ability to raise searching difficulties on both sides of a subject will enable us to detect more easily the truth or error of an issue. Thus, the role of dialectic is a purely critical one — it is a process or method of criticism, not a means of attaining reality.

The first fact that strikes one in an examination of dialectic in Hegel is its resemblance to that of Plato. For dialectic is a long process toward science which is at rest in the "Absolute." However, there is a fundamental distinction of which Hegel is very conscious. The process toward science, for him, is not what is primarily imagined by leading the unscientific consciousness up to the level of science. There is the same progress toward form with the same supersedence of lower by higher that we find in Plato's use of hypotheses. However, the distinctive contribution of Hegel lies in the natural imperfections of the form, the reason for its supersedence, as an inherent opposition with which it combines in mutual destruction, out of whose ruins there rises, phoenix-like, the higher category. This elaboration of the inherent imperfection of form into a progress by stages of thesis, antithesis, and synthesis which in turn becomes thesis, is what Hegel

---

"The other way in which the manner of being is expressed is a manner of being which belongs to all beings in general. And this manner may obtain in a twofold fashion. First, in that it belongs to all beings in themselves; secondly, in that it belongs to all beings in their ordered relation to another being.

"In the first case it is so spoken of because it expresses something affirmative or negative in the being. Nothing however is found to be affirmatively said in an absolute way that can obtain in every being except its *essence*, according to which it [*res*] is said to be. In this way the name *thing* is imposed. Thing differs from being, as Avicenna says in the beginning of his Metaphysics, in that being is taken from the *act of existing*, while the name thing expresses the *whatness* [*quidditas*] or essence of the being. The negation which attaches to all beings absolutely is indivision, and this is expressed by the term *one;* for one means nothing else but individual being.

"If however the manner of being is considered in the second way, namely, according to the ordered relation of one being to another, this may occur in a twofold way. First, with respect to the division of one thing from another, and this is expressed by the term *something* [*aliquid*]. Wherefore just as being is said to be one inasmuch as it is undivided in itself, so it is said to be something inasmuch as it is divided off from the others. Secondly, according to the agreement of one thing with another; and this, of course, cannot be unless it be understood as something which by its very nature agrees with all beings. Now this is the soul, which in a certain way is all things, as it is said in the third book of the *De Anima*. For in the soul there are two powers, namely, *cognitive* and *appetitive*. The agreement of being with the appetite is expressed by the term *good*, as it is said in the beginning of the Ethics: 'The good is that which all desire.' The agreement of being with the intellect is expressed by the term true."

To complete the synopsis given in the above quotation, it is fitting to add here a few texts on *beauty*.

". . . beauty and goodness," says St. Thomas (I, q. 5, a. 4, ad 1) "are the same in their subject; they differ only by reason." And again he says (*De Veritate*, q. 22, a. 1, ad 2), "Whoever desires the good, thereby desires also the beautiful."

adds to the Platonic dialectic. Though based on a universe of pure intelligibility and positing a conceptual progress like Plato's, there is an autonomy of this process which roots Hegelian dialectic even more firmly in the realm of metaphysics than that of Plato, for essentially the dialectics of both Plato and Hegel are metaphysics of being as opposed to Aristotle's location of dialectic in the realm of logic.

§ 5. A METAPHYSICS OF BEING

Although one strong current of thought in the history of western metaphysics has looked on metaphysics as dialectic, another stronger current has always considered metaphysics to be a demonstrative science.

What is metaphysics? The most complex problem of contemporary philosophy and the one that has given rise to bitter controversy is precisely the nature, origins, and justification of metaphysical thinking. The transliteration of metaphysics into epistemology with the consequent elimination of metaphysics as anything but illusory knowledge has been the result of the attempt to constitute physics as a legitimate science and to locate it as an academic discipline in the university curriculum.

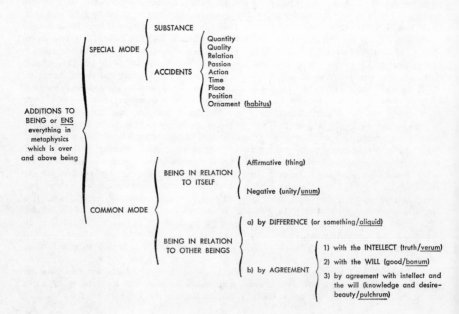

The history of epistemology is the chronicle of the progressive discrediting of metaphysics — but we shall discuss this later.[5]

The closest thing to a definition of metaphysics is still the formula of Aristotle: metaphysics is the study of being *as* being. This definition has as many variations as the proverbial wax nose. Each thinker interprets the fundamental meaning of this formula in accordance with his own conception of what metaphysics is.

When we read the formulas of the different philosophers and try to get inside them, to relive the intuitions and mental life of the thinkers as they constructed these formulas, certain very basic evidences confront us. The first and primary evidence about being seems to be its opposition to nothingness, its separation from the gulf of emptiness, of nonentity. When we say of something that it *is,* we are recognizing that it is *not nothing.* To use the vocabulary that has become traditional in the history of western metaphysics, *to be* is *to be set apart from nothingness, to be placed outside of its causes.*[6]

Being seems to be the most elemental and primary predicate. After we have enumerated the indefinitely complex intelligible notes that can be predicated of every thing we reach the bare bones, as it were, the ultimate and most basic characteristic so fundamental that there is nothing beyond it — it *is!* When we recognize that something is or exists we perceive the foundation on which all characteristics and the character of being itself are built. Before existence nothing else is. After existence all that happens, does so![7]

The metaphysical intuition of being is rooted in our concrete experience and we can search our experience to make it comprehensible.[8] Just as being is the *last* and most fundamental thing we can say about anything because it is the foundation of all other characteristics and of the predicates in which we embody them in the economy of lan-

---

5 Cf. *infra,* Chap. IV, 7, p. 86 ff.

6 Cf. E. Gilson, *Being and Some Philosophers,* (Toronto: 1952).

7 Cf. L. Wittgenstein, *Tractatus Logico-Philosophicus,* (London: Routledge and Kegan Paul, 1958); s. 6, 44. Cf. also W. Carlo, *The Ultimate Reducibility of Essence to Existence in Existential Metaphysics* (The Hague: Martinus Nijhoff, 1966), pp. 18–19, n. 3.

8 We agree with Professor Feyerabend that the only foundation for a metaphysics is experience although this has been by no means a unanimous decision in the history of metaphysics.

"Even the most determined metaphysicians who intend to discuss Being in Itself, and who are upset by the most insignificant sensual element, have a hard time, and it is likely that they will never succeed in keeping experience out of their account" (Paul K. Feyerabend, "Problems of Empiricism," *Beyond the Edge of Certainty: Essays in Contemporary Science and Philosophy,* ed. Robert G. Colodny [Englewood Cliffs, N. J.: Prentice-Hall, 1965], p. 146).

guage, so it is the *first aspect of the thing which we contact intellectually.* We know with intellectual deliberation *that* a thing is before we know *what* it is. A plethora of examples can be marshaled in illustration.

Let us consider examples from the intellectual utilization of the basic senses of sight, touch, and hearing. Imagine yourself standing in the center of a road looking down a highway which slopes away from you all the way to the horizon. What is the very first thing we know about something seen far down the road? We know *that it is!* It is something! As it approaches us, we know that it moves. It is alive, an animal. As it comes closer we see that it walks upright, a primate of the order of mammals. As we get a closer view we know it is a man. Finally we see standing before us, John Smith. Even a cursory view of our knowledge as it comes in contact with some concrete individual thing shows us that it moves from the general to the particular. What we know first in our initial point of contact with any one thing is the most general characteristic which all things have in common — *being!* The fact that they *are!* Our knowledge then becomes progressively delineated and differentiated till we know the individual, not as being, not as animal, not as man, but in its concrete individuality, as *John Smith.*

This fundamental experience can be duplicated in the intellectual utilization of the sense of touch. By the intellectual utilization of the sense of touch we do not mean the raw crude sensations, nor their unified structure in the image, but that which the intellect knows as a result of sensible contact with the concrete individual in the experience of touching.

Consider yourself coming out of a set of revolving doors from a department store. The doors revolve quickly under the impetus of a sharp thrust by an impatient patron and as you exit you stumble . . . over something? Things may happen so quickly that you are not yet aware of *what* it is, a dog on a leash, a baby carriage, a box? But you do know *that* it is. It is something in your way as you struggle for equilibrium.

When we turn to the intellectual utilization of the sense of hearing we find a similar movement of the mind from the general to the particular, from the abstract to the concrete. Once the intellect is put in contact with the thing through the vital act of sensation, the properly intellectual movement in its natural inclination, undisturbed by the imposition of some arbitrary, conventional, so-called philosophic method is, by its connatural impetus as it were, from the general to the particular, from the abstract to the concrete.

Imagine yourself standing in a meadow, in the evening stillness. Even the singing of birds is hushed. Through the quiet hum of accustomed sounds comes a faint unfamiliar note. You stand straining to catch the sound. You know *that* it is before you know *what* it is. It must become progressively louder till it reaches the point at which you recognize it. Someone is trying out his bugle before blowing taps. But you knew that you heard something before you knew what it was that caught your attention. Just as the sleeper who awakens in the dead of night listens with concentrated intensity, and ultimately realizes that the clock has stopped ticking. He knows *that* something has happened to the sounds about him but he does not yet know *what* it is.

The "Vague Being of Common Sense," as Jacques Maritain calls it, and the "Concrete Being" of a sensible quiddity or nature, as Cajetan terms it, is not that being which is the object of metaphysics. If the Being of Common Sense were the object of metaphysics even a child would be a metaphysician. A transmuting process is necessary before the primitive content with reality as a sensitive-intelligible totality can be refined by the further penetration of the intellect to the core of being, i.e., existence. It is existence *(esse)* which is at the origin of the universe because it is at its core and its circumference. Existence is all-encompassing.

By a refinement of the Being given in Common Sense through the metaphysical "abstraction" called "separation"[9] in the negative existential judgment the intellect makes its first contact with that existence with which it is to be so completely preoccupied. A being is called "being" precisely because of its existence, not because of its essence.

In the negative existential judgment the intellect achieves its intuition of being against the backdrop of "nothingness." Profoundly beneath the intellectual recognition that beings are of certain kinds, that to be is to be a kind of thing, a man, a dog, or a rose bush, lurks in the depths of mystery the explanation of why it is at all that principle by which it is *set apart from nothingness* and *placed outside its causes.*[10]

But one-term and two-term propositions express the existential judgment. We can say that *Mary is,* meaning *Mary exists,* or we can say *Mary is blonde,* meaning that, translated into its existential foundations: *Mary exists as blonde, intelligent, young, a coed,* etc. All these determinations are modes in which Mary *is,* ways in which she *exists;* essential

---

[9] Thomas Aquinas, *In Boethium de Trinitate,* ed. A. Maurer, *The Divisions and Methods of the Sciences* (Toronto, 1953), pp. 28, 31.

[10] Cf. Milton Munitz, *The Mystery of Existence* (New York: Appleton-Century-Crofts, 1965).

determinations are *modes of existence*.[11] Being is not only at the origin of the universe because it is at its very core and at its circumference. It is all-encompassing.

The mind does not grasp existence conceptually although it does grasp existence *intellectually* in a properly human and scientific fashion. Immanuel Kant's oft quoted example of the hundred dollars is of vital importance here.[12]

Metaphysics as a rational science has always been the dream of thinkers — and its attractiveness has never been more strongly felt than it has by some thinkers in our own day. For one of the functions of the discipline called metaphysics, ontology, or first philosophy has been the integration of all the human sciences and knowledges. No science seems to be able to examine its own nature. It must go to a higher science for the understanding and explanation of its nature and its own first principles.[13]

§ 6. FREEDOM: A TEST CASE

To better illustrate the metaphysical analysis of the nature and classification of the sciences and knowledges, let us examine a burning contemporary problem, human freedom, with which existentialism is preoccupied almost to the point of obsession.

A. Freedom and Natural Science

Freedom will never enter into the natural sciences as a constitutive element of the object of these sciences. Freedom as an immaterial and spiritual reality lies outside the scope of knowledges such as physics, chemistry, and biology. If the physical scientist does attempt to include freedom within the sphere proper to his knowledge, the presumption is inexcusable and the result disastrous. The culmination of such a misapprehension of the nature and method of the natural sciences is of course the complete elimination of freedom and the substitution of the necessity of physical law to a field of human behavior utterly foreign to it. If the physicist is concerned with matter and motion, then freedom must be reduced to a function of matter or vacate its claims to reality. This is the origin of a determinism

---

11 Cf. G. B. Phelan, "The Being of Creatures," *Proceedings of the American Catholic Philosophical Association*, Vol. XXXI (1957), pp. 118–125.

12 Cf. Gilson, *Being and Some Philosophers*, appendix, pp. 216–227.

13 Cf. chart, p. 72.

that would resolve all free action into a multiplicity of causes so complex that we are not able, at one particular moment, to discover and evaluate the precise contribution of each to any human action; consequently, it designates freedom of action as our substitute for ignorance of its real causes. Therefore, we reiterate, freedom is not a constituent of the object of the natural sciences, and, as a result, the natural scientist is not qualified, in his office of scientist, to judge the existence or nonexistence of freedom as a basic component of reality. This does not mean that as a man, in his daily experience of commonsense knowledge, he ignores the obvious presence of freedom as an experimental datum. He well knows that he can or need not, as he wills, reserve a hotel room at the end of his trip. He is perfectly aware of his ability to take the car or walk to work. We have again that basic contradiction of two legitimate knowledges indicating the erroneous conclusion of one. But the precise knowledge for which the natural scientist is respected, and from which flows whatever authority is attached to his statements, has no bearing at all on the question involved. We might as well ask the professional mathematician the best method of high diving. He might know. But then he would have to be a diver as well as a mathematician. Thus, the scientist rejects free will because it introduces an element of disorder into the physical universe, an element which is not predictable. But freedom is not anarchy, and in casting a doubt on the absoluteness of whim or noting the absurdity of uncontrolled behavior, the free man is by no means losing sight of the everyday meaning of freedom. He is merely doubting or denying the existence of any such thing as a core of indetermination at the root of an ordered, orderly thing. In this sense he agrees with the scientist who refuses to admit in a measurable, predictable world the presence of a fundamental anarchy or disorder at the heart of that supreme artistic production of nature, the human being. But such an indetermination does not make sense because it does not exist. Freedom is harmony, not anarchy. The anthem of freedom is not sung off key, it is in tune with the universe. It is an ignorance of the true nature of freedom that causes so many erroneous notions of freedom.

Along with the common experience of the fact of freedom that the physical scientist shares with the rest of mankind, there is a precise and important way in which freedom does enter into his office as a scientist, but not as a constitutive element of the object of his science. For freedom does enter into the initiation and direction of research, into the control that he exercises over his productions. Science is not an autonomous being pursuing its own solitary aims. It is not some juggernaut that must advance even though it entail the destruction of every obstacle. Science is an operation of the human being and like all the operations of man it has as its end and purpose the perfection of man. Therefore, the pattern of control is laid very clearly. If this instrument will be disastrous for man, should I produce it? When the scientist can make a bomb that will destroy the world, is he free to make it? It is here that the problems of freedom with their inextricably tangled implications are to be found. This is one of the crucial decisions of our age.

The physicist seems to have greater personal freedom in his rejection of scientific theory, but only because his scientific judgment lacks the urgency of the concrete prudential judgment with its necessity of action. A man who is standing on the edge of a cliff awaiting the charge of an angry bull cannot remain indifferent or in a state of suspended judgment like the scientist. The particular circumstances of his situation make a decision imperative. Likewise in the political and social areas the urgency of a situation demands immediate assent or dissent. Therefore, the freedom proper to the professional physicist within his own field could never be extended absolutely to the areas of political and social affairs. Such an extension would be disastrous. Certain eminent physicists seem to be completely unaware of this fact. It is for this reason that Jean-Paul Sartre condemns "scientific neutrality" as socially vicious, because it militates against that involvement in the concrete social order in the performatory acceptance of which he finds the foundation of moral value.

B. Freedom and Practical Knowledge

If our immediate purpose is to know freedom, to understand its nature, then we are concerned primarily with speculative knowledge. But, if we want to do something about freedom, if we want to defend it, to preserve this precious possession, then we must look to the practical knowledges for help. Those practical knowledges in which freedom plays so important a part are medicine, or more properly, psychiatry, law, and art.

Since medicine is characterized in large measure as art, freedom enters into its scope only in the way that it is common to any strictly human activity. Both doctor and patient are aware of their freedom as men. If the empirical methods and observational modes of procedure of this knowledge are not meant to attain to human freedom in some proper and profound way, why is it that in our society there is a branch of medicine that is especially concerned with freedom? It is the board of psychiatrists that certifies responsibility. A human being can be committed to an institution for life on the word of medical men. This certainly seems to imply a real insight into the nature of freedom as a function of psychiatry, since one should know the nature of that which one judges. What kind of knowledge of freedom does the psychiatrist really possess? Does he know what freedom is ultimately, the fundamental nature of freedom? The methods and techniques of his knowledge seem to argue against such a claim. But does that mean that his power of certification of the mentally irresponsible is invalid? It is true that the court and not the psychiatrist makes the legal decision and orders the execution of the committal but it does so on the basis of the knowledge of the psychiatrist. Does the psychiatrist know the nature of freedom, or does he rather recognize the influence of specific organic and functional diseases on the normal behavior of man? Through his experience and practical knowledge gained from the examination of a variety of cases, he can determine whether or not the conditions of freedom are present, a domination of passions and emotions by the intellectual powers. All this can be done, and very effectively, without the proper knowledge of the nature of freedom. However, curative treatment might be more effective in mental cases if the nature of man's intellectual powers and their free exercise were better understood by the psychiatrist.

The professional jurist (by jurist we mean all those involved in the construction and operation of a legal system), the lawmaker, the judge, the lawyer, also work in the practical order. Therefore, they do not investigate within their own proper field the nature of freedom anymore than the geometer questions his first principles; for instance, that the whole is greater than any of its parts. They start with the fact of freedom, an irreducible datum of reality, and proceed from there. If freedom is questioned by the legist, then the whole structure of responsibility and punishment collapses. To demand responsibility for an uncontrollable action is unjust. Even if we consider the role of punishment to be merely that of a deterrent, freedom must be assumed as a necessary constituent of human actions.

To look upon the law positivistically, as the mere practical instrument for the preservation of order, possessed of no ontological roots, with an appeal to precedent as the ultimate authority, is not to deny the fact of freedom, though its nature may be ignored. The very fact that a legal system can work even when it prescinds from a scientific knowledge of the nature of freedom is a significant indication that perhaps such an examination does not fall within the authority of the jurist. A commonsense knowledge of the results and conclusions of freedom is the general framework of law, and a practical, prudential judgment is the characteristic core of legal decision. That is why precedent can perform so valuable a service in law, although so valueless to science. What was done intelligently in the past is perhaps a practical guide to what should be done today in the area of individual and social behavior. The fundamental legal structure, the court, is a good example of the exercise of the precise type of knowledge involved in the law. In the court, the prosecuting attorney and counsel for the defense each presents his case in all possible strength, so that the judge or jurist may make a concrete prudential judgment on the basis of the facts involved. In such a situation, the office of the attorneys is concerned primarily with presenting the strongest points of their clients, not in making a personal moral judgment in respect to the case. That is the primary function of the jurist.

Thus, the role of the psychiatrist and psychologist as strictly consultants to the court is an eminently sensible one. Their knowledge of freedom, basically nonscientific as it must be, does not possess the certainty and necessity to give it absolute authority. And although certain members of the medical profession have been very vocal in their dissatisfaction with their present consultative status, the fact remains that their knowledge is just as much a knowledge of results and conclusions as that of the experienced jurist, and it is of greatest value when used in conjunction with the jurist's own practical knowledge, at his own discretion.

It is not the duty of the jurist, then, to explain what freedom is, to analyze its nature, but it is his obligation to provide, in the construction and operation of a legal system, the profoundest guarantees and the most effective protection for the freedom of his fellowmen. What are the limitations that society can place upon individuals consonant with the dignity of free men? It is important to note that the only reason for placing limitations on the freedom of individuals is, paradoxically, to gain for him the greater freedom that he possesses as a member of a just, smoothly articulating society.

Perhaps one of the most hotly contested areas of freedom is that of the arts. Art must be free. Censorship and control stifle artistic genius, we are told. Time and again daily newspapers, and especially their Sunday supplements, repeat the slogan. Controversial cases of censorship make excellent copy, at times meriting headlines. Of course art should be free, but there is no such thing as an absolute freedom in a contingent world. Can a man sculpt any statue he wishes, or paint any canvas as the whim moves him? Can he produce lewd and vulgar representations as he wills? If art is one intellectual operation of man, having as its object the perfection of man, the ministering to his wants, and the fine arts, in particular, to the more spiritual and aesthetic needs, then any artistic production that is in conflict with man's perfection is by that fact invalidated. Such production does not further the end of art as an operation of man contributing to the perfection of the whole man, including his moral exigencies.

In theory, therefore, art is not possessed of some fictitious absolute freedom. But in practice man must bend over backwards in order not to infringe on the free artistic exercise. One must be very careful lest one transgress the legitimate liberties of the artist. But legitimate authority has not only the right, but even the obligation, of censorship. Men of a practical common sense, who know their people, their level of education, and their customary modes of thought and expression, are in a very good position to make a prudential judgment on whether such and such a work of art will be definitely harmful.

C. Freedom and Philosophy

Looking back over our analysis of the nature of knowledge and the illustration of this nature by the application of the different knowledges to freedom, we realize that if we are to initiate our examination of the nature of freedom, our treatment must be philosophical, because philosophy alone of all the forms of knowledge is properly concerned with essences or natures; and the foundation of psychology, for instance, and indeed of all knowledges, is laid in metaphysics.

We use the word "free" to designate a being which is master of itself though influenced by external things and jostled by irrelevant events. Of course this is no definition, it is the mere beginning of a description on the level of common sense. In order to describe more fully the realm of freedom, we must explore the recesses of human behavior open only to philosophical science.

It is not within the scope of this introductory study to begin the analysis of freedom itself. However, we should like to call attention to the first two philosophical divisions of freedom. Much of the confusion and difficulties that surround modern questions of freedom flow precisely from the twofold aspect of freedom itself, due to which freedom seems often to be in conflict with itself. This mortal contradiction is revealed on all levels of human thought and activity. It has been the object of a variety of names and distinctions, but initial freedom and freedom of autonomy seem to be as accurate as any.

Basically, freedom is something that an intellectual being possesses and expresses in its ability to make choices. Human acts are termed free acts because of the relation they have to an intellect. It is precisely in the ability of the human mind to form the concept of goodness that we discover one of the elements of freedom. The transcendental concept of the good is the very distillation of whatever good there is in the universe, and as such it is precisely the crystallized object of the profoundest yearnings and deepest hungers of this human nature of ours. Having once lost itself in this vision of total splendor to which all the rest of the universe is blind, the will cannot be completely ensnared by any partial good, because it is enamored of *all* good. This freedom of choice, however, is not an unmixed perfection. The ability to do what is contrary to the exigencies of nature is not entirely enviable. Freedom is a responsibility of frightening proportions. For a being of finite, limited intelligence to be able to will exactly as it wishes, leaves it with a basic insecurity and fear of the results of its actions. To be faced with a world that I can and will change, for better or worse, when I am not sure of what better or worse actually is, presents a problem of disquieting implications. Freedom, in that sense, is a painful thing and a liability to the creature that is free. Thus, this initial plunge into motion by being hitherto under the rule of the determination and necessity that flow from nonintellectual nature — this initial freedom must find its completion or fruition in the achievement of that good which is proper to man and in which his perfection consists, what has been known as freedom of autonomy. The virtuous man, for instance, has brought the entire complexus of causes of human behavior into harmony with the end perceived by his intellect, so that the dissonances of appetite are reconciled in the symphony of the soul where every faculty is intent upon its contribution to the whole without violation of its due autonomy. That man, then, is truly free who restricts freedom of choice to the choice of means consonant with his end, and there is a progressive advance in freedom paralleling the progressive achievement of his destiny.

Freedom is not merely and exclusively freedom of choice. It is not only the exercise of a choice of means, each of which can be assigned the character of goodness itself by a being that looks through a partial goodness to the vision of absolute goodness of which it is the expression. In a fuller and more complete sense, freedom is found in the realization of the end of the nature, wherein the person is independent of the remainder of reality, as only a being which has realized its perfection is free and thus no longer is enslaved by the means through which it achieved its autonomy. Thus, in the examination of the nature of freedom, both these aspects must be studied.

The metaphysical location of freedom is of prime importance, because the analysis of freedom will vary with the particular metaphysics involved. It is no secret that there is a plurality of metaphysics. A metaphysics of essence will emphasize the proper role of intelligence in the specification of the will and the spontaneity of the volitional act will be explained as an ultimate operation of nature, a tendency flowing from the immanent principle of immanent action of a spiritual being. The ultimate explanation of freedom is thus located on the level of the philosophy of nature.

On the other hand, an existential metaphysics provides the explanation of the autonomous operation of the will, the ultimate spontaneity of the volitional act, on a properly metaphysical level. *The act of existence,* the fundamental metaphysical principle, is the dynamic aspect of being that expresses itself in human acts in the spontaneity of the will. The ultimate, irreducible fact of freedom is this ability of the will to be the source of its own movements. The freedom of an act is possible because of the dynamism of existence, the source of its own energy expressing itself through the specification of the intellect; just as essence delimits existence, *esse,* so in the free act, the intellect specifies the operation of the will.

It is the office of philosophy to examine the natures of things while the other knowledges, as we have seen, are more concerned with freedom in practice; they want to know how to attain and conserve freedom. In the larger perspective of things these knowledges are all complementary and supplementary. They are not mutually exclusive or contradictory.

The fact of freedom is evident and is written on the hearts of all men as a basic human value unless obscured by an erroneous theory of freedom. But to understand the nature of freedom is a complex scientific and intellectual venture of which not all are capable. Therefore, they must accept the results of those who ought to know, the scientists. This places a sobering responsibility on the intellectual and the scientist. He cannot follow any intellectual will-of-the-wisp he pleases. He cannot scribble off any chance phrase simply because it delights the ear and tickles the sensibilities. He is thinking for the human race and his thought, whether he will or no, is affecting the lives of many more people than he suspects. The parading of one's ignorance in public as the height of scientific method is unforgivable.

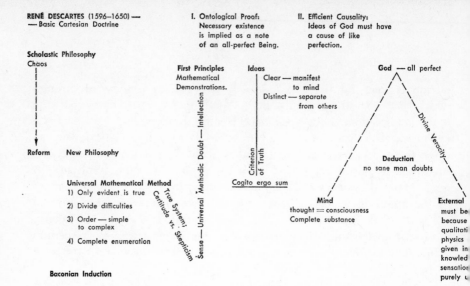

RENÉ DESCARTES (1596–1650) —
— Basic Cartesian Doctrine

I. Ontological Proof:
Necessary existence
is implied as a note
of an all-perfect Being.

II. Efficient Causality:
Ideas of God must have
a cause of like
perfection.

Scholastic Philosophy
Chaos

Reform   New Philosophy

First Principles
Mathematical
Demonstrations.

Ideas
Clear — manifest
        to mind
Distinct — separate
         from others

God — all perfect

Divine Veracity

Universal Mathematical Method
1) Only evident is true
2) Divide difficulties
3) Order — simple
   to complex
4) Complete enumeration

Baconian Induction

Sense — Universal Methodic Doubt — Intellection

True System:
Certitude vs. Skepticism

Criterion of Truth

Cogito ergo sum

Deduction
no sane man doubts

Mind
thought = consciousness
Complete substance

External
must be
because
qualitati
physics
given in
knowled
sensation
purely ι

§ 7. EPISTEMOLOGY

The term epistemology can have a variety of meanings. In general it is a study of human knowledge, the nature and the validity of knowledge. By usage epistemology has come to be centered around this problem of validity. When are we sure that our knowledge is true? It seems to be primarily a question of method. And this is the function of the criterion, the methodical examination of the knowing process to decide whether or not it can attain reality. Epistemology thus conceived is the judge of metaphysics and holds her fate in its hands.[14]

A. Descartes and the Origins of the Critical Problem

This conception of epistemology, as concerned with what is commonly called *the critical problem,* began with René Descartes. The most important thing to remember about Descartes is his starting point. This is almost a truism since the *Cogito* is the very model of a correct and technical starting point for a philosophy that aspires to be more than a naïve and vulgar knowledge. It is the necessary point of departure for a technical, professional philosophy if it is to achieve a scientific stature. However, this explicit starting point is not Descartes's real and primary starting point. His implicit starting point is not the famous *Cogito* which dominates contemporary philosophy, it is a mechanical material universe completely intelligible in terms of the principles of mechanism. The object of Descartes's total effort is to establish mathematical physics as the supreme and only science of the physical universe in order to gain for it an academic legitimacy and a rightful place in

---

[14] Cf. Kant, *Critique of Pure Reason,* Preface.

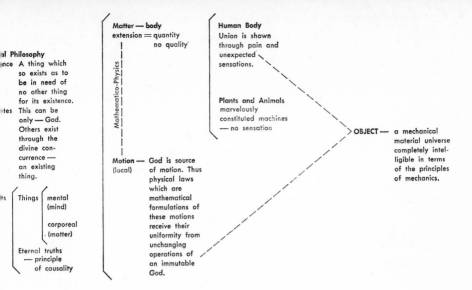

Matter — body
extension = quantity
no quality

Mathematico-Physics

Motion — (local)
God is source of motion. Thus physical laws which are mathematical formulations of these motions receive their uniformity from unchanging operations of an immutable God.

Human Body
Union is shown through pain and unexpected sensations.

Plants and Animals marvelously constituted machines — no sensation

OBJECT — a mechanical material universe completely intelligible in terms of the principles of mechanics.

al Philosophy
nce   A thing which so exists as to be in need of no other thing for its existence. This can be only — God. Others exist through the divine concurrence — an existing thing.

tes

rs   Things   mental (mind)
             corporeal (matter)

Eternal truths — principle of causality

the university curriculum of the day, which hitherto had found it unacceptable and inadequate according to the standards of scientific judgment of the seventeenth century.

Since the *Cogito* enabled Descartes to reach his own knowledge before he confronted external physical reality, it permitted him to strip reality of all the aforementioned forms and qualities and relocate them somewhere else. We do know them. The perception of qualities is so fundamental a human experience that these qualities cannot be denied. They cannot be reduced to nothingness, annihilated. But they can be relocated in the geography of reality. They can be taken out of things and pushed back into the mind where they become the direct object of thought even while the mind is still doubting the very existence of external physical reality. Thus was idealism born as an unsought and unwelcome by-product of the attempt to bestow on modern physics its charter as a science. The epistemological problem as a pseudoproblem finds its plausibility in the origins of modern critique as an historical accident. Descartes, in attempting to find a niche of honor in the realms of science for modern empiriological physics, constructed a material universe which was absolutely and exhaustively interpretable in terms of the laws of mechanics, matter, and motion. In order to present us with a universe wherein matter was reducible to its quantitative aspects, he was forced to push all quality into the mind. He could not completely neglect such basic facts of awareness, and therefore he made them a part of mental life. Thus was born the "idea" of Descartes, this strange mental phenomenon that owed its origin to a mind so inspired with the vision of the future glory of mathematical physics that it exalted it to the office of unique and supreme arbiter of the material universe.

B. The Idea and the Concept

It is in the existence of this mental fact, the "idea," *as the direct and immediate object of knowledge* that we find the hidden assumption that would make of the epistemological problem a pseudoquestion. If in our posing of the critical problem we imply in any way that in the *primary operation* of knowledge a mental act can be the object of our knowing processes, then we have placed ourselves in an inextricable position, linked arm in arm with Bishop Berkeley, and our answer, if logically rigorous, must be essentially identical.

These are the basic facts of this approach briefly sketched. We make no attempt at justification. Much abler students have already done so. We state them merely as background for a further question. Without conceding the truth or falsity of this interpretation, the question that we would like to pose, and the one in the answer to which we contend that this difficulty lies, is this: Is the "idea" of Descartes a mental monstrosity? What did Descartes find when he went within himself? Was a mind as brilliant as his the victim of a delusion? Were the gifted thinkers who accepted his principle of the idea as the direct, immediate object of knowledge repeating by rote his formula, or when they went within themselves did they come face to face with some reality that fitted his definition? What did Descartes find within his own mental processes that served as justification for his notion of "idea"?

In attempting to answer this question, we think that we shall find a key to an epistemology. Thomas Aquinas, for example, never called the principle of knowledge an "idea." The term which he used was usually *conceptus,* or concept. However, there was a mental content which Aquinas did refer to as an "idea." This mental fact fits the formulation of Descartes perfectly. It is our contention that when Descartes went within himself, he was not the author of some metaphysical monstrosity. There was a reality there which he saw and of the nature of which he was aware. But he made an error in allocating its proper function.

The idea seems to differ from the concept by the fact that it is made the object of a direct intellectual examination. The artist, when he understands in himself the form of house in matter, is said to understand the house, but when he understands the form of the house considered in itself, from the very fact that he understands himself to understand it, he understands the idea or *ratio* of the house. The idea is the concept having assumed the role of object of the intellect that it might be the exemplar of something produced.

Now to relate the results of our study to its epistemological background. Being is the first and adequate object of the intellect, and knowledge is an immanent action which possesses the form of the thing in the same way that a living being possesses food. When you know a tree, it is not like examining a snapshot which you have acquired after the fashion of the camera, a Cartesian machine; it would be more accurate to take an example from biology as Thomas Aquinas does. When you know a tree, it is as if you plunged your arm up to the armpit into the tree and there you grasp the core of reality of the tree, its form, in an immaterial relationship, of course — a profoundly immanent union. If this ontological theory of knowledge is true, then the question "How do I know that I know?" in the critical sense, is the same type of question as "How do I eat that I eat?" There is no eating without a being to eat, and there is no knowing in the primary act of knowledge without a being to know. The only way such a question makes sense is if, when you know, you know directly your own mental contents, your ideas. But then the problem is, of course, to relate the two, the knowledge and reality, an impossible task.

In conclusion then, let us say that if the idea is not the direct object of intellectual examination, then there is no critical problem. However, how could Descartes confirm psychologically his metaphysical principles? We suggest, as the whole point of our discussion, that one of the reasons for the success of Descartes was that when he went within his own consciousness in an *act of reflection,* he actually did discover a psychological entity which is the direct object of an act of reflection, and so did his followers when they entered their own mental life to relive his philosophical experience. They found something there, Aquinas would say, but it was not what they estimated it to be. It was not the principle of knowledge functioning as the principle of knowledge, but the principle of knowledge functioning as the principle of artistic production. Descartes mistook the idea for the concept — an easy mistake, but one with terrible consequences.

Knowledge itself, in its initial movement, is a physical tendency. We have no control over the initial movement, the primal operation of our own knowledge. We do not say: "Now I am going to know!" We have to know with the same necessity a hungry dog has to eat. We have even less control and free deliberation over our knowing than we do over our breathing and our other determined, instinctive, or physical tendencies and operations. We cannot in fact *not* know. As an experiment try not to know or to not know! Try to think of nothing! It cannot be done. We have more control over our breathing than we do over our knowing. We can at least hold our breath for a few minutes.

But we cannot know as a free deliberate act of volition. Our knowledge is as necessitated and outside of our control in its initial movement, in the primal spark of consciousness, as our heartbeat.

When I know, to the extent to which I am knowing, to the degree of concentration or intensity of attention, to that extent I am unaware of the fact that I am knowing, of my own knowledge, or, indeed, of myself. For example, when I am at a motion picture theater, to the extent to which I am knowing, to the degree of cognitive absorption in the events of the picture, to that extent I am completely unaware of myself or my environment. I am literally outside of myself, beside myself, and lost in the events on the screen. The movement of knowledge is thus a centrifugal one. It is characterized by an *exstasis,* an ecstasy, a literal going out of oneself and becoming completely absorbed in the cognitive object or thing known — as is the case in the ecstasy which characterizes the most intense moments of sensory knowledge, which is, after all, knowledge.

Thus, I think that experience would seem to support the theory of the concept as an immaterial relation (biological, logical, or otherwise) between two beings rather than a collapsing of the object of knowledge upon the knowing subject and the location of the thing known within the field of consciousness.

Certain contemporary theoreticians of knowledge accept as an axiom the statement that when we know, we know our own sensations. The corollary is that therefore we know for sure *only* these sensations. Consequently sensation cannot be trusted. The purpose of sensation or its function is not, for example, the perception of dimension. It is touch which has dimension for its proper object. We perceive dimension secondarily under color. Color only lays bare the formal structure, the intelligibility or intelligible structure of the things. We see things through color. If in a completely dark room we were to dash a can of luminous white paint on the furniture, we could see the furniture. There is a bureau, there a chair, that is a bed, etc.! Likewise, in looking at the curtain at a stage play, as it billows out we can perceive form or shape. That is an actor, that a piano, etc.! We can see a face because of the difference of shadows. Color lays bare the form, structure, and/or meaning underneath.

But color is only the proper object of sight; color is not the being or thing with which sight puts us in contact. Sight can easily be deceived regarding dimensions and many artificial situations can be constructed or fabricated as illustrations — but this is the influence of art. Art perfects nature. When I put on a pair of glasses I see things smaller and clearer. Therefore, am I justified in concluding that my eyes are not to be trusted? This is also true of the famous flower pot reflected in a concave mirror and thus displaced in height — which is checked by the sense of touch. Also, in the Hanover experiments, for example, we look through a peephole and see three rectangles, one a surface, another a wire frame, and the third a drawing — but through the peephole they look the same. The senses are not being deceived. Knowing the laws of sight we can experiment with them. But this can only be done by one who knows and respects the reliability of necessities of sensation. To reiterate, color and sound, etc., are only the "objects" of sensation, not the things or sensible structures known.

Conception is not an inference. It is biological. Just as we possess food when we eat, so we grasp the form when we know — a true biological operation and not merely an analogy. The word *conceptus* is not chosen at random.

Epistemology then, within a philosophy which possesses a radical psychological dichotomy, which perceives the differentiating characteristics of sense and intellectual knowledge as a complete separation — epistemology here serves the purpose of attempting to span this separation, to find the point of contact between the intellect and the thing, the knower and the known.

However, in a philosophy where metaphysics is queen, where there is only distinction and not separation of sense and intellect, that knowledge is a unity, the components of which are sensation and understanding, whose natural function is the grasping of reality, the direct apprehension of the thing — in such a philosophy there is no room for a critique in the sense in which it was defined above. If there is to be an epistemology, it must be radically transformed. It must be a metaphysical and not a purely methodical instrument. It becomes merely an explanation of human knowledge and its possibility.

The problem of the concept is a representative case in point. If we argue that the object of human knowledge is the concept, if we hold that what the knower knows is merely the idea in his own intellect, then an epistemology as the study of the validity of human knowledge is perfectly acceptable. But there are two fundamental errors inherent in such a view — first a divorce of sensation and intellection and second a divorce of essence and existence, for knowledge has become the systematizing of abstract essences which have little if any relation to things.

If, however, we hold that there is a unity of sense and intellect in knowledge, that the concept is not a pure being of reason but a *passio* possessing the real being of an accident, a formal sign whose very essence consists in designating its object, whose own being as a representation is nothing but the formal presence of the thing in the mind, if there is such a unity between the species in the mind and the thing that they are not only of the same species but more correctly they are the very species itself under consideration, if St. Thomas can call the concept and the thing one in number, then there is no possible room for a criterion. As soon as we have knowledge we know the thing. And since the critique is knowledge it cannot claim priority, either temporally or by nature, to its own origin.

C. The Idea in Psychology, Epistemology, and Logic

Our aim in this brief analysis is to discover the fundamental rationale in the locating and differentiating of psychology, logic, and epistemology. We shall attempt to establish their peculiar orbits as specified by a central problem, which like so many of the really fundamental problems of philosophy, span in a common question, the arbitrary division of sciences that is essentially a unity of wisdom, namely the problem of the idea or concept which we have already discussed.

Beginning with psychology, for the idea likewise takes its origin there, we find the concept as the fruit of the natural processes, of abstraction. It is itself an entity, it has a being subordinated to and depending on the faculty in which it comes to birth, a being which in Aristotelian terminology may be called *accidental*.

With logic, we consider the concept in itself, as a being of reason, divorcing it from the intellectual processes of which it is the term, divesting it of all contamination with reality, in order to consider the rules and standards by which these mental contents may be measured, related, and combined in proposition, judgment, and reasoning — a fascinating exercise in which the agile and facile mind can build a magnificent systematic superstructure, absolute in consistency and complete in detail.

In epistemology, or to be more consistent when speaking from the point of view of a realistic theory of knowledge, in metaphysics, the idea is nothing else but the thing itself. There is a direct and intimate contact of the intellect with reality, a union of knower and known by which the object is in the knower in the full reality of its formal presence. The idea is this formal presence of the object in the intellect, when considered from the point of view of the mind's contact with reality, for purposes of asserting its validity in an epistemology.

In conclusion then, metaphysics is interested in things, psychology in the processes of knowledge and of life, and logic in the relation of concepts in thinking and reasoning.

The *critical problem* arose historically as the accidental adjunct of the attempt to provide physics with its own charter as the legitimate science of the physical world. We can go one step further in the dissolution of the critical problem by providing a legitimate status for mathematical physics among the sciences. For St. Thomas, we need not reduce the universe to a giant machine in order to respect the scientific claims of the natural sciences. We can locate these knowledges in the realm of science and at the same time preserve the integrity of the traditional knowledges, the mathematical, the philosophical, and the theological sciences. It is precisely this consideration which provides the transition from epistemology to the classification of the sciences.

§ 8. THEOLOGY

Granted the Christian economy, theology, too, must be considered a science precisely because it is the most *certain* and *necessary* of all knowledges — founded as it is on the word of God.

The history of modern philosophy and contemporary philosophy has certainly shown us that natural reason alone is too delicate and sensitive an instrument to rely on when the salvation of a human being is at stake. Religion must be rooted in some more reliable certitude, the authority of God revealing, or faith.

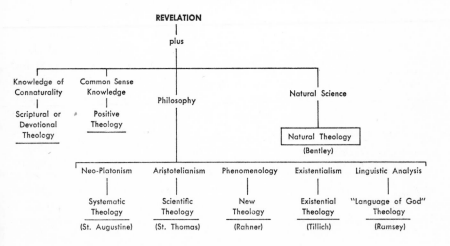

Thomas Aquinas defines theology as the *science of God and all things in relation to God (sub ratione Deitatis)*.[15] This certainly is not the only definition of theology. For Augustine the subject of theology was the *Christus Totus*, the *Integral, Whole Christ*. Just as the definition of theology, the attempt to grasp just what theology is, has had a history of variety and conflict, so the very structure and development of the knowledge has come in for a variety of experiments.

First of all, theology must be distinguished from religion. Religion is a way of life, of salvation, while theology is a knowledge and must not be confused with the virtue of religion, the significance of which it seeks to explain and the understanding of which it serves to deepen.

Theologies vary by the knowledges that inform them. The attempt to make a theology out of simple religious knowledge by the addition of commonsense knowledge to inform and develop the content of the faith as found in Scripture, gives rise to what we may call a *positive theology*. If philosophical conceptions are used to organize and construct a theology then we have a *scientific theology* such as that of Thomas Aquinas. Bentley, the Protestant divine, attempted to construct a theology out of Newtonian science as part of the movement known as *natural theology*. The Protesant thinkers, reluctant to rely on scholastic philosophy for fear that they might be attracted back into the orbit of the Church, tried to fashion a viable theology out of the impressive contributions of natural science in the seventeenth, eighteenth, and nineteenth centuries. This was the movement which caused Darwin so much trouble in the nineteenth century. Since religion used the scientific notions of the day to construct a theology, these notions received an approval and psychologically powerful confirmatory strength from religious conviction. This is what happened to the Linnean classification of species. When Darwin pointed out that these biological classifications were inadequate and that actually biological species were not fixed (he was not concerned with philosophical species), religion which had a vested interest in the Linnean classification became panicky. After all, the Linnean species had come from the hand of God in direct creation! This baptism of outmoded scientific notions is what has made natural theology suspect in our time and lies at the basis of the modern conflict between science and religion. But it is not really a conflict between science and religion but between one set of scientific notions

---

15 Thomas Aquinas, *In Boethium de Trinitate*, Prol., ed. Pecker, p. 46.
"Theology is a poem, with God for subject," quoted by M. Bishop, "Petrarch," *Renaissance Profileo* (New York: Harper and Row), p. 14.

and another set, between one scientific theory and the other outmoded one which it seeks to replace. We shall see more of this in our discussion of Darwinian evolution.[16]

Theologies vary by the knowledges that inform them and scientific theologies vary by the philosophies that inform them. St. Augustine used the neo-Platonic philosophy to organize and structure theology. His magnificent effort may be characterized as theology becoming aware of its own proper nature as a science. His contention that theology was the one and only science may be excused for failing to see the proper autonomy of the other knowledges against the blinding brilliance of his discovery of a new science. His position is similar to that of Descartes relative to the construction of a mathematical physics. Augustine took the positive theologies, the scriptural and devotional theologies of the Fathers of the Church, and produced a *systematic structure* for theology through the instrumentality of a neo-Platonic philosophy. In this sense Thomas Aquinas was, and so looked upon himself as, an Augustinian.

The Augustinian systematic theology was the attempt to move from the level of commonsense knowledge or the practical knowledge of connaturality to a truly explanatory level, a knowledge of causes — that scientific theology which was to reach its maturity in Thomas Aquinas.

In using the term "systematic" we intend no overtones of the Cartesian "closed system"; we only mean to describe the way in which Augustine organized positive theology into at least that descriptive phase of the knowledge which was its initiation into the stage of scientific knowledge, yet to become truly explanatory. St. Augustine's philosophical tools were not equal to his theological effort, but in spite of this he was able to construct what was truly theology out of what had been essentially religious knowledge. However, the utilization of the Aristotelian philosophy and particularly the mode of demonstration, plus the addition of completely new and unique metaphysical notions, enabled Aquinas to construct a mature science which respects the rights of things and the claims of the natural knowledges while at the same time it propounds the ways of God with the world.

These are not in every case separate and distinct theologies but they are *the types* of theologies determined by the kinds of knowledges employed to organize, structure, and develop the content of the faith. All too often theological quarrels are due not so much to the theology involved as to the epistemological conflicts between the knowledges used to inform the theologies concerned. This is particularly true of the *new*

---

[16] Cf. *infra,* Chap. VI.

theologies which attempt to apply phenomenology and existentialism to the contents of the faith. This serves to set the proponents of a scriptural or devotional theology with its propensity for mysticism and "sermon exhortation" against a scientific theology with its emphasis on explanatory, logical structure and academic preoccupation. For existentialism is a philosophical rethinking of the fundamental poetic intuition and literary and aesthetic experience and thus serves to give academic legitimacy to the kind of knowledge informing a scriptural or devotional theology, accounting for its value and current popularity.

Experimentation is the breath of life for theology as for any other knowledge. No knowledge is closed, finished, and completed like the mathematical ideal of the Cartesian system. Theology is perennially open to further development and even innovation.[17] For example Bentley attempted to construct a theology out of Newtonian science as part of the movement known as *natural theology*. Today there are attempts to construct new theologies by using phenomenology as an informing principle, as in the case of Karl Rahner, or existentialism, as in the case of Paul Tillich. To this can be added the employment of linguistic analysis to fashion the "language of God" theological approach of Ramsey, for example, and Hartshorne's utilization of Whitehead's metaphysics to similar purpose.

One of the contemporary attempts to construct a theology modeled after Bentley's attempt to use science (albeit Newtonian science) is the effort to employ the quasi-sciences to structure and model theological thinking. Such are the dangers of reducing theology to the exigencies of a "social apostolate." Following the thrust of a neo-Marxian existentialism, thinkers such as Harvey Cox (*The Secular City*) attempt to use politics and sociology as the scaffolding for the evolution and development of the content of the faith as found in Scripture. The influence of August Comte is seen in Cox's reduction of the knowledges to the causal efficacy of social institutions. Comte's positivism is the basic inspiration for Cox's reduction of myth to rural society, metaphysics to the medieval town, and liberal scriptural theology to the urban society, the city. Whether such a causal relationship is anything more than metaphor is difficult to see since no historical justification is given or even attempted.

Such an experiment is a stimulus to political and social justice but

---

17 Karl Rahner in theology and Bernard Lonergan in philosophy are examples of thinkers who have innovated fruitfully from an historically sound theological and philosophical foundation. The same can, unfortunately, hardly be said of all their disciples.

runs the danger of substituting action for spirituality and social work for religion. Social justice flows from religious virtue but cannot be equated with it. One of the ever present dangers of the theologian, *otherworldliness,* is always present as a by-product of a recognition of the primacy of the supernatural. It is easy to forget the natural and its exigencies in the preoccupation with the supernatural. In this conception grace replaces nature and is surrogate for it.

St. Augustine was of course primarily concerned with the primacy of the supernatural and the devotional. But this theological aim was reinforced to a point of extremity by the natural momentum of the neo-Platonic philosophy he used to constitute his theology.

But there are *conditions* to innovation and experimentation. We must know, and know well, the history of theology if we are not to make the same mistakes over again, and repeat the same heresies. For example, Scripture is certainly the foundation of any theology. But if one tries to develop a sophisticated doctrine like that of grace, scriptural passages are not enough for scientific understanding. The theologian must go to the medieval formulations as crystallized in the councils or he is in danger of simply repeating old errors and heresies.

Too many younger contemporary theologians think that the history of theology is irrelevant and that innovation means utilizing, for example, the philosophies of today to reconstruct and reinterpret religious truths and thus revitalize them.

The situation is similar to the student of contemporary art. The neophyte artist wants to begin with abstract and nonrepresentational painting. He wants to paint like Picasso right from the start. He does not realize the hard disciplines he must first master. He must know perspective, anatomy, and representational drawing. He forgets that Picasso could and did paint representational canvases to rival the masters in quality. Only when one has this kind of training can he then safely experiment and innovate.[18] Otherwise he is skimming the icing from the cake and the result can be theological indigestion.

The situation in philosophy is at times analogous. Those philosophers so involved with contemporaries that they discard the ancients and medievals as irrelevant are guilty of the same lack of perspective. In philosophy one must know the major philosophies in the major documents of

---

[18] "Inasmuch as they help us to share in the primordial intuitions of the faith, the texts of the past are never wearisome. They lead the mind into postures that are always new, which we leave refreshed, not only towards the problems and situations of to-day. There is only one way in which a tree can prove that it lives, and that is by sending out new shoots and new flowers every spring. Thus, to be always truly itself, the theology of the Church should be always abundant in new consequences.

the major philosophers of the ancient, medieval, modern, and contemporary periods if he is to achieve an intellectual liberation. The same is even truer of theology. An unbalanced immersion in one period or theologian to the exclusion of all others means lack of perspective, and a jaundiced theological vision.

The reaction of some contemporary thinkers against the excesses of a Thomism of the *Ipse Dixit* type is understandable and might have been predicted. The authority of Thomas Aquinas is only as good as the cogency of his arguments, as he himself states so bluntly. It had become common to hear speakers preface their own unique ideas with "St. Thomas says." But excesses beget excesses and reactions are to be distrusted, as C. S. Lewis puts it so well:

> For my own part I hate and distrust reactions not only in religion but in everything. Luther surely spoke very good sense when he compared humanity to a drunkard who, after falling off his horse on the right, falls off it next time on the left. I am convinced that those who find in Christ's apocalyptic the whole of his message are mistaken. But the thing does not vanish — it is not even discredited — because someone has spoken of it with exaggeration. It remains exactly where it was. The only difference is that if it has recently been exaggerated, we must now take special care not to overlook it; for that is the side on which the drunken man is now most likely to fall off.[19]

But the theology of Thomas Aquinas must not be overlooked in this age of theological renewal. He was a theologian first and foremost. He manufactured new philosophical conceptions only because he needed them to develop his theological doctrines. The doctrine of being as existence *(esse)* was conceived to express and explain the theology of creation.

The point that theology should be structured by a metaphysics is a valid one. But the problem goes one step further. If theology is to be structured by a metaphysics, does this mean that it is the metaphysics in a "sea of change"? It is precisely here that I think this position is the strongest. For although theologies are the result of the organization of the faith or religious premises communicated to some community

---

How should we ever have perceived them unless we had been guided by the writings of our contemporaries, whether theologians by vocation or otherwise? — and those that are not so are occasionally the more sensitive to vibrations coming from worlds that are still in formation" (Charles Journet, *The Church of the Word Incarnate* [New York: Sheed & Ward, 1955], p. xxx).

19 C. S. Lewis, *The World's Last Night* (New York: Harcourt, 1960), pp. 94–95.

by a revelation, by some particular knowledge, the theology must always which provides the criterion of truth and shapes the theology it informs be in control. It sets the problems and outlines the solutions. The theologian must use some natural human knowledge; the theologian uses metaphysics, and invariably finds it a two-edged blade.

Augustine could use the neo-Platonic philosophy and come through unscathed. But John Scotus Erigena, a poorer theologian but a better philosopher, would follow the natural, almost gravitational inclination of his metaphysical principles and conclude that God could not know himself, and the Son could not know the Father because when the *Nous* or Intelligence knows, it defines and sets limits to a thing, makes it to be a certain kind and gives it an essence. Therefore if the Intelligence were to know the One, the One would be limited and finite; if the Word were to know the Father, Erigena concludes, driven by the force of the philosophical doctrine, then the Father would be limited, defined, and finite. But Augustine was too sensitive to the theological exigencies of the doctrine to permit the metaphysical principles he used to assume control of the complete formulation of theological doctrines. Augustine's philosophical tools were not equal to his theological effort, but in spite of this he was able to construct what was truly theology out of what had been essentially religious knowledge. Such evidence, multiplied many times, is the reason why I think this position is so strong, namely, that "theological questions have to be settled in accord with theological principles of judgment." Theology must always be in control of the particular knowledge it employs, whether metaphysics or something else.

In the light of the conception of theology as a science, the relations between freedom and authority are clearly delineated. The charge that the Church is undemocratic makes sense only to a mentality that exalts the sociopolitical order to the supreme pinnacle of reality, that makes politics a metaphysics by which it judges all things. Democratic is an adjective that belongs to the order of politics and applies especially to that method of deciding issues by the vote of the majority, claiming this to be the best way of preserving the freedom and dignity of the individual citizen. It rebels against political coercion.

But to call a church undemocratic because it does not permit opinion to run roughshod over religious truths is to make that same mistake of confusing two orders of knowledge. Do we settle the time of the rising of the sun by the vote of the majority, or the rate of acceleration of a falling body, or the boiling point of water? It is a fact that God either exists or he does not. Can that be settled by the vote of the majority?

The vote is of value only in concrete prudential decisions where certitude cannot be arrived at and a course of action must follow.

If we lived in a world where there was no revelation, then an absolute and unbridled freedom of thought and of religion might be countenanced. But if revelation is a fact, then never again can man reason as if he were unaware of these same fundamental truths. We do know that God exists, that he created the world and that, as a part of creation, we owe him love and obedience. And in this lies our fulfillment and the completion of our natures. It is ignorance that is the worst slavery, because when you do not know something, then precisely you *do not know*. The most terrible thing about ignorance is that the ignorant man does not know what he does not know. He is not even aware of his own ignorance, because otherwise he would know in some way that which he does not know.

Dogma, then, should be not an obstacle but an aid to man's freedom precisely because it frees him from that ignorance which makes freedom impossible. Man must know what he is and how to act in accordance with what he is, if he is to achieve the estate of a free man. Dogma was not meant to coerce and enslave the mind. It was meant to guide it. The history of the councils of the Church is there to show us that definition of doctrine was made precisely when great danger of error was present, when men needed guidance to see the truth. In this sense dogmatic theology, as paradoxical as it may sound to the contemporary mentality, is an instrument of freedom, especially of the freedom of autonomy.

PART TWO

THE SYSTEMATIC RELATIONS OF PHILOSOPHY AND SCIENTIFIC THEORY

IN ANY treatment of the relations of philosophy and natural science there are five major points of discussion:

1) According to the theory of the "substitutional" role of natural science in the history of man's intellectual development, natural science alone is the true interpreter of reality and supplants both theology and philosophy as valid human knowledges.

2) Philosophy explains to science its own nature. No science, except metaphysics, judges its own nature or its own first principles, but it receives them from a higher science, ultimately metaphysics.

3) Philosophy criticizes the philosophical claims of scientific theory. The atomic theory in physics and chemistry, the theory of relativity in mathematics, and the theory of evolution in biology have only an accidental philosophical significance.

4) Philosophy can provide a principle of unification for the diverse sciences, one which is directive of research and a valuable aid in the development of the sciences.

5) Philosophy has its own proper work which lies beyond the scope and techniques of the sciences. It is the human voice of theology, and

it examines basically immaterial realities such as being, the soul, and its two fundamental powers, knowledge and love.

Many philosophers spend too much time in the analysis of natural science. Their purpose is apologetic and the results negative. Natural science has little to give which is of philosophical value and the philosopher can be wasting energies that should be harnessed to properly philosophical work.

Even though philosophy has been called the science of generalities, I dislike speaking of generalities in generalities. Therefore I should like to take the first theme, perhaps the most important for evaluating the place of philosophy in the world of modern science, and develop it in some concrete fashion. In view of the mixture of professional backgrounds that any reading public represents, I think that an historical approach to a philosophical problem will be of more general profit than an analysis and critique of one of the more specialized sciences. The more technical themes can be handled later.

The most common and most powerful contemporary argument against scholastic philosophy is that since it was built upon Aristotelian science, when Aristotelian science was discarded it lost whatever validity it might have had. A new philosophy had to be built to explain the facts discovered by the new science.

This viewpoint is faulty for two reasons: (1) the underlying assumption is incorrect. Philosophy does not have to start with scientific facts (although it is mindful of them); it can begin with the knowledge of common sense. You can start with a tree, a dog, and a man and from them reach directly the philosophical notion of form, the principle of organization of matter; (2) as an historical fact, the medievals were conscious of the shortcomings of the Aristotelian physics and were in the process of correcting it. St. Thomas, for instance, kept his science and his philosophy in two different compartments and was well aware of the provisional nature of scientific theory and of Aristotelian science as one way of "saving the appearances" of things. Even a cursory reading of his *In De Caelo* (*On the Heavens*) makes this point evident. This is the question I should like to discuss.

If all scientists saw in the atom, in the living cell, and in the galaxy the evidences of the supreme intelligence which fashioned them (which is the proper vision of the scientist), the work of the philosopher and the theologian would be immeasurably simplified. Unfortunately such is not the case. Instead of the confirmation and corroboration which could do much toward psychologically disposing men's minds for the truths that theology and philosophy have to teach, all too often the facts, methods, and theories of modern science have been used to equip the arsenal of the opponents of philosophy and theology. In fact, Science, with a capital *S*, has been offered as an alternative view of the universe in direct opposition to the teachings of theology. Such is not the true role of science, such is not the belief of many competent scientists, but such is the intellectual perspective that dominates contemporary university teaching and present-day popular thinking.

CHAPTER V. / THE SUBSTITUTIONAL THEORY OF SCIENCE

TO THE modern mind, the role which science plays in the history of human intellectual progress is what may be termed the "substitutional" one. According to this view there are three phases of intellectual development applicable to both the individual and society. They are the theological or supernatural phase which treats of the behavior of things as directly dependent upon supernatural agents; the philosophical phase where essences are merely observable constancies of phenomena and the result of natural forces; the third and final phase, the scientific, where the uselessness of inquiry into causes and essences having become obvious, the interest lies only in observation and classification of phenomena in their relations and resemblances — the discovery of the laws of phenomena. The most primitive or theological way of expressing human ignorance is to ascribe life and intelligence to inanimate things. This results in fetishism, polytheism, and ultimately monotheism. Philosophy substitutes fanciful essences natural to the phenomena themselves. But science is the true interpreter of reality and supplants philosophy in its turn. Averroës in the Middle Ages and August Comte in modern times have been eloquent proponents of this "substitutional" view of modern science. But it was never more alive than it is today. Sir William Dampier keynotes his *History of Science* with a self-authored poem.

1) At first men try with magic charm
    To fertilize the earth,
    To keep their flocks and herds from harm
    And bring new young to birth.

2) Then to capricious gods they turn
    To save from fire or flood;
    Their smoking sacrifices burn
    On altars red with blood.

3) Next bold philosopher and sage
    A settled plan decree,
    And prove by thought or sacred page
    What Nature ought to be.

4) But Nature smiles — a Sphinx-like smile
    Watching their little day
    She waits in patience for a while —
    Their plans dissolve away.

5) Then come those humbler men of heart
    With no completed scheme,
    Content to play a modest part,
    To test, observe, and dream.

6) Till out of chaos come in sight
    Clear fragments of a Whole;
    Man, learning Nature's ways aright,
    Obeying, can control.

7) The great Design now glows afar;
    But yet its changing Scenes
    Reveal not what the Pieces are
    Nor what the Puzzle means.

8) And Nature smiles — still unconfessed
    The secret thought she thinks —
    Inscrutable she guards unguessed
    The Riddle of the Sphinx.[1]

One scientific educator writes:

Scientists have a special responsibility to help adults and adolescents to find new conceptions and ideas to replace the traditional religious beliefs about the nature of the universe, man's place therein, and the meaning and value of human life, which science has made untenable.[2]

Science has even been invoked as the arbiter of ethics:

And because this is true, scientists can and do pass ethical judgment

---

[1] Sir William Cecil Dampier, *A History of Science* — and its relations with philosophy and religion (New York: Cambridge University Press, 1949) , p. vi.

[2] B. C. Grunberg, *Science and the Public Mind* (New York, 1953), p. 4.

on human behaviour; those things which are based on the scientific attitude, or encourage it, are good, those which stultify or deny it are to that extent bad.[3]

The most frightening obstacles to the very existence of theology and philosophy, however, have not come from the pure scientist, or the science educator, but rather from the scientist turned philosopher, giving rise to a new type of professional philosopher. On the ground of the new science there arose a new philosophy, which began as a by-product of scientific research.

> The mathematician, the physicist, or the biologist, who wanted to solve the technical problems of his science, saw himself unable to find a solution unless he first could answer certain and more general philosophical questions. It was to his advantage that he could look for these philosophical answers unburdened by preoccupation with a philosophical system. And thus . . . he found answers unheard of in the history of philosophy.[4]

The history of philosophy finds its continuators, not in the modern classical or traditional philosophers, mere imitators of a decadent past, but in the new philosophers who grew out of science. Thus the new philosopher is trained in the techniques of the sciences, especially mathematics.

> The philosopher of the traditional school has often refused to recognize the analysis of science as a philosophy and continues to identify philosophy with the invention of philosophical systems. He does not realize that philosophical systems have lost their significance and that their function has been taken over by the philosophy of science.[5]

The notion of the "substitutional" nature of science is the fruit of a peculiar historical and philosophical perspective. For centuries the nature and origins of modern science have been obscured. It had no history. The scientific method sprang fully formulated from the mind of Galileo. This reporting of the history of science is part of a more general interpretation of history, namely the "Dark Ages" conception. Between the glory of classical times and the rebirth of the Renaissance there was only superstition, ignorance, political chaos, and social misery. Translated into the history of philosophy the thesis states that Descartes, the father of modern thought, followed upon Greek philosophy as if there were nothing in between. One of the characteristics of this interpretation is to lay all blame for such a state at the doors of the Church.

---

[3] C. H. Waddington, *The Scientific Attitude* (Cambridge, 1948), p. 3.
[4] Hans Reichenbach, *The Rise of Scientific Philosophy* (Berkeley, 1951), p. 118.
[5] *Ibid.*, p. 119.

Happily, the myth of the Dark Ages has been long exploded, as any serious historical scholar can attest.[6] Also, it has been recently recognized that modern philosophy makes sense only if we recognize its continuity with medieval philosophy. It has no point of rapprochement with Greek thought. In a very real sense Descartes is still a scholastic philosopher. Finally the myth of medieval science is currently being destroyed. The absence of science in the Middle Ages has long been a favorite theme of historians of science. Evaluations such as the following have been stylish.

> During this era, the peculiar flowers of scholasticism blossomed all over Europe. The keenest minds were engrossed in the dispute about the metaphysical reality of universal ideas. As to particulars, they were deemed unworthy of detailed study. The story is told somewhere of a crowd gathering in a mediaeval marketplace, hotly divided in an argument on the question of the number of teeth in a horse's mouth. The matter could not be settled because no copy of Aristotle's works was at hand. But when a young friar suggested that the question be decided by counting the teeth of one of the animals which were standing by waiting for their masters, his remark was taken by some as a joke, by others as shameful impudence. It is not surprising that this period was unproductive of contributions to Physics, and that the one great discovery which was made should be obscure and not connected with a definite name. I am referring to the use of the compass needle.[7]

The verification of sense perception, the recourse to experience, so the accusation goes, was not the basis for medieval thought, which was concerned with revelation or abstractions. This is a half-truth. Scholastic thinkers were very much concerned with natural causes of things. As early as the twelfth century inquiring minds were seeking to explain the cryptic facts of Genesis by rational causes. The entire problem

---

6 For example: "The hospital, like the university, was a mediaeval institution. The foundation of large numbers of charitable hospitals for the relief of the poor and treatment of the sick was a product of Christian civilization. The Emperor Constantine is credited with the first hospital of this kind, and hospitals became numerous in Byzantium. One hospital in the 11th century had 50 beds in separate wards for different kinds of patients, with two doctors and a staff attached to each ward" (A. Crombie, *Augustine to Galileo* [London, 1952], pp. 209–210).

7 Dampier, *op. cit.*, p. 176.
"It is generally agreed that the Middle Ages preserved for the use of later times the science of the ancients. Therein lies both the scientific achievement and the scientific failure of the Medieval civilization. . . . What the Middle Ages took over they did not very much enrich. Indeed so small was their own contribution, that historians of science are apt to regard the Middle Ages as something of a pause" (M. Postan, "Why Was Science Backward in the Middle Ages?" *The History of Science* [Glencoe, Ill., 1951], p. 25).

of the introduction of Aristotle and his Arabian commentators into the West was that of a valid rational science of nature, the autonomy of philosophical disciplines. Along with this, and part and parcel of the same question, was the organization of a complete system of scientific thought, the basis of which were the works of Aristotle.

> Early in the 12th century men asked how the facts recorded in the book of *Genesis* could best be explained in terms of rational causes. With the recovery of full tradition of Greek and Arabic science in the 12th and early 13th centuries, and particularly of the works of Aristotle and Euclid, there was born, from the marriage of the empiricism of technics with the rationalism of philosophy and mathematics, a new conscious empirical science seeking to discover the rational structure of nature. At the same time a more or less complete system of scientific thought was provided by Aristotle's works. The rest of the history of mediaeval science consists of the working out of the consequences of this new approach to nature.[8]

As early as the twelfth century, Adelard of Bath points up the new approach to nature in his *Quaestiones Naturales:*

> Why do plants spring from the earth? What is the cause and how can it be explained? When at first the surface of the earth is smooth and still, what is it that is then moved, pushed up, grows and puts out branches? If you collect dry dust and put it finely sieved in an earthenware bronze pot, after a while when you see plants springing up, to what else do you attribute this but to the marvelous effect of the wonderful divine will?[9]

Adelard answers that even though the divine will is a cause, this growth is "not without a natural reason too." In reply to the further question: Is it not "better to attribute all the operations of the universe to God" since natural explanations are not available for all of them?[10] Adelard says:

> I do not detract from God. Everything that is, is from Him and because of Him. But nature is not confused and without system and so far as human knowledge has progressed it should be given a hearing. Only when it fails utterly should there be recourse to God.[11]

Adelard is clearly studying nature for its own sake and is concerned more with the cogency of reasoning than authority.[12]

---

[8] A. Crombie, *op. cit.*, p. 14.
[9] *Ibid.*, pp. 12–13.
[10] *Ibid.*
[11] *Ibid.*
[12] *Ibid.*

Those who are now called authorities reached that position first by the exercise of their reason. . . . Wherefore, if you want to hear anything more from me, give and take reason.[13]

There is no clearer statement of the medieval attitude toward scholastic authority. An authority is precisely that because of the cogency of his thought.

Historically speaking there are three phases in the development of scientific theory: induction, experimentation, and mathematization. Aristotle contributed induction when he laid the foundations for the science of biology. The contribution to scientific method in the seventeenth century was thought to be the notion of experiment and the construction of an adequate mathematics of motion. Galileo afforded scientific method a generality which it had never before possessed but which was still related strictly to the experimental facts. We now know that both experiment and the mathematization of motion were products of the twelfth and the fourteenth centuries respectively, the work of medieval Latin Christian thinkers. The elaboration of induction into experimental theory occurred in the twelfth century. Robert Grosseteste, Bishop of Lincoln and Chancellor of Oxford, delineates the theory of experiment:

This therefore is the way by which the abstracted universal is reached from singulars through the help of the senses. . . . For when the senses several times observe two singular occurrences, of which one is the cause of the other or is related to it in some other way, and they do not see the connection between them, as, for example, when someone frequently notices that the eating of scammony happens to be accompanied by the discharge of red bile, and does not see that it is the scammony that attracts and withdraws the red bile; then from the constant observation of these two observable things, he begins to form a third unobservable thing, namely, that scammony is the cause that withdraws red bile. And from this perception repeated again and again and stored up in the memory, and from the sensory knowledge from which the perception is built up, the functioning reason therefore begins to wonder and to consider whether things really are as the sensible recollection says, and these two lead the reason to the Experiment, namely, that he should administer scammony after all the other causes purging red bile have been isolated and excluded. When he has administered scammony many times

---

[13] "With this remark the medieval conception of nature began to cross the great watershed that divides the period when man looked to nature to provide illustrations for moralizing from that in which men began to study nature for its own sake. The realization of such a conception became possible when Adelard demanded 'natural causes' and declared that he could not discuss anything with someone who was 'led in a halter' by past writers" (*ibid.*).

with the sure exclusion of all other things that withdraw red bile, then there is formed in the reason this universal, namely, that all scammony of its nature withdraws red bile, and this is the way in which it comes from sensation to a universal experimental principle.[14]

Another example of scientific sophistication is this description characterized by observational accuracy and precision of detail:

Aaron's Beard has leaves which are thick in substance, nearly a span broad and long, and it has two little beards to each leaf. The leaves are divided down to the root. It has a tuberous root in the ground, from which a cosmetic ointment is made, and it sometimes has blotched leaves. It forms its flower in a capsule, contrived by a marvellous artifice and having this yellowish capsule around it, in the center of which is a sort of finger, with two little "apples" below it, wonderfully contrived. The plant which has blotched leaves is masculine and that without blotches on the leaves is feminine.[15]

The theory of experiment had its origin in the twelfth century. We are not speaking of its practice. The initial applications of mathematics to motion occurred later, especially in the fourteenth century, at Oxford. In this century we see the transition from a finalistic interpretation of motion exerted by the natural place of body to an interpretation in terms of external forces. William of Ockham, for example, reduced motion from a qualitative phenomenon demanding a form for its explanation to quantitative determination, a varying spatial relationship with other bodies. Ockham is here approaching the concept of inertia which revolutionized the physics of the seventeenth century.[16]

The most fundamental contribution to scientific method made in the seventeenth century was the construction of an adequate mathematics of motion.

The special contribution that Galileo's conception of science as a mathematical description of relations enabled him to make to methodology, was to free it from the tendency to excessive empiricism which was the main defect of the Aristotelian tradition, and to give it a power of generality which was yet strictly related to experimental facts to a degree which previous Neoplatonists had seldom achieved. This Galileo did in the first place by not hesitating to use, in his mathematical theories, concepts of which no examples had been or could be observed. He required only that from such concepts it should be possible to deduce the observed facts. For example,

---

[14] A. Crombie, *Grosseteste and Experimental Science* (Oxford, 1953), pp. 73–74.

[15] Lynn Thorndike, *The Herbal of Rufinus* (Chicago, 1946), p. 54, quoted by A. R. Hall, *The Scientific Revolution, 1500–1800*, p. 277.

[16] Cf. J. A. Weisheipl, *The Development of Physical Theory in the Middle Ages* (New York: Sheed & Ward, 1960), p. 62 ff.

there is no such thing as a perfectly functionless plane or an isolated body moving in empty, infinite, Euclidean space, yet from these concepts Gàlileo first constructed the seventeenth-century theory of inertia.[17]

This included the formation of certain unempirical notions such as a perfectly functionless plane and a body in isolation moving through empty, infinite, Euclidean space. From these notions Galileo developed his theory of inertia which was later made more precise by Newton's laws of motion. Newton did not change Galileo's method, he improved and extended it in the form of his three laws which became the basis of classical mechanics. Newton was validating again Galileo's method of controls, which regards a body as inert and equivalent to the forces and factors maneuvering it from the outside. This conclusion is written into each of the three laws. But these notions, too, have a history.

John Buridan in his investigation of the continued movement of projectiles and the acceleration of freely falling bodies rejected the theory of natural place and formulated his own theory of *Impetus*. This impetus is a motive power which would maintain the body at uniform velocity indefinitely if it were not for the action of external forces. In projectiles this was naturally reduced by air resistance, and natural gravity acted as an accelerational force adding successive increments of impetus. Force was something that altered motion and did not merely maintain it. This is the very definition of force on which Newton built his mechanics. Impetus in Buridan is analogous to momentum in Newton, except that motion is always in straight lines. To explain the trajectory of projectiles, Albert of Saxony used a compound impetus plus the frictional value of air resistance. He perceived that freely falling bodies move with a uniform acceleration and that

---

[17] Cf. Galileo Galilei, *Due Massimi Sistemi, ii* (Opere, VII), pp. 48 ff., 171 ff.

"The momentous change that Galileo, along with other platonizing mathematicians like Kepler, introduced into scientific ontology was to identify the substance of the real world with the mathematical entities contained in the theories used to describe the 'appearances.' The important practical result of this identification was to open the physical world to an unrestricted use of mathematics. Galileo had removed the worst inconveniences of Aristotle's notion that there was a science of 'physics' outside the range of mathematics, by declaring the substances and causes postulated by that physics to be mere names. The success of his mathematical method convinced him that he had shown how to read the language in which the book of the universe was truly written. In other words, he believed that the world of appearances was the product of an underlying mathematical structure and that he could discover what the structure was. What logical inconveniences this form of 'mathematical realism' could bring are shown by his unsuccessful attempts to prove that the heliostatic theory was necessarily true. The most extreme seventeenth-century form of this mathematical ontology was that advanced by Descartes" (Crombie, *Grosseteste*, p. 310).

the work done is equal to the product of the weight multiplied by the vertical distance.

In the pre-Galilean attempts to formulate a mathematical description of motion, such thinkers as William of Ockham, John Buridan, Nicole Oresme, and Albert of Saxony did remarkable work in both dynamics and statics, especially in the measurement and computation of velocities. It is significant to note that Galileo was familiar with the work of these medieval thinkers. Their books have been found in the catalog of his personal library.[18]

In conclusion we can say that the "substitutional" theory of natural science as a matter of historical record is incorrect. Theology, philosophy, and natural science are not successive stages in the movement of the human mind from ignorance to knowledge, but three ways of understanding a reality too rich in intelligibility for any one alone. They are supplementary sciences, not conflicting ones. They existed side by side through history and each plays its part in explaining a universe flung from the one hand of God and wheeling back in its appointed time, boomerang fashion, to nestle lovingly in the other hand.

§ 1. PHILOSOPHY EXPLAINS TO SCIENCE ITS OWN NATURE

Having eliminated the "substitutional" notion of science as an historical explanation, our next step is to see whether such a theory serves as a causal explanation, to outline precisely what it is that philosophy can contribute to the modern world of science. There are, as we have seen, four other basic functions which philosophy exercises:

1) Philosophy explains to science its own nature.
2) Philosophy criticizes the philosophical claims of scientific theory.
3) Philosophy can provide the principle of unity so necessary to science.
4) Philosophy has its own proper work to do beyond the realm of science.

No science judges its own nature or its own first principles but it receives them from a higher science; as Aristotle says, optics takes its principles from the physics of light. The mathematician does not set his own first principles, such as the whole is greater than any of its parts, things equal to the same thing are equal to each other; nor does he ask what a number is, what of reality does a number seize. He simply proceeds to use these principles and notions. The quantitative unity which is at the basis of number finds its ultimate explanation

---

[18] Cf. William A. Wallace, *The Scientific Methodology of Theodoric of Freiberg* (Fribourg, 1959).

in the metaphysical unity of substance and ultimately of being. Thus, as we have seen in the nature and classification of the sciences, philosophy explains to science its own proper nature.

Science is a speculative human knowledge of causes and thus differs from the knowledge of common sense which is concerned only with effects and results. For example: fire was once explained scientifically as the result of a liquid flowing from a burning object, namely phlogiston. But this loss of material was extremely difficult to reconcile with the increase in weight of a burnt object. Charred wood is heavier than natural wood and rusted metal is heavier than it was prior to rusting. And both are heavier precisely by the same mathematical proportions as that of the oxygen in its compounds. Thus the newer conception of fire as an oxidation, an increase in weight by the addition of oxygen, succeeded the old. Although science does not give us the ultimate causes of a thing, it does tell us something about what a thing is. When we call fire an oxidation we still do not know what fire is as it leaps and dances in the grate, but we do know something about it. Translated into scholastic terminology we use the expression "ultimate and proximate causes." The classic law of acceleration is a good example. When a body is dropped from the Empire State Building we know how long it will take to get to the ground, the speed at which it is traveling at each point in its descent, and the rate of increase per second per second. But the data are the same as long as the weights and dimensions of the bodies considered are the same. It makes no difference whether the bodies concerned are those of men, sacks of potatoes, or barrels of flour. The physicist is not concerned with what things are but only how they operate, only insofar as they are matter in motion.

We are not in complete agreement with thinkers such as Bridgman who consider science as merely art, primarily a form of control of nature. They point out, for example, that the engineer can make an electric light without knowing what electricity is. However, Faraday's experiments of the reciprocal relations of electricity and magnetism do tell us something about what electricity is, a minimum it is true, and in terms of proximate causes, but they are real causes nonetheless. The point that the philosopher would like to emphasize is that none of the sciences attempts to tell what man is, to give his definition. As we have stated repeatedly, for the physicist, man is an articulating system of stresses and strains; for the chemist, man is a complexus of elements and compounds; for the biologist, he is a mammal of the order of primates, that is, he has a skeletal framework so constructed that he walks upright, and he has a certain type of gland by which he suckles his young; for the economist, he is a producer and consumer; for the *philosopher* he is a rational animal. Only the last really attempts to explain what man is. None of the other knowledges, individually or all together, arrives at a definition of man that explains him in any adequate way.

§ 2. PHILOSOPHY CRITICIZES THE PHILOSOPHICAL CLAIMS OF SCIENTIFIC THEORY

One of the functions of philosophy is to criticize the philosophical claims of scientific theory. As long as common sense ruled the human perception of reality it was comparatively easy for metaphysics, so to speak, to rule the intellectual roost. Metaphysical principles were abstracted from the general experience of common sense. Notions such as being, existence, cause, effect, substance, unity, truth, goodness made sense and could be reduced to the common sense experience from which they arose.

But one of the first things that the scientific revolution did was to discredit sensation and the common sense experience based upon it. It could be used as a principle of verification but it had to wait in the antechamber. It could never be admitted into the interior domain of science. The raw stuff of human thought was now a reality distilled through scientific interpretation. Scientific theories and laws were the raw materials out of which metaphysics had to fashion its fundamental doctrines. This is one of the tasks that lie before the metaphysician in this day — to become as familiar with the basic theories and concepts of the natural sciences as his predecessors were with the facts of sense experience, and out of that draw inductions which are couched in the language of science and yet translatable into traditional metaphysical conceptions and vocabulary.

This can be done. It is actually in the process of being accomplished. All that remains for its achievement is time.

Once philosophy lost its privileged position as interpreter of the world about us, the scientist, faced with the perennial philosophical questions, had to use the only materials he had, his scientific techniques, to answer them. The atomic theory in mathematical physics and the theory of evolution in biology are two examples.

CHAPTER VI. / EVOLUTIONARY THEORY AND PHILOSOPHY

THE general theory of evolution, at least in the Walt Disney "Fantasia" version, is common knowledge. Out of the tumult of the forces of nature, scorching temperatures, crushing pressures, and hurricane motion, out of the cataclysm of transient action, somehow arises the original germ of life. After the tumult of wind and wave and earth's belching eruption, a single cell goes floating peacefully in the calm waters to a pizzicato sound track. Out of the passion of inanimate nature is born the germ of life.

Somehow this granddaddy of all jellyfish develops into a fish. The fish in turn becomes an amphibian, leaves its watery home for a land existence, and develops ultimately into some form of mammal. Then follows the ape or primate and finally, the crowning glory of this process, man.

Strictly speaking, there is nothing in all this which cannot be reconciled with the basic truths of religion, as long as the direct creation of a spiritual soul is safeguarded. For a spiritual soul cannot develop from a material form. In fact St. Augustine taught a sort of evolution with the spiritual soul infused at some point in the human body.

Even though the theory of evolution, if and when it is proven, can be fitted into the framework of religious doctrine, it has been seized upon by antireligious thinkers as an alternative to the Christian doctrine of creation. So employed, it has given impetus to modern materialism. It suggests that the whole man, including the spiritual operations he possesses, evolves from the forces of material nature and that there is no need to posit such a thing as a soul.[1]

Originally the theory of evolution received its strongest support from Darwin and Wallace. They had many forerunners and the theory was certainly in the air. But it was Darwin's work in geographical distribution that gave a scientific basis to the theory of evolution. The variety of finches on the isolated Galapagos Islands served to illustrate the principle he formulated as natural selection.

However, what served to win popular support for Darwin against tremendous opposition from paleontologists such as the brilliant Cuvier, was the embryological work of Von Baer later popularized by Haeckel and formulated in the slogan, *Ontogeny recapitulates Phylogeny*. The infant in its development traces out the history of the species. No reputable biologist today subscribes to this theory, which is based on superficial similarities, but it served at the time to fire the public imagination and gain for Darwin's work popular support. Despite current disfavor there are still certain embryological facts that demand an explanation — teeth in the baby whale, the temporary coat of hair on both the human and whale embryo, and vestigial organs, to mention but a few.

Today, however, the strongest and most vocal supporter of the evolutionary theory is paleontology. In the fossil record, organic materials by a process of substantial change have been transmuted into organic minerals, retaining however the original characteristic forms of the animal skeletons and plant tissues embedded in the rock.

---

[1] "It is equally obvious, however, that until teleological thinking and acceptance of any supernatural force, being, or authority are completely and utterly removed from men's minds and the full implications of biological evolution are known to, and accepted by, all scientists (especially teachers of science) and then by all people on this earth, little can be done in a systematic logical way to further man's evolution. Organized religion, with its dependence on belief in supernatural authority for its continued existence, is the chief obstacle in the way of an intellectually emancipated mankind. It is the urgent responsibility of scientists in general and biologists in particular to be aware of the implications of evolution as they apply to man and for each to spread his understanding among the general population. The philosophy we should strive for is not devitalized by the lack of a supernatural mystic element; man is an animal, although a unique one, and his emotional sounding board, as Homer Smith calls it, will continue to be present and to give 'colour' to his perceptions. For the further development of man this sounding board must be controlled with reason and logic, rather than allowed to beat so loudly we cannot hear ourselves think. Man's possession of the power to reason makes it his responsibility to use it" (Bruce F. Crocker, "A Biochemist Looks at Evolution: Past and Future," *Evolution*, T. W. Cameron, ed. [Toronto: University of Toronto Press, 1960], pp. 147–148).

It is a matter of fact that rocks in their function obey a certain temporal sequence, the more recent strata overlying the earlier in a customary pattern. This time clock seems to apply also to the fossil remains preserved in the temporal levels of the rock formations. These fossils differ in a graded sequence from the animal and plant forms we know today. As we come down the time scale more and more types seem to have become extinct. In fact in a few cases, such as the horse, a recognizable series of forms seems to be able to be traced to a very different ancestor.

In spite of these examples, it remains true, as every paleontologist knows, that *most* new species, genera and families appear in the record suddenly and are not led up to by known, gradual, completely continuous transitional sequences. When paleontological collecting was still in its infancy and no clear examples of transitional origin had been found, most paleontologists were anti-evolutionists. Darwin (1859) recognized the fact that paleontology then seemed to provide evidence against rather than for evolution in general or the gradual origin of taxonomic categories in particular. Now we do not have many examples of transitional sequences. Almost all paleontologists recognize that the discovery of a complete transition is in any case unlikely. Most of them find it logical, if not scientifically required, to assume that the sudden appearance of a new systematic group is not evidence for special creation or for saltation, but simply means that a full transitional sequence more or less like those that are known did occur and simply has not been found in this instance.[2]

Any idea that human prehistory can be reconstructed from an examination of fossil remains is naïve. There simply are not enough fossils. The scarcity of fossil remains, when compared to the millions of animals, makes of the fossil record a book with too many pages torn out, obliterated by time and the forces of nature.

The chances that remains of an organism will be buried, fossilized, preserved in the rock to our day, then exposed on the surface of dry land and found by a paleontologist before they disintegrate are extremely small, practically infinitesimal. The discovery of a fossil of a particular species, out of the thousands of millions that have inhabited the earth, seems almost like a miracle even to the paleontologist who has spent a good part of his life performing the miracle. Certainly paleontologists have found samples of an extremely small fraction only of the earth's extinct species, and even for groups that are most readily preserved and found as fossils, they can never expect to find more than a fraction.[3]

---

[2] G. G. Simpson, *The Major Features of Evolution* (New York: Columbia University Press, 1955), p. 360.

[3] *Ibid.*, p. 359.

BIOLOGICAL SPECIES

Much of the sound and fury surrounding evolutionary theory is due to a misapprehension of sorts. Evolution initially had no pretensions to the status of a *Weltanschauung,* nor did it seek to serve as a substitute for the Christian doctrine of creation, which we shall discuss at length in relation to the origin and evolution of the universe. The theory of evolution actually grew out of a conflict between *two distinct and opposing biological theories.* It was a family quarrel. The dominant biological theory was that of *a fixed and immediate creation of species.* This of course has little or no reference to the theological doctrine of creation *ex nihilo.* Nor is the concept of the fixity of species a logical deduction from the philosophical doctrine of the immutability of essence, although the genus and species of Linnaeus do carry some of the logical and conventional characteristics of the Aristotelian genera and species.[4]

The notion of fixed and separate species among the chaotic varieties of plants and animals provided the foundation for classification and systematization. It served a very useful purpose in spurring and motivating the fundamental and crucial work of description and classification that was necessary before biology could even set its foot on the first rung of the ladder to a scientific status. But like most successful theories its very success led it to resist modification and even improvement. As useful as the biological concept of the fixity of species was, it could not be extended to certain very fundamental facts about biological species.[5]

In fact Linnaeus himself as a biologist did claim for his arbitrary morphological classification the cooperation of God, although well aware of hybrid and mutational forms:

> The species that come from God seem to me superior to those contrived by gardeners. The former have existed ever since the beginning of the world. But the latter are growths contrary to nature and can only claim a short life. If they are neglected they disappear and vanish like fugitive shadows. I ignore them.[6]

---

4 Linnaeus himself recognized that "his system was not a natural one but still he was not an evolutionist and saw no alternative to the absolute fixity of species."

5 Cf. W. C. Dampier and Margaret Dampier, *Readings in the Literature of Science* (New York: Harper Torchbooks, 1959), p. 187.

6 Linnaeus, quoted by Wendt, *In Search of Adam* (Cambridge, 1956), p. 50.

"One answer to the problem of how life originated is that it was created. This is an understandable confusion of nature with technology. Men are used to making things; it is a ready thought that those things not made by men were made by a superhuman being. Most of the cultures we know contain mythical accounts of a supernatural creation of life. Our own tradition provides such an account in the

The observations that underlay this statement were of course correct. Artificially cultivated plants, as Linnaeus knew from his gardening experience, soon lose their characteristic features if they are not duly tended, and apparently regain their former wild estate.[7]

Under the hypothesis of separate creation, or as it is sometimes called, *special creation*, the distinctions between true species,[8] at least according to its opponents, should be absolute and the members of the same species must all trace to the same originally created individuals, while members of different species can have no common ancestry whatever. Consequently, much of the difficulty in evaluating contemporary evolutionary theory is the confusion involved in the very formulation of the problem. Some sort of development in living things is admitted by all. One form of this development is the presence in a group of communication of genetic characteristics and the modification of the character of the whole group by the selectivity of these genetic characteristics. In some groups better adapted offspring will find mates more easily and thus exert a greater influence on the general character of the entire group.

But apart from this type of development, which is known to every gardener and animal fancier, the theory of evolution implies a development from group to group and, in its extreme formulation, of complex multicellular organisms from simple unicellular organisms. (But the evidence for the latter is by no means validated by the canons of scientific experiment.) These two kinds of development have been

opening chapter of Genesis. There we are told that beginning on the third day of the Creation, God brought forth living creatures — first plants, then fishes and birds, then animals and finally man" (George Wald, "The Origin of Life," in *The Physics and Chemistry of Life* [New York: Simon & Schuster, 1955], p. 50.

[7] *Ibid.*, p. 50.

[8] "But species appear to be genetically distinct, that is to say, the individuals of a species reproduce organisms of their own kind only. And so, in spite of the suggestions contained in such words as 'genus' and 'family,' natural historians of earlier times felt compelled to assume that species had been established separately at some remote date in the past. The doctrine of the separate creation of species was not an invention of priests, designed to buttress a system of theology, but the best guess that could be given at the time. The theory put forward by Darwin and his successors is simply an hypothesis to the effect that what we call specific differences have come about through the accumulation of many small differences between individuals of successive generations. The laws of genetics show what can be accomplished by selective breeding. Whether, and, if so, by what stages, the organisms we know have been evolved from organisms of simpler types is a question of historical fact. It is extremely unlikely that biologists will ever be able to trace all the steps by which all the known species have been established, but they have apparently found enough to convince themselves that the general hypothesis of evolution is as probable as an historical hypothesis of that kind can be" (W. Kneale, *Probability and Induction*, pp. 105–106).

confused in the history of evolutionary theory since the days of Linnaean classification.[9]

\/There are three basic ideas, often confused, which must be distinguished and delineated here. Evolutionary affirmation of some sort of development was a reaction against the doctrine of fixed and immediate creation of species. But whether there is development from one species to another becomes a question not of progressive change from one group to another or one individual to another, but rather a question of essential differences. The definition and characteristics of species are thus crucial questions in arriving at conclusions on the validity of evolution.[10]

Biological species from Linnaeus to the present have little in common with the philosophical species because they have no (philosophically speaking) specific differences, only accidental differences. Linnaean classification was based primarily on *morphology*; by other criteria, such as the production of viable and fertile hybrids, many species are coalesced and become subspecies, the tiglon for instance; even different genera such as the pigeon and the dove produce fertile hybrids from their matings.

The evidence in favor of evolutionary theory has never been completely satisfying. Strictly speaking, evolution has yet to be scientifically proven.

The old conceptual framework of taxonomy was static — a museum pigeonhole sort of convenience. But since animals propagate themselves by generating other animals, the hypothesis can not be far from the mind that those animals which resemble each other most are genetically closest related, others less. This guess is corroborated, and corrected in details, by further study of relationships between extant animals, and by the cooperative clarities elicited by other approaches. I may as well make the important aside here for the first time: all of the approaches I shall mention are valid, all give information about evolution; but it is the quantitative and qualitative accumulation of all brands of evidence that builds the "fact" of evolution. It is the convergence of probabilities and certitudes

---

[9] "The doctrine of the special creation and fixity of species had become the orthodox teaching of the Church, enforced in Protestant countries by the emphasis on the Bible and the literal interpretation thereof" (W. C. Dampier and Margaret Dampier, *Readings in the Literature of Science*, p. 187).

[10] There are thirteen major groups or phyla. According to Linnaeus, they are divided into four major classifications: class, order, genus, species. The modern breakdown is into phylum, class, order, family, genus, species. A typical example of each of these is: phylum — chordata, sub-phylum — craniata, class — mammalia, sub-class — euthenia, order — Carninora, family — felidae, genus — felis, species — felis tigris. Cf. M. Guyer, *Animal Biology*, pp. 133 ff., 140 ff.

that causes the firm adherence of biologists to the master idea of evolution, a principle which is inescapable in my opinion.[11]

The fact that no missing link has ever been discovered is perhaps the most pronounced weakness in the evolutionary scheme of things. The *theory* of evolution remains just that, a theory, for it has never been demonstrated.[12] Not one link between the species has been found. That is why these transitional forms have been referred to as "missing." That is their normal condition.

A very interesting argument has been recently proposed by a contemporary historian of science. It contends that viability is one of the marks of the permanent species as opposed to the transitional forms of those species. Therefore, missing links, because they are transitional forms, are of course not viable. Thus to expect to find missing links is incorrect. If they existed, they would not be transitional forms but permanent species and thus would not be the link to a more enduring form of living being.

The implications of evolution contradict our daily experience. When a fish comes out on dry land it dies. Evolution as commonly taught also involves a contradiction of one of the first principles of the human mind, the principle of causality. In our experience every cause is greater than its effect. Dogs give birth to puppies and not human infants. In evolution as so commonly taught every effect is greater than its cause, referring to the development of the major species. By a gradual process of perfection it culminates in the most perfect being of all, man. The world as we know it does not support this view.

Actually the real and factual basis of evolution is that in a world which is not a hodgepodge things resemble each other. Even the coelenterate, a living intestinal canal, resembles the structure of the human trunk; there are homologies or likenesses in the wings of a bird and the forelimbs of the mammal. Now, since animals do generate themselves, the next step is to say that since living species resemble each other they must have come from each other. That similarity or analogy implies causality is the assumption of evolutionary theory! But does resemblance demonstrate causality?[13]

---

[11] J. Franklin Ewing, "Precis on Evolution," *Thought*, XXV (March, 1950), pp. 59–60.

[12] "Since his [Darwin's] theory would not have served for predictions then, it is not adequate for an explanation now. It is a scheme of explanation, but the details are yet to be filled in" (John Kenneny, *A Philosopher Looks at Science*, p. 20).

[13] "A first examination of any complex mechanism (a car, a watch) will naturally involve its superficial form and its general behaviour. Closer study will involve an analysis of the mechanism into its several parts and observation of the form of each of these. The final stage in arriving at a complete understanding of the mechanism

We can arrange the Indian teepee, the log cabin, the suburban colonial, and the modern apartment house in order of resemblance, from simpler to more complex. But does that mean that one developed from the other or was generated by it? If things exist in the same

---

will involve a gradual reassembly of the parts with observation of behaviour at each stage until the whole is once again reached. This is a perfectly general method applicable in all cases — for the living organism just as truly as for the watch.

"In the case of the living organism we have seen this method at work. The morphologist (be he zoologist, botanist, or microbiologist) studied the form and behaviour of animal, plant, or micro-organism. He then began the process of analysis, studying (in the case of the zoologist) the individual bones, muscles, blood vessels, nerves, gland cells, etc., of the animal. The comparative anatomy of diverse forms indicated a basic similarity between for example, the flipper of the whale or of a walrus, paw of a rat, foot of a horse, wing of a bat, and hand of a primate. This sort of observation, multiplied several thousandfold, extended by the botanist to the field of plant life, by the micro-biologist to the microscopic and submicroscopic world of micro-organisms, and by the palaeobiologist back along the time axis for hundreds of millions of years has been the basis of our concept of biological evolution. The geologist and the astronomer had already laid the basis for this development by providing evidence that the non-biological world has *evolved* into what it is now" (Crocker, "A Biochemist Looks at Evolution: Past and Future," *op. cit.*, p. 138).

"Analogy (like function) as well as homology (like structure) serves as an heuristic principle for scientific discovery. The theories of Kirchoff in mechanics provide an example. The equations of equilibrium of a thin rod bent or twisted by couples at its ends are identified with the equations of motion of a rigid body turning about a fixed point. The use of analogy in biology can be found in the comparison of analogous organ systems, e.g., the neurosecretory system of invertebrates and vertebrates. The crustacean has a cistern where the hypophysis is located in the vertebrate. There are, also, the well-known analogies between the wings of the insect and the clavicles of the mammal.

"Analogies do serve as instruments which are useful in solving problems. Investigators in the field of applied physics who are concerned with solving practical problems of engineering, as for instance Nemenyi (see Truesdell, 1952) are very much interested in analogies (Nadai, 1931)." A question of the introduction to Chapter 16 entitled "Analogies" by Mindlin and **Salvadori** in the *Handbook of Experimental Stress Analysis,* edited by M. Hetenyi (1950), may best describe the significance of analogies in one field of applied physics, i.e., stress analysis: "It frequently occurs that the characteristics of two or more apparently different physical phenomena can be expressed in identical mathematical form. When this is so, the physical systems are said to be analogous. Although one may speculate on the possibilities of discovering a fundamental law of nature which might explain the existence of analogies, such a law is not a prerequisite for either the discoveries or the use of the analogies themselves. It is sufficient to consider an analogy as a chance coincidence of mathematical forms (E. Scharrer, "The Concept of Analogy," *Pubbl. Staz. Zool. Napoli,* XXVIII, 204–213 [1956], 206 ff.) .

An example of just such analogies is provided by the theories of Kirchoff, particularly his equations of equilibrium, as we saw above.

Modern methods of analyzing electric circuits are of inestimable value in the theory of mechanical vibration. The formal identity of the fundamental equations of mechanical and electric wave systems permits the formulation of analogies. Maxwell used mechanical analogies to clarify electrical phenomena.

physical universe and are subject to the same physical laws, there must be similarities among them. The teepee needs a hole at the top for smoke and ventilation. It must have walls for protection and a door or opening of some sort for entrance and exit, since bodies are not compenetrable. A man cannot walk through a wall. In like fashion, the apartment house has a chimney, walls, roof, etc. These dwellings resemble each other because they are subject to the same natural necessities. In like manner, animals live in the same world and are subject to the same physical laws. If they move they must move according to some variation of the lever or the wheel. They must breathe the same atmosphere, which indicates some sort of lung structure. As they increase in size they must nourish themselves with a type of circulatory system. Homologies or resemblances between living beings do not *necessarily* mean that one produces the other.

In the theory of evolution, natural science has not been able to explain causal links satisfactorily, even to its most ardent disciples. The theory has never been scientifically proven. Resemblance does not demand causality. It is very easy for a speculative knowledge of things as they are to be transformed, gradually and unawares, into an artistic knowledge, a production of things as the mind would like them to be. There is a bit of the creator in all of us, a legitimate heritage.

Darwinian evolution is not simply a theory of movement or change, or movement toward perfection or change for the better. Historically, philosophers and scientists from Thales to Darwin's own contemporaries had taught variation after variation of a static structure of perfection

---

"That the biologist has made so little use of the analogy principle is due to his century old preoccupation with the concept of homology, i.e., the comparison of organs that have the same origin irrespective of their function," for example, the foreleg of the mammal and the wing of the bird (*ibid.*, p. 210).

"The prestige of the homology concept is well deserved for it provides the documentation for the theory of evolution" (*ibid.*).

"What does biology have to gain from the application of the analogy principle, i.e., the comparative study of parts and organs having the same function rather than the same origin? A great deal, in that analogy principle permits the analysis of structures as solutions of functional problems" (*ibid.*, p. 211).

Chemistry also provides examples of analogies. Compounds of similar structure, but having different atoms of the same valence and usually of the same periodic group, such as H_2O, M_2O, M_2S, M_2Se, and M_2Te, form a series called *isologous*. Compounds whose structures differ by some radical $-CH_2$, forming neighbors in the same series, are called homologous. An analogous series is a group of compounds with similar electronic structures but different atoms. Analogy here means the resemblance of relationships. Analogous compounds are in some cases similar or antagonistic; e.g., Look for an antagonistic of serotonin which has the property of raising the blood pressure, etc. Such agents for control were found in 1953; meprobamate and tranquilizers.

of reality informed by some dynamism that led creatures on to some definite or indefinite ultimate perfection through progressive stages and sequential phases.[14]

This was pretty well accepted and not at all the great innovation of Darwin. Darwin's real contribution to biological thought was quite definitely not a philosophical one. He attempted to offer an interpretation of what philosophers like Thomas Aquinas had, after all, called "the return of creatures to God," but he offered it on a truly *empirical scientific basis*. His magnificent hypothesis and its intelligible structure were fashioned out of the materials of a scientific theory and not the principles of philosophy.

We can better understand what Darwin was attempting to do if we compare his conception of the changes of living beings, or life, with its generation and corruption, with the revolutionary transformation that Galileo worked in the Aristotelian conception of physical or local motion. Aristotle had attempted to explain the possibility of motion in bodies by asking the question: What must be the structure of material things if they are to be susceptible of change or engaged in movement? His answer was couched in terms of qualitative principles. In order to change, a thing must have a composition of matter and form. Form accounts for the qualitative *difference* in a change, for example the difference between a lump of coal and its burnt-out ash, while matter explains the *continuity* of a being through change. After all, if nothing perdured there would be annihilation of being and a new creation out of nothing. Every time we ate an apple we would starve to death. Something must carry over if nourishment is to be acquired. The continuity of weight in physical and chemical changes, which serves to balance the equation or formula and so permits the finding of unknowns, also demands some principle of continuity underlying change. This principle precisely was termed *matter*.

---

[14] "Philosophically, evolution is nothing new. Every great philosopher from Plato on has either accepted some evolutionary system or been prepared to accept it. For Plato it was simply the further unfolding of the superplenitude of the Forms in the material world. For Aristotle it was the actualization of the potentialities of the sources whence higher entities emerged; that is, since the higher comes from the lower, it was in potency in the lower and was educed from the lower by sufficient causes.

"Aristotle deserves a closer look. He gets quite metaphysical about evolution. Aristotle maintained that the same elements that make up non-living beings also make up living beings. Furthermore, we do not know where non-life leaves off and another form begins. Hence, all we can say is that degrees of material being are different and higher degrees of organization of the elements. The higher forms are, thus, the higher proportions of the elements, the fulfillment, through higher forms, of the potentialities for existence" (Leo Foley, *Cosmology* [Milwaukee: The Bruce Publishing Co., 1963], p. 282).

Galileo, at the term of a long developmental movement beginning with William of Ockham, looked at this movement of things in terms of *extrinsic causes* and not *intrinsic principles*. If things are emptied of natures we can interpret their motion in terms of the external forces applied, for example, to a moving projectile. In fact, the rate of speed and variation of direction are found to be ultimately the sum of the *external* applied forces.

This elimination of *intrinsic principles* and the interpretation of movement in terms of *extrinsic causes* or *external forces* was the crux of the Galilean revolution in the science of motion and provided the dramatic point of departure from a *philosophy of nature* to an *empiriological physics*.

This too was the framework for Darwin's thought. He attempted to interpret the fundamental fact of the movement of living things toward their perfection in terms of extrinsic causes. This is the function of such elaborations of the theory as *natural selection, geographical isolation of species, survival of the fittest, the communication of acquired characteristics, genetic mutation, DNA, RNA* — all these provide extrinsic causes to determine the rate and direction of evolutionary movement.[15] Not that Darwin deliberately recognized this transition, though he has told us that he was doing for biology what Galileo accomplished for physics, but he, as a scientist, was aware of the type of explanation which was meaningful to the scientist, which made sense to the scientist working within an empiriological physics. Thus Darwin made an explanatory science of biology out of what was a descriptive natural history.

The concept of the soul, however, is a notion which is scientifically legitimate and can provide aid in the theoretical formulation of evolution. It is more concrete than an abstract natural selection conceived at times as a Platonic form.

Can we use abstract natural selection to explain concrete mutations? The soul can provide the concrete vital force present in each living being from its conception to its dissolution in order to provide the dynamic energy behind natural selection, to be shaped and modified by it.

---

[15] ". . . we have given enough information to show how modern genetical evolutionists consider the processes of evolution and speciation occur. Besides the four major factors of mutation, recombination, isolation, and selection, which have been described in some detail, there are many others. Indeed it should be obvious that the whole environment is the laboratory of evolution. Unknown or little known factors tend at present to be grouped under the heading of selection which Wright described as 'a waste basket category that includes all causes of directed change in gene frequency that do not involve mutations or introductions from without'" (P. G. Fothergill, *Evolution and Christians* [London: Longman, 1960], pp. 229–230).

Evolution, whether scientific fact or theory, fits beautifully into the dynamic developmental metaphysics of Thomas Aquinas. His notion of the developmental movement of the creature from its initial grant of existence (*esse*), to its mature perfection, and finally its ultimate end, implies some sort of evolution. The appropriation of further *esse* or existents by an incomplete *esse* or existent, in the process which St. Thomas calls *esse tendere*, is a dynamic act, completing itself in a continuous movement toward perfect actuality. An evolutionary development present at the very marrow of reality can certainly have no quarrel with a progressive development of the superficial integument of being, the living material world.

An imperfect existent appropriates to itself other existential quanta, thereby expanding and becoming more perfect in nutrition, in knowledge both sensible and intellectual, and finally in that crystallization of all the higher operations of a spiritual being working in harmony, called the moral act, the ultimate perfection of man in the natural order. In this process, I should say that the real problem is not whether some development or evolution is possible, but to what extent this is so. There is no doubt of the progressive development of the individual from its embryonic state to the mature perfection of the adult, but does evolution go deeper than the individual material differences which we would call biological species? Can beings be transformed substantially? Is that primary limitation of existence (*esse*) which we call essence a rigid or an elastic one? Can a concrete *esse* in its developmental aggrandizement break the bonds of essence by the very transcendence of the perfection realized?

The two doctrines of traditional philosophy for which the theory of evolution has, in the hands of certain thinkers, attempted to substitute, are the doctrine of creation and the doctrine of the soul.

What I would like to do next, then, is to examine the major theories of embryology in order to locate the soul within the modern form of its original biological context; to see whether evolutionary theory has eliminated the soul, not as a biological scientific concept but as a philosophical scientific concept; whether, in other words, it has been emptied of all meaning save perhaps some vague religious one — the ghost hovering in disembodied fashion about the machine of science.

CHAPTER VII. / EMBRYOLOGY
AND THE SOUL

DESCRIPTIVE and comparative embryology dates its beginnings from the work of Karl von Baer in the early part of the nineteenth century. A cataloging was made of the structure and appearance of different embryos as they passed from one stage to another, from egg to clear specific types. When the embryos were arranged in an order from simple to more complex species, a certain sequential and progressive structural development could be seen. Naturally, the thesis that *ontogeny recapitulates phylogeny* helped to fire the imagination of evolutionary thinkers. In the process, of course, this interest was reflected upon embryology, giving it an impetus whose momentum is felt down to the present.

The history of embryology shows in its basic emphasis a movement from the examination of the embryo as a whole with Aristotle to a preoccupation with progressively smaller parts.

It can be argued that embryos were first studied as whole organisms (Aristotle, Fabricius, Harvey, Malpighi, Wolff), then in terms of their constituent layers (Wolff, Pander, von Baer, His, Haeckel, Spemann), next in relationship to their constituent cells (Roux, Driesch, all the students of cell lineage, Spemann, Harrison), and finally with reference to the components of cells, through the 19th century largely nuclear (O. Hertwig, Boveri), though in some cases visible cytoplasmic inclusions were also investigated (Boveri, E. G. Wilson, Conklin). It is hardly necessary to point out that the 20th century continues

127

the process by describing and analyzing both the visible and invisible nuclear and cytoplasmic elements of the cell in terms of their constituent molecules.[1]

§ 1. GERM LAYER THEORY

The germ layer theory provided a formal, theoretical organizing concept for the construction of a scientific embryology. All embryological phenomena were to be interpreted in terms of the primary germ layers, endoderm, mesoderm, and ectoderm. From these can be traced the development of the four distinct tissues differing in embryological origin, in arrangement, and in function. Epithelium — sheaths and surface tissues in tightly packed layers with little or no intercellular material — has no typical embryological location. It arises from all three germ layers. Connective tissue, such as bone, cartilage, and blood, has its origin in mesoderm. Muscle also arises from mesoderm. Nervous tissue has its source in embryonic ectoderm. Each tissue has a different embryonic origin, and consequently there is a different source of the organs they constitute. Thus, the individual embryonic change can be *explained* by reducing it to its original germ layer and the total embryonic development can be scientifically organized and *explained* in terms of the reciprocal interactions of these germ layers. These enable embryology to move from the descriptive stage to the explanatory stage of a natural science.

§ 2. CELL THEORY

The referral of embryonic developmental processes to the cell instead of the germ layers was a normal result of the analytic process. The cell, as many embryologists have pointed out, is a natural unit for the embryo. Not only is it a natural structural or anatomical unity, but the twentieth century has found it to be also a natural functional or physiological unit. The cell seems to work with a certain integrative unity of its own. Its parts act as parts of a whole.

A cell-to-cell relation which explains embryonic changes seems to have an explanatory advantage over germ layer relations because aggregation seems to be the result of the selective migration of individual cells. The cell therefore is conceived as a dynamic independent entity. All embryonic changes may therefore be explained as reducible basically to cell division. The work of microbiologists has this in common with

---

[1] Jane M. Oppenheimer, "Embryological Concepts in the Twentieth Century," *Survey of Biological Progress*, III (1957), 7.

cell theory, that they recognize that cells are not only single cells but whole organisms in their own right.

§ 3. THEORIES OF TOTAL ORGANIZATION

The living body, however, is not a chaos or an undisciplined mob. It is an organized whole, each part of which has a specialized function that makes sense only in terms of its contribution to the totality. Any definition of life must somehow include and to some extent explain this organization.

> The integrative powers of the embryo, at all of its levels, are, however, so pervasive that they never permit themselves to be overlooked by those who avail themselves of the privilege of looking at the embryo at all. The result has been that when each of the practices just enumerated became fashionable, the previous one was never completely outmoded; and when, at each stage of its development, embryology has added a new dimension to its studies, it has never wholly discarded the old ones. Spemann, for instance, who analyzed the relations between layers in terms of cellular interactions, never lost sight of the whole embryo. These effects have, as a matter of clear cold fact, been cumulative throughout the centuries, with the result that even in the 20th century the embryo is still being actively investigated at all of its levels: as a whole, in terms of its layers, of its cells, and of their microscopic and submicroscopic constituents.[2]

Several theories have been formulated whose purpose is to explain the embryo as a whole, in its organizational totality. The earliest was, of course, Aristotle's theory of the soul, or *entelechy,* which was, among other things, an embryological conception. In recent times, the axial gradient theory, the organizer theory, and the field theory of Harrison have been constructed to explain just the basic organization of the embryo, a role which Aristotle had consigned to the soul.

§ 4. AXIAL GRADIENT THEORY

The axial gradient theory of Child has exerted a certain influence on contemporary embryological thinking. Its attractiveness lies partly, I suppose, in the fact that it is a purely quantitative explanation of embryological development. But the fact that there is a gradient or gradation along the axis of development from the head and brain to the caudal section in the speed of development does not seem to be more than a descriptive fact. There is a time in the newly formed

---

[2] *Ibid.,* pp. 7–8.

foetus when the head is one third the size of the body. With consequent development the relative sizes are adjusted until finally the adult proportions are reached.

There is always a relation between the structure of the body, or rather the spatial disposition of parts, and the speed of development. In the starfish there are five processes, each connected with a central ring or system of nodules of the central nervous system. But even this pentagon has an order — in activity one process leads and the rest follow. Then another leads and the other four cooperate as did the four powers in Austria — sharing a rotating leadership. And it works rather satisfactorily. And in embryonic development the same is true. One process begins to develop ahead of the others. Then they catch up and another forges ahead, but one always seems to dominate. In humans the theme is a gradient of speeds of development from front to back.

This at least gives a quantitative basis in the spatial disposition of parts for a qualitative configuration of organs. But its precise weakness seems to be that it is merely descriptive of the facts and not truly explanatory.

An explanation would be, perhaps, the apparent sensitivity to light of the forepart of the foetus — resulting ultimately in front-end development and an optic system. But this leads into the further question of preformation and epigenesis.

A great deal of work has gone into the effort to isolate embryonic cells. Hans Driesch actually performed this delicate operation in 1891. He isolated the cells of the sea urchin in a flask of sea water without injuring the individual cells. Later he nurtured each cell into a complete sea urchin larva. He was actually able to separate sixteen cell embryos and from each he incubated a complete sea urchin. Driesch found that operational interference did not hinder the development of the whole animal, as long as no injury was done to the individual cells. There seemed to be a teleological principle informing the embryo that would achieve its purpose, the complete organization, despite experimental interference. He was of the opinion that the operations of the living organism could be explained only on the hypothesis that a directing principle, or *entelechy*, the Aristotelian word for soul, foresaw its end in some way.

> Driesch's conclusion was that: here the physico-chemical explanation of life reaches its limit, and only one interpretation is possible. In the embryo, and similarly in other vital phenomena, a factor is active which is fundamentally different from all physico-chemical forces, and which directs events in anticipation of the goal. This factor,

which "carries the goal within itself," namely, the production of a typical organism in normal as well as in experimentally disturbed development, was called "entelechy" by Driesch, using an Aristotelian notion.[3]

§ 5. ORGANIZER THEORY

Spemann and his followers, using the same simple techniques that Driesch found so effective, produced some startling results.

Spemann constricted a salamander's egg with a single loop of hair parallel to the silver crescent. Two embryos resulted. The one with the nucleus developed first and the other later. Following the same line of thought he tied off the egg parallel to the gray crescent and got a complete embryo and a "mole" or mass of tissue. His conclusion was that the gray crescent introduced a necessary organizing factor for development. When he tied off the egg with a loop passing through the silver crescent he got two complete salamanders. Thus, he demonstrated that the cells of the gray crescent are necessary for organization and development.

Perhaps the most striking experiments of the organizer theory are those of transplantation. If cells at an early embryonic stage are transplanted, i.e., if an area of mesoderm which would normally result in muscle, for instance, is transplanted to an area of ectoderm, for example presumptive brain, the potential muscle actually becomes nerve tissue. This implies that the organizer material has a control over the primary germ layers, organizing them into the whole animal despite experimental disturbance and interference. The conclusion is again that certain cells, the "organizer," provide a principle of organization for the whole embryo.

Potency and act, long considered metaphysical principles in an absolute sense, are found to be extremely useful on the frontiers of natural science. One example is that of the "Totipotens" principle of the role of primary germ layers in the production of the embryo. The fact that an apparent indetermination of function of endoderm, mesoderm, and ectoderm at the blastula stage can enable one layer to substitute for another is currently being interpreted as the "prospective fate" of a layer as compared to the "potential end" of ectoderm which can become any of the other structures.

§ 6. FIELD THEORY

The third and last theory of organizational totality with which we

---

[3] E. Mascall, *Science and Theology* (Oxford, 1955), pp. 255–257.

are concerned is Harrison's field theory. It is not easy to grasp just what a "field" is, but certain quantitative characteristics can be shown, especially in relation to the embryonic structure of the ear. The embryonic ear is an area of ectoderm. Transplanting another ectoderm provides interesting results. These pieces of ectoderm will form embryonic ears. To sum up these results, the closer to the ear region a piece of ectoderm is transplanted, the more complete will be the ear growth. The further away, radially, it is transplanted, the more abnormal and defective will be the new embryonic ear structure.

The field thus varies in potency in a quantitative way. The field center gives an ear in every case of transplant. At the periphery of the radial area called the field, the production of anything like an embryonic ear would be entirely rare, if at all. The field then seems to be much larger than the organ or structure that forms within it.

In conclusion, the field theory implies partial principles of organization spatially located and quantitatively measurable from the radial center to the periphery.

§ 7. THEORY OF THE SOUL

What has been responsible, as much as any other single factor, for the discrediting of the doctrine of the soul as a scientific principle in modern times is the substitution of the Platonic notion of the soul for the Aristotelian. It was the notion of the soul as a complete substance in itself, separate from the body and not needing it for its existence and operation, that became dominant in the history of ideas. If we consider the soul as the mover of the machine that is a body, then we would be perfectly correct in eliminating the notion of soul from biology. All that biology needs to study is the body which has a self-sufficiency about it.

The Aristotelian notion of the soul fits beautifully into current theories in a way that the Platonic and Cartesian conception does not. If the soul is conceived as a disembodied spirit hovering in ghostly fashion around the body of which it is the animating principle, then it is rightly ignored and its existence cast into doubt by biological science. But if the soul is the very form of the body, the very organization of the body itself, then it must play an intimate part in any analysis of the intelligible patterns throughout biological theory.[4] Every theory then becomes a partial elucidation of its structure and function, its causal efficacy and its effects. The major theories of embryo-

---

[4] Cf. *supra*, Chap. II, 5, p. 31 ff.

logical total organization must articulate with the doctrine of the soul.

Certainly the axial gradient theory needs a *directive energy* to account for the descriptive facts it sets forth. There is an order of *importance,* apparently, in the development of organs running from the front to the rear, from the head to the caudal area.

Likewise, what is the hidden mechanism that makes this protein complex group of agents we call the organizer? What is the organizing principle or directive energy, or dynamic act, which explains the teleological patterns formed through the organizer? The theory of the organizer would seem only to locate more precisely one of the points of contact or areas of operation of the silver crescent, of the dynamic energies of the principle of organization, as badly needed as ever to account for the facts of the organizer theory.

The field theory attempts to locate even more precisely than the organizer theory the more determinate operations of the principle of organization, and in that sense it is a development of the organizer theory. Neither it nor any other contemporary biological or embryological theory, however, serves as a substitute for the soul, this general principle of organization, whatever it may be called.

Embryological theories, despite the heat generated by controversy, do not seem to be mutually exclusive. Theories of germ layers and those of cells, are not, as theories, as antagonistic as their scientific proponents. The axial gradient and the organizer seem to me to work on different levels. The organization of the whole manifests itself on various levels of organization. The total pattern may be resolved into a myriad of subpatterns which enter into its constitution.

This organization which Aristotle terms *form* appears on all levels of reality and on all levels of science. Not only are macroscopic entities distinguished by their organization, but the same is true of microscopic entities. It is not true to say, as has been said, that "a cell is nothing but a bag of enzymes." Structure means something even in terms of function. There are general structural principles of complex organization in the cell, systems of double membranes and cytoplasmic components. This is not a rigid, mechanical, cast-iron structure, as seen in electron microscopy. It is more flexible and fluid. It possesses the elasticity of all living organisms, the fundamental elasticity and flexibility of all living phenomena as illustrated by nutrition, growth, and reproduction. The nuclear, conjugated proteins are strictly localized in a predictable fashion, as are substances other than proteins — nucleic acids, for instance. The mitachondria, the Golgi apparatus, chromatin, Nissl bodies, are all components of a highly structuralized organization; and, although at this stage it is very difficult to correlate structure and function, there are sufficient experimental evidences of a teleological character to provide a certain respectability to such correlations.

The same appears to be true even below the level of electroscopy in the infinitesimal depths of the atom and even the atomic nucleus. It is interesting to speculate on the way in which what is supposed to be a purely quantitative approach to physical reality gives us a reality of such highly organized structure. Electrons, protons, neutrons, and the whole gamut of newly discovered particles indicate a complexity of organization not one whit less intricate than that to be found on the level of the macroscopic universe.

The atomic physicist and the electromicroscopist, like the celestial physicist, the astronomer, see a complex intricate pattern in their universes, hardly understanding what these tracings spell out. But there is a message there which is being progressively decoded.

If we were to attempt an interpretation of the relations of contemporary embryological theories to the Aristotelian doctrine of the soul, we might say that these theories are syntheses, more or less explanatory, of proximate formal causes, of accidents, or to put it more loosely, of what the substantial form does to the matter in its progressive stages of organization. Embryological theory can explain the mechanisms involved in the total organization of the body, but it cannot explain away the soul, dispense with it altogether, or itself serve as a substitute for the soul; it cannot be a total principle of organization. At every point there is still necessary, even more so than in Aristotle's day, an energizing force, a principle of organization, one that is directive of both structure and function — in ancient scientific terminology, the soul, amenable only to philosophical analysis.

§ 8. CELL DEATH

The phenomenon of *cell death* is another piece of evidence which militates against the theory of living beings as mere aggregates of cells.[5]

---

[5] "When we think of normal development, we naturally think of an increase in the number of cells, their subsequent differentiation into specialized cells, and the grouping of these cells into organs and organ systems. This process is a dynamic and creative one, and you may consider it incongruous to characterize cell death as a vital and necessary aspect of development. Cell death, however, plays two very significant roles in development. The first of these, metamorphosis, has long been known; the second, the role of cell death in the shaping of organs and body contours, is only beginning to be appreciated as a phase of development.

The last type of cell death we will consider is that involved in the shaping of organs. Form, therefore, can be achieved by relative rates of cell death as well as by relative rates of cell growth. As organs develop during morphogenesis, for instance, excess cells are often a hindrance, and these transient cells that are of use to the embryo or larva but not to the adult must be removed (the tail of the tadpole is a case in point). Or when an organism forms secretory ducts, cells die instead of pulling apart to provide for the central hole or lumen. Many organs form by the infolding of tissues which then fuse along their edges — for example, the eye and part of the nervous system — and the seams where fusion takes place are removed by cell death. Fingers and toes are separated from each other in the same way; if the separation is incomplete, a webbed condition results.[6]

Some principle of organization would seem to be in directive control. If the cell is the fundamental unit of development alone, conceived

---

"Metamorphosis involves a change in shape (the transformation of a larval form of an organism into an adult shape) and a change in organs when one mode of life is exchanged for another. Two well-known examples are the metamorphosis of a tadpole into an adult frog, and of a caterpillar into a pupa and then into a butterfly or a moth.

"A tadpole is transformed into a frog without an appreciable change in size, and in the common American leopard frog the process takes about a year. The tadpole that emerges from the egg, and the large tadpole about to metamorphose have the same general shape; in its conversion into a frog, it grows legs and loses its tail, which is devoured by wandering cells, or phagocytes, that are carried by the blood stream to the tail region where they gradually consume the muscles, nerves, skin, and other tissues. The skin shrinks and eventually the tail is reduced to a mere stump. In addition, the tissues in the digestive and excretory systems are extensively reorganized. We can speed up or slow it down experimentally, for in the frog metamorphosis is, at least in part, under the control of an iodine-containing hormone from the *thyroid gland*. More thyroid hormone accelerates the process, less reduces its speed and may even prolong larval life and shape indefinitely.

"The character of metamorphosis in insects varies quite widely, and cell death is not always a major aspect of change. In the simplest type of metamorphosis, the cells of a particular larval tissue are retained to form the corresponding tissue in the adult, and only minor differences in growth and differentiation are needed to bring this about. In these cases of *incomplete metamorphosis*, the form of the insect is only slightly altered as the larva matures to adult proportions. Good examples of this type of metamorphosis are found in the locust, grasshopper, or cockroach.

"In *complete metamorphosis*, the larval and adult forms are totally different from each other. The larva, or caterpillar, is converted into a pupa, the larval skin hardens and shrinks into the outer skin, or *puparium*, of the pupa, and the larval tissues are almost completely destroyed. The adult develops during pupation, and adult tissues arise from *imaginal buds* that form in the larva and that escape cell death. These buds can be regarded as zones of persistent embryonic tissue in which the potentiality for growth and differentiation is suppressed during larval life, and is only realized when the *juvenile hormone* controlling larval growth lessens its activity and the hormone concerned with metamorphosis takes over" (Carl P. Swanson, *The Cell* [Englewood Cliffs, N. J.: Prentice-Hall, 1960], pp. 99–103).
    6 *Ibid.*

according to a mechanical mode, or a mechanistic model, how can one account for the fact that it dies? The instinct for survival and self-preservation would be expected to dominate the behavior of the cell, as in the case of the cancer cell. But these cells "die on schedule"!

> One of the most arresting instances of cell death as a morpho-genetic phenomenon is the one that frees the elbow of the wing of the chick from the body wall and gives the wing its characteristic shape. . . . These cells die as a line of cellular destruction moves from the body area along the front and back of the wing towards its tip, thus separating the elbow region from the body wall. Most fascinating of all, however, is the fact that when these cells are re-moved and transplanted to another part of the embryo, the cells *die on schedule* (at approximately 4 days of age) as if they were still in their original site. Their time of death had already been deter-mined by some unknown change that had taken place within them, and once embarked on their course of destruction they could not escape. If we can, in the future, understand the mechanism responsi-ble for this phenomenon, we may well be on our way to comprehend-ing the larger problem of aging and of fixed life spans.[7]

The conclusion seems logical then that these cells are under the control and directive of a principle of development, a principle of organization which is concerned with the interests of the whole organism, rather than the individual cells.

§ 9. REDUCTIONISM AND EMERGENCE: MECHANISM AND
VITALISM REVISITED

A great number of recent publications have been preoccupied with the old dilemma of *mechanism* versus *vitalism* under a new form, *reductionism* versus *emergence*.[8] What seems to be at stake is the notion of "explanation" proper to biology and, actually, the very claim of biology to the status of an autonomous science. Can the theoretical autonomy and integrity of biological science be preserved or must it be reduced to the "mechanistic" formulations of physicochemical proc-esses? Is biology a science in its own right or is it merely an indirect

---

7 *Ibid.*
8 R. Schubert-Soldern, *Mechanism and Vitalism*, P. G. Fothergill, ed. (Notre Dame, Ind.: University of Notre Dame Press, 1962); M. Beckner, *The Biological Way of Thought* (New York: Columbia University Press, 1959); E. E. Harris, *The Foundations of Metaphysics in Science*, Muirhead Library of Philosophy, H. D. Lewis, ed. (London: Unwin Brothers, and New York: Humanities Press, 1965); E. Nagel, *The Structure of Science* (New York: Harcourt, Brace & World, 1961); W. R. Thompson, *Science and Common Sense* (Albany: Magi Books, 1965); P. Caws, *The Philosophy of Science* (Princeton: D. Van Nostrand Co., 1965); David Bohm, *Causality and Chance in Modern Physics* (New York: Harper & Brothers, 1961).

approach, through more complex objects, to chemistry and ultimately to physics? Are there properly biological phenomena to serve as the object of biology, phenomena which are irreducible to physicochemical processes and thus "emergent" over and above "mechanistic" theory and sciences?[9]

It would seem that contemporary efforts to reconcile mechanistic and vitalistic interpretations by such doctrines as "organismic" biology are a movement away from the theoretical formulation of the problem of "vital principle" under Platonic inspiration to a more philosophically sophisticated notion first formulated by Aristotle.

The experimental evidences of embryology, for example, which led Driesch to postulate a "vital principle" have necessarily to be incorporated within a more philosophically sophisticated formulation of "vital principle" than Driesch was able to fashion out of his neo-Kantian materials.

When the current conflict between reductionism and emergence is reexamined in the light of the philosophical themes determinative in the historical confrontation of the Platonic and Aristotelian doctrines of the soul in medieval controversy, a remarkable conclusion can be drawn: *Both contemporary mechanism or reductionism and contemporary vitalism or emergence have moved from the Platonic formulation of the soul as a separate substance and mover of the body, constituted as body in its own right (the "ghost in the machine") to an Aristotelian formulation of the soul as the principle of organization of matter constituting body as body and identical with its structure.*

The argument follows five basic steps:

1) mechanism as a stage in the development of scientific theory, later supplanted by a less quantitative and more qualitative stage;

2) the old vitalism as an instance of the Platonic formulation of the problem of properly biological processes;

3) Darwinian theory as based on and contributory to a mechanistic model of biological development;

4) the contemporary conception of antimatter as a key to the inadequacy of a mechanistic interpretation of biological phenomena (It shows the inadequacy of even a mechanistic model of physics, not to speak of biology.);

5) organismic biology and the Aristotelian formulation of the problem, with emphasis on regulative and directive processes, in a hierarchy of organizational levels.

1) Mechanism is a stage in the development of scientific theory.

---

[9] M. Beckner, *The Biological Way of Thought,* p. v.

Scientific theory invariably begins materialistically and mechanistically. It is initially preoccupied with the quantitative in each science and then, as the science matures, it becomes qualitative. The mechanistic phase of a science corresponds to its childhood, as its descriptive phase corresponds to its infancy.[10]

In fact, as science develops from its simple descriptive stage it becomes more dematerialized and philosophical in the process of achieving maturity and in the process of becoming explanatory by a reduction to causes. Its arrival at full maturity seems to be marked by an increasing preoccupation with problems which at a more primitive stage would have been labeled "abstract metaphysics." In fact, so-called philosophical and metaphysical problems are being currently discussed within the competence of scientific method.[11]

The question of vitalism and mechanism and in its more subtle form, that of a qualitative versus a quantitative interpretation of reality, has been hotly debated in every period of human intellectual history. It was not restricted to the seventeenth and nineteenth centuries. In fact, the origins of the difficulty lie as far back as Aristotle's criticism of Democritus and Galen's criticism of Erasistratus.

It is the selfsame problem that underlay the fourteenth-century treatises on the intension and remission of forms and Descartes's discussion of Harvey's quantitative methods in his formulation of the theory of the circulation of the blood. It is due to this difficulty that a Faraday finds the mathematical recasting of his patterns of magnetic force by a Maxwell so baffling.

The picture, now largely passé, of a scientific method exclusively qualitative and vitalistic until the seventeenth century, then replaced by the modern mechanistic interpretation, is historically inaccurate. Both vitalistic and mechanistic explanations existed side by side at every period of scientific history. For instance, Galen used a mechanical explanation for the filtering action of the kidneys and this type of interpretation was common throughout the Middle Ages. The *De Corde* of Alfred of Sareshal is a good example. What was an innovation was the extension of mechanical explanations to certain phenomena long considered purely qualitative. The furor was caused by the prestige

---

[10] Anatomy moves out of its descriptive stage and becomes explanatory with the theory of evolution. Embryology became scientific by explaining the development of organs in terms of germ layers, ectoderm, endoderm, and mesoderm. Organs of the nervous system are explained by deriving them from or reducing them to ectoderm. Connective tissue, muscle for example, is explained by deriving it from or reducing it to mesoderm.

[11] David Bohm, *Causality and Chance in Modern Physics*, pp. 1–3.

of Newton in favor of a corpuscular theory of light. Qualitative phenomena seem to be expressible, at least indirectly, in quantitative terms. To what extent such a theory comes to grips with reality or simply "saves the appearances" of things appears to be closer to solution at present than at any other period in history.

In twentieth-century biology, mechanism seems to be presented in an ever attenuated and diminished form so that the "mechanism" advocated by as competent a thinker as Ernest Nagel has little in common with mechanism as originally conceived by the Cartesians.[12] In fact, in its new form it seems to be only a reduction of biological structures to physicochemical structures or processes.[13] Descartes would have looked on these processes as qualitative phenomena, not reducible to matter, i.e., extension and local motion. Even Locke would have located such explanations within the subjective world of secondary qualities rather than in the relatively objective world of primary qualities. In fact, Nagel's explanation would fit under a broad interpretation of the Aristotelian and Thomistic philosophy of form or formal structures.[14] It is only the naïve, Platonically inspired forms of vitalism such as the neo-Platonic, Augustinian, Bonaventurian, and Cartesian which contemporary mechanists are attacking within Driesch's Platonic, neo-Kantian formulations.[15]

2) Both contemporary "mechanism" and contemporary "vitalism" or "organismic biology"[16] seem to be fighting straw men of their own construction and to be using the traditional terms as banners to bear into battle rather than as accurate labels of their respective doctrines. These doctrines, it would seem, are fast approaching one another and

---

[12] E. Nagel, *The Structure of Science*, p. 430.

[13] "The main question of Vitalism is not whether the processes of life can be properly called purposive: it is rather the question if the purposiveness in those processes is the result of a *special constellation of factors known already* to the sciences of the inorganic, or if it is the result of an *autonomy* peculiar to the processes themselves. For that there is, as a matter of fact, much that is purposive in vital phenomena is merely an immediate deduction from the definition of the concept of purpose itself, and from the application of this definition to living beings" (H. Driesch, *The History and Theory of Vitalism* [London: Macmillan, 1914], p. 1). Cf. Peter Caws, *Philosophy of Science*, pp. 311, 308, 309.

[14] "However, biological mechanism so understood must not be taken to deny that living bodies have highly complex organizations. On the contrary, most biologists who adopt such a standpoint usually note quite emphatically that the activities of living bodies are not explicable by analyzing 'merely' their physical and chemical compositions without taking into account their 'ordered structures or organizations'" (E. Nagel, *The Structure of Science*, p. 430).

[15] On the conception of Driesch as an Aristotelian, cf. W. R. Thompson, *Science and Common Sense*, p. 173 ff.

[16] E. Nagel, *The Structure of Science*, pp. 428–429.

actually only seem to be distinguishable by a matter of emphasis and *a theory of the primacy of certain sciences,* reductionism and emergence, based as much on disciplinary biases and particular practical interests as on really clear-cut points of issue.[17] In fact, with some so-called "mechanistic" thinkers "mechanism" seems to be more or less innocuously identified with "operations."

Vitalism has formulated the problem of a vital principle or soul thus:

elements + organization + vital principle → living being

It is this vital principle providing some sort of energy or life force to an already constituted or organized body which Lotze finds such a problem with Driesch and which Moritz Schlick finds so difficult to understand.[18] It is this kind of unscientific principle which Darwin was intent on eliminating, a vitalism which is an instance of the Platonic formulation of the problem.

3) The Darwinian theory was based on and contributory to a mechanistic model for evolution.[19]

4) The contemporary conception of antimatter is a key to the problem of reductionism, of a mechanistic interpretation of biological phenomena. It shows the inadequacy of even a mechanistic model of physics, not to speak of biology. In order to understand reductionism we must understand the nature of the causes, the explanatory level to which biological operations are to be reduced in order to explain them. Microphysics and the subatomic particles of which it treats are the principle instruments of contemporary reductionism, even though physicochemical processes in a broad sense are advanced as the causes for a mechanistic reduction.

5) Modern microscopic discoveries indicate a complexity of organization at least as intricate as that found on the macroscopic level.[20]

The atomic theory is of little help here, because there is a hierarchy of increasing complexity. On the molecular level, the changes are few and simple. In muscular changes, for instance, there is much more, e.g., the same enzymes, in all animal muscular changes. Once the level of tissue is reached, the changes are more complicated. In fact, as a general rule, the higher the level, the more complex and intricate the

---

[17] Cf. Ludwig von Bertalanffy, *Problems of Life.* An organismic conception of life overcomes the mechanistic-vitalistic conception of life by strict adherence to scientific method. This approach is fundamentally positivistic and antimetaphysical in character according to his own admission and philosophical claims.

[18] M. Schlick, "Philosophy of Organic Life," *Readings in the Philosophy of Science,* Feigl and Brodbeck, eds. (New York, 1953), p. 525.

[19] For a development of the Darwinian theory in the context of biological development, see Chap. VI, pp. 118–126.

[20] Cf. Chap. VI.

changes. The complexity of higher levels cannot be completely explained by the simple changes of the lower levels of structure.

Even the use of chemistry as a "mechanistic" science or as mechanistically interpretable is a debatable point. *Form* in Aristotle and *prehension* in Whitehead seem to indicate levels of organization on the inanimate level which are continuous with the levels or organization on the biological level of which the Aristotelian vital principle or soul is explanatory.

The neo-Kantian philosophy of Driesch caused him to interpret his truly impressive experimental findings by a vital principle fundamentally Platonic in inspiration.

But his experimental findings fit just as well into an Aristotelian conception of the vital principle as the principle of organization of matter, as the first actuality of the body constituting it as body, rather than a simple mover or source of motive energies.[21]

The problem can be discussed and resolved on two levels, the psychological and the metaphysical. In psychological reduction, *form* is located on all levels of the universe from the macroscopic to the microscopic. There are always identifying qualitative differences of things even if they are not readily distinguishable or distinguished. Levels of organization or possible organizations are what Aristotle meant by form or soul as the principles of organization of matter, but not principles separate from the bodies which they constitute as bodies:

$$\text{elements} + \text{organization} \rightarrow \text{living being}$$
$$\text{(matter)} \qquad \text{(form)}$$

Thus, according to Aristotle, "to say that a living organism has a soul, is the same thing as to say that it is one."[22]

---

[21] "If, then, we have to give a general formula applicable to all kinds of soul, we must describe it as the first grade of actuality of a natural organized body. That is why we can wholly dismiss as unnecessary the question whether the soul or body are one: it is as meaningless as to ask whether the wax and the shape given to it by the stamp are one, or generally the matter of a thing and that of which it is the matter" (Aristotle, *On the Soul*, II, 1, 412b, 4–10).

[22] Experimental evidence for a principle of organization in living beings is not diminishing. Continued research is multiplying such confirmatory experiments. The phenomenon of *cell death* is another piece of evidence which militates against the theory of living beings as mere aggregates of cells mechanically multiplied. Cf. Swanson, *The Cell*, pp. 99–103. Some principle of organization would seem to be in directive control. If the cell is the fundamental unit of development alone, conceived according to a mechanical mode, or a mechanistic model, how can one account for the fact that it dies? The instinct for survival and self-preservation would be expected to dominate the behavior of the cell, as in the case of the cancer cell. But these cells "die on schedule"! *Ibid.* The conclusion seems logical then that these cells are under the control and directive of a principle of development, a principle of organization which is concerned with the interests of the whole organism, rather than the individual cells.

In conclusion, a universe which is viewed as a hierarchy of organizational levels by Thompson, Nagel, Beckner, Harris, Foldy, Schubert-Soldern, and Bohm is an original rethinking of the Aristotelian formulation communicated within the contemporary methodological perspective.[23]

In the metaphysical reduction, kinds of beings or essences, as metaphysical transformations of forms or natures, are reducible to levels of existence. Thus motion and change are interpretable in terms of appropriations of further *esse* or being.[24]

There is a real danger in giving to form or essence a being of its own, so that vitalism has formulated the problem of a vital principle or soul thus:

---

[23] E. E. Harris, *The Foundations of Metaphysics in Science,* pp. 260–261.

"*The meaning of structure.* To turn now to our principal topic, the structure of the neutron and proton, it is perhaps appropriate to dwell for a moment on the question, 'What constitutes structure?' One may have intuitive notions concerning this, but when encountering something new one cannot be certain that intuitive ideas are inadequate to the situation. Thus one might immediately think in terms of a structural situation extended in space or in space-time; it is perhaps justifiable, but the possibility cannot be overlooked that there exists internal structure which is not of this character.

"The internal symmetries of particles such as those associated with isospin or SU (3) invariance, for example, have not yet been identified as possessing a spatio-temporal connection" (L. L. Foldy, "The Structure of Nucleons," *Physics Today,* 18 [Sept., 1965], p. 28.

"Symmetry properties" seem to be a basis for classification of the increasing number of elementary particles according to Foldy. Cf. *op. cit.,* p. 44. Cf. also E. E. Harris, *op. cit.,* p. 483 ff., also pp. 260–261, 277–278, and W. Beckner, *The Biological Way of Thought,* pp. 173–190. Although Beckner is a reductionist, his conceptions of functional analysis and teleological explanation are compatible with emergent and organismic theories. Schubert-Soldern's "holistic" position is also reducible to a vitalism of the Aristotelian brand, particularly his concepts of the "morphe" and the "forma corporis" in *Mechanism and Vitalism,* pp. 207–227. David Bohm uses "modes of being," a phrase neutral with regard to mechanistic characteristics and yet identical with levels of organization the "qualitative infinity" of things. Cf. D. Bohm, *op. cit.,* pp. 153–157.

"Form is an essential constituent of the whole realm of organic chemistry . . . nor can it be excluded from 'inorganic' chemistry or nuclear physics. Eventually it blends, we might say, into order and organization as such. . . . The only two components required for the understanding of the universe in terms of modern science [are] Organization . . . and Energy" (Joseph Needham, "Biological Aspects of Form and Growth," Whyte, ed., *op. cit.,* pp. 79–80 [quoted by H. Rugg, *Imagination* (New York: Harper & Row, 1963), p. 122]).

[24] M. Schlick and B. Russell recognize at least the possibility of just such a metaphysical reduction. In fact B. Russell's notion of neutral monism is an actual attempt to subsume mind and matter under a common principle — exactly what we are doing in this instance with the employment of the metaphysical principle of existence (*esse*). Cf. M. Schlick, "Philosophy of Organic Life," Feigl and Brodbeck, eds., *op. cit.,* pp. 523–524. Cf. also B. Russell: subsumption of matter and mind into neutral monism. He shows how the problem of matter and mind can be reduced to a metaphysical problem and solved on that level.

elements + organization + vital principle → living being

But if *essence* is a mode of existence and *form* thus a mode of being, without a being of its own, then organization and structure are reducible to an intrinsic limitation of the basic act of existence, or limitation of *esse* of each concrete existent:

elements (matter) + organization → living being

The ultimate question of the ontological status of form is not a question legitimately posed or answered on the level of the philosophy of nature or psychology. As soon as the question, "If the soul is not a substance separable from the body, what kind of being is it?" is asked, we enter metaphysics. Here we are concerned with such issues: What kind of being is an ontological principle? Must it be a substance to be a being or can it be a mode of being antecedent to substance in nature if not in time? Both matter and form are modes of existence (*esse*) and find their ontological status as stages of limitation of being. Form properly is a limited *esse* which needs other *esses* for its perfection, and in this aggrandizement and diminution of *esse* are located the modalities of being by which they are called matter and form. But I have tried to deal with this topic elsewhere.[25]

A major point to be kept in mind is that the reduction to physico-chemical processes is, strictly speaking, outside the province of the biologist. It is precisely to do the work of the chemist or physicist.

The biochemist might claim that he is demonstrating the ultimate dependency of biological processes when he crushes genetic materials, titrates and centrifuges them and gets a yield of DNA and eventually RNA. To the mind of the chemist he has "explained" a biological phenomenon, the gene, by a chemical phenomenon, DNA. This seems to be a model of the procedure advanced by the reductionist theoreticians.

When, however, we examine this situation from the point of view of the biologist we find that to his mind this is not a biological answer to the enigma of the gene, but a *chemical* answer. His inquiry has as its object a properly biological answer. Just as he once explained heredity, the phenomena of skin pigmentation, eye color, hemophilia, etc., by the *nucleus* of the cell, he was able then to explain this state of affairs, to give its properly biological cause in the *chromosome*. In penetrating even deeper for an explanatory biological "mechanism" (it is difficult to avoid the word), or cause, he was able to explain the role of the chromosome in the communication of hereditary characteristics by discovery of the *gene*.

---

[25] Cf. W. Carlo, "The Ontological Location of Matter," *Proceedings of the American Catholic Philosophical Association* (1964).

Does the biologist expect at this point to discontinue his search for a more basic biological phenomenon to explain the *gene* and rest content with the reduction by the chemist to RNA? He certainly will not. The biologist will note the fact that on any level of the living organism the hereditary materials can be destroyed and the resulting carbon compounds analyzed with man, the tissue, the cell, the nucleus, the chromosome — as well as the gene. The biologist wants a properly biological answer to a biological question and with the aid of the electron microscope he will get it.

CHAPTER VIII. / CELESTIAL PHYSICS AND CREATION

THE recent surge of interest among philosophically minded scientists in the origin of the cosmic universe provides another example of the articulation of scientific theory and philosophical doctrine. Some scientists and certain religious thinkers are fascinated by the prospect of marshaling the argumentative strength and popular prestige of scientific theory to confirm the Judaeo-Christian doctrine of creation.

Yet an examination of current theories in Astronomy and Biology raises many doubts as to the validity of the idea of necessary conflict between the concepts of Evolution and Creation. In Astronomy the advent of nuclear physics has brought with it a reaffirmation of the possibility of creation. One group of current theories, indeed, derives the known universe from an initial explosion concentrated in time and space, an act of creation as clear and simple as a command from the Lord. And in Biology a leading current speculation, the notion of emergent evolution, is nothing but the concept of creation thinly disguised as a mechanism. Let us ask to what extent these ideas, now at least respectable if not universally accepted by the more philosophical among scientists, indicate a convergence of scientific and religious thinking on this issue.[1]

Let us summarize briefly the state of scientific theory of celestial physics and reexamine its significance for the philosophical and theological explanation of the doctrine of creation. In just the last century

---

[1] W. Etkin, "Science and Creation," *Judaism*, IV, 2 (Spring, 1965) , p. 132, n. 2.

tremendous strides have been taken in our understanding of the universe and its stellar and solar constituents. A scientific explanation of the origin of our sun and, with it as the model, the origin and formation of any star, is a very recent innovation, and the heady wine of such discoveries has stimulated cosmological thought to aspire to the intoxicating heights of the explanation of the whole universe of beings.

The naïve (by present standards) view of the structure of the sun a century ago was that which Herschel had already formulated in 1795. The sun itself was conceived as a cool solid, most likely able to support some forms of life. Its burning radiation came from a "self-luminous envelope or photosphere" which enclosed a "cooler planetary atmosphere."

§ 1. TERRESTRIAL PHYSICS AND CELESTIAL PHYSICS

The tools which were to transform this naïve scientific view into the highly sophisticated and technical modern theory in just one hundred years were already being forged in the early part of the nineteenth century. This period of rapid development saw the formulation of the theories of the atomic structure of matter, the conservation of energy, and the laws of electromagnetism. It was the application of these advances in terrestrial physics to the explanation of solar and stellar constitution that has brought astrophysics of age scientifically. It was just about the middle of the last century that an astrophysical phenomenon was for the first time formulated in terms of the new ideas of the conservation and convertibility of energy by J. R. Mayer and J. J. Waterston.

Naturally, any body as far distant from the observer as the celestial bodies must be investigated indirectly, through its luminosity in this instance. Fraunhofer had already mapped out the line spectra of the sun in 1814, and it was then a matter of establishing mass, radius, and luminosity correlations, first within one body and then in relation to other stellar bodies. Beginning with a certain mass in isolation and using nothing but the known laws of terrestrial physics it was possible to set up the empirical *luminosity-class relations* and the *empirical mass-luminosity relation*. It is this empirical uniformity between mass, luminosity, and spectral classes that hold true for most stars and provides us with the "Main Sequence" system of stars. However, white dwarfs, red giants, super-giants, and cepheid variables do not exemplify these relations.

Without attempting a technical physical description which would have to be done mathematically, there are certain steps in the formation of a star according to the laws of atomic physics on which many astrophysicists are agreed. In a very general way, the theory begins with the expansion of an initial matter giving a "perfect" gas at a tremendously high temperature resulting in a spherically symmetrical body. (1) Temperature sensitivity at about twenty million degrees now provides the occasion for the release of subatomic energy. (2) Hydrogen nuclei, with the carbon-nitrogen cycle as catalyst, become helium nuclei. (3) Consequent on this process there is an outward flux of radiation and the transmutation of the chemical elements by "thermonuclear reactions." (4) This results eventually in a stable-state "star" in which hydrogen, by all calculations, is still present much in excess of all other elements.

These seem to be the steps, in a very schematic and general way, in the hypothetical development of any star and its properties, explained in terms of the fundamental particles of laboratory physics. The theory is certainly not worked out in detailed fashion, but most astrophysicists would agree on the corroborative evidence of its general correctness.

There seems to be, in the minds of most of these scientific cosmological speculators, a certain confusion between their scientific theories and philosophical-theological speculations.

> The problems of cosmogony, that is the theory of the origin of the world, have perplexed the human mind ever since the dawn of history. Among the ancients, the origin of the world was necessarily associated with a creative act by some deity, who separated light from darkness, raised and fixed the heavens high above the surface of the earth, and fashioned all the other features that characterized the highly limited world picture of early man.[2]

As a matter of fact, the "substitutional" theory of the nature of modern science is as popular as ever and serves as the general historical-philosophical framework for locating recent discoveries.

> As the centuries rolled by and men gradually accumulated knowledge about the various phenomena taking place in the world that formed their environment, the theories of cosmogony took a more scientific shape. The names of Buffon, Kant, and Laplace characterize the scientific era when the first attempts were made to understand the origin of the world exclusively as the result of natural causes. The theories of that time, which were limited essentially to the original of our solar system, later underwent a process of multiple evolution.[3]

[2] George Gamow, *The Creation of the Universe* (New York: Mentor, 1962), p. 20.
[3] *Ibid.*, p. 3.

Modern cosmogonical theories can be located in two basic classes:

1) On the one hand we have what we might call the "big-bang" theory of Canon Georges Lemaitre (1930), as outlined in his pioneer work which has influenced all later thinking, *The Primeval Atom.* This includes the concept of the expanding universe, as indicated by Hubble's work on the red shift of the Nebular Spectra in 1919, as well as the more recent modifications of the theory as the "universe in equilibrium," both expanding and contracting, of George Gamow, 1952.

2) On the other hand, we have the "steady-state" theory of the origin of the universe by Fred Hoyle, of Cambridge University, based on the continuous creation of hydrogen atoms.

§ 2. THE BIG-BANG THEORY

Both theories begin with the premise that the red shift can only be interpreted as evidence that the galaxies of the universe are moving farther and farther apart at tremendous speeds, faster in the case of the outlying galaxies. Canon Lemaitre claims that this fact can be explained on the basis of an initial explosion of a "primeval atom," and, using the laws of physics alone, he traces mathematically the evolution and progressive division and differentiation of the cosmic system from this primal catastrophe.[4]

George Gamow describes in popular fashion the mathematical theory of Lemaitre. Beginning with a primal "ylem," or matter, which had

---

[4] "The purpose of any cosmogonic theory is to seek out ideally simple conditions which could have initiated the world and from which, by the play of recognized physical forces, that world, in all its complexity, may have resulted.

"We believe that we have shown that the hypothesis of the primeval atom satisfies the rules of the game. It does not appeal to any force which is not already known. It accounts for the actual world in all its complexity. By a single hypothesis it explains stars arranged in galaxies within an expanding universe as well as those local exceptions, the clusters of nebulae. Finally, it accounts for that mighty phenomenon, the ultra penetrating rays. They are truly cosmic, they testify to the primeval activity of the cosmos. In their course through wonderfully empty space, during billions of years, they have brought us evidence of the super-radioactive age, indeed they are a sort of fossil rays which tell us what happened when the stars first appeared.

"We shall certainly not pretend that this hypothesis of the primeval atom is yet proved, and we would be very happy if it has not appeared to be either absurd or unlikely. When the consequences which result from it, especially that which concerns the law of the distribution of densities in the nebulae, are available in sufficient detail it will doubtless be possible to declare oneself definitely for or against" (Canon Georges Lemaitre, *The Primeval Atom* [New York, 1950], pp. 162–163).

been squeezed into pulp, there is a consequent elastic expansion ultimately reaching certain limits and again contracting.[5]

---

[5] "A picture of the creative process begins to emerge — somewhat hazy and frag-
mentary, but in its general outlines quite definite. In the dim pregalactic past we
perceive a glimpse of a metaphysical 'St. Augustine's era' when the universe, whatever
it was made of, was involved in a 'gigantic collapse.' Of course, we have no information about that era, which could have lasted from the minus infinity of time to
about three billion years ago, since all 'archaeological records' pertaining to that
distant past must have been completely obliterated when the cosmic masses were
squeezed into a pulp. The masses of the universe must have emerged from the Big
Squeeze in a completely broken-up state, forming the primordial ylem of neutrons,
protons, and electrons. As the ylem cooled rapidly through expansion, these elementary particles began to stick to one another, forming aggregates of different complexities which were the prototypes of the atomic nuclei of today. During this early
period of 'nuclear cooking,' which lasted not more than an hour of time, conditions
throughout the universe closely approximated those existing in the center of an
exploding atomic bomb. Cosmic space was full of high-energy gamma radiation, the
mass-density of which greatly exceeded the density of ordinary atomic matter. The
temperature throughout the universe was in the neighborhood of a billion degrees,
but the density of matter was comparable to the density of atmospheric air at high
altitudes.
  "Following that highly productive first hour of the history of our universe, nothing
in particular happened for the next 30 million years. The gas, consisting of the
newly formed atoms, continued to expand and its temperature became lower and lower.
Radiant energy, which at the beginning played a predominant role, in the evolutionary process, gradually lost its importance and by the end of the thirty-millionth
year yielded its priority in favor of ordinary atomic matter. As soon as matter took
over, the force of Newtonian gravity, which represents one of the most important
characteristics of 'ponderable' matter, came into play, breaking up the hitherto
homogeneous gas into gigantic clouds, the proto-galaxies. In that era, the temperature
dropped to approximately that which we call 'room temperature,' so that space was
still rather warm, although completely dark. While the original proto-galaxies were
being driven farther and farther apart by continued expansion, material in their
interiors began to condense into a multitude of much smaller aggregations, called
proto-stars. Because of the comparatively small size of these proto-stars their contrac-
tion progressed quite rapidly. Very soon the temperature in their interiors reached
the value at which nuclear reactions between hydrogen and various light elements
would take place, and space became bright again — illuminated by myriads of stars.
When the stars were formed by the condensation of the gaseous material of the
proto-galaxies, some of that material was left over in their vicinity and from it
sprang planetary systems. The planets were too small to create their own sources
of nuclear energy; they cooled off fast and developed solid rocky crusts. With the
help of the radiations from their respective suns, certain chemical compounds which
were present on the surfaces of these planets went through an evolutionary process,
as yet not well understood, by which organic materials of higher and higher complexity were developed. Thus the naked rocky surfaces of the planets were presently
covered by the green carpets of woods and meadows. Animals appeared, first primitive
and then more and more complicated, finally evolving into the human being who
is intelligent enough to ask and to answer questions concerning the events which
took place billions of years before he came into existence.
  "Probably one of the most striking conclusions from our inquiry into the history
of the universe is the fact that the main evolutionary events of physical development
occupied only such a tiny fraction of the total period. This, of course, only means

§ 3. THE STEADY-STATE THEORY

Hoyle claims in his steady-state theory that there is a continuous creation of hydrogen atoms. His approach is a mathematical one and developed in the framework of the theory of relativity. The question he proposes is this: If the galaxies are moving farther and farther apart, why does not space become more empty? He answers that newer galaxies are constantly being formed, their rate of formation just compensating for the separating effect of the expansion. So a stable situation is preserved. His theory (in his own interpretation of it) leads to the conclusion that the universe has no beginning and no end, that space and time are infinite, and that matter is being constantly created throughout space.

If all chemical substances are reducible to hydrogen by atomic weight, then Hoyle, in accounting for a supply of hydrogen atoms, has the material at hand to fashion the rest of the universe.[6]

---

that organic evolution takes place at a much slower rate than the large-scale physical processes in the universe.

"Indeed, it took less than an hour to make the atoms, a few hundred millions years to make the stars and planets, but three billion years to make man!" (G. Gamow, op. cit., Conclusion, pp. 137–139.)

[6] "At first sight the creation of matter may seem a queer concept to be invading scientific thought. But the origin of matter must enter all cosmologies. Nowadays we are coming more and more to realize that hydrogen is the original material — the material out of which the other elements have been produced by nuclear reactions inside stars. This transmutation of hydrogen is going on all the time.

"Why is there any hydrogen remaining in the universe? Why was it not all used up in the production of heavy elements eons ago? If we assumed that the hydrogen of the universe has existed for an infinite time, there would be two conceivable answers. We might suppose that the hydrogen has not had sufficient time to become transmuted into other elements because the stars were born only recently, that is, within the last five billion years or so. But it would follow from this that the hydrogen remained stable for eons of time and then suddenly five billion years ago began to condense into stars and galaxies. This seems less than plausible. The other possibility, assuming the hydrogen is infinitely old, is that we still find it on hand because the higher elements formed from it break down to hydrogen again. The chief objection to this idea is the difficulty of explaining how the energy necessary for the breakdown would be supplied. Decomposition of the heavier elements into hydrogen requires absorption of energy — the reverse of the release of energy that occurs when hydrogen nuclei combine. To provide an amount of energy adequate to account for a sufficiently large-scale reconversion of the heavier elements, nothing less than an implosion of the whole universe (as opposed to an explosion) apparently would suffice.

"We are thus led to the conclusion that the hydrogen we observe is not infinitely old: it has originated within some finite time and has not yet been converted to heavier elements. Both the evolutionary and the steady-state theories of the universe agree on this point. But there the similarity between them ends. The evolutionary theory argues that all the hydrogen was created in an explosive beginning some five and a half billion years ago. The steady-state hypothesis holds that hydrogen

When we come to examine the precise relations of these astronomical theories of the origin of the universe in relation to the Judaeo-Christian doctrine of creation, the striking fact is that they have no relation at all. One begins only where the other leaves off. The problem of the creation of being begins only at that point where the astronomical theories which seek to explain the problem fail.

The big-bang theory and the steady-state or continuous-creation theory are both concerned only with a further organization of an already existing matter. The relations between these two theories are usually posed as that between a "beginning for the universe" and an "eternal universe." Lemaitre's big-bang theory, with its modifications as commonly held by contemporary astronomers, is taken as indicating a beginning for our universe in its present condition. The steady-state theory, on the other hand, as we have seen, is used to support the view that the universe has always existed in its present form. But actually neither theory is concerned with creation, because strictly speaking creation does not depend on a beginning. Even Gamow begins with a primeval "ylem" or matter. These theories, then, are concerned with a progressive organization of an already existing being.

§ 4. THE JUDAEO-CHRISTIAN DOCTRINE OF CREATION

Creation, on the other hand, is concerned with the question of being, *why something is,* rather than is not being. Even the primordial stuff is being and, therefore, needs an explanation. Many problems are involved here. The notion of being is basic, and it must be understood if we are to understand the difference between "creation" and the astronomical theories of the origin of the universe.

For the Greeks the universe was eternal. A basic stuff, whether the chaos of the theological poets or the matter of the philosophers Plato and Aristotle, can be traced through all the Greek thinkers. The water of Thales, the *apeiron* of Anaximander, the air of Anaximenes (a gas, it should be noted), the fire of Heraclitus, the mathematical entities of Pythagoras, the One of Parmenides, the four elements of Empedocles, the atoms and the void of Leucippus and Democritus, and the mind or *Nous* of Anaxagoras are all eternal. It actually never occurred to any of these thinkers that the universe was created. Matter was eternal and was acted upon or was organized in a variety of ways. It was only with the Judaeo-Christian tradition that the question of

has been created at a steady rate throughout infinite time and is still being created at the same rate today" (Hoyle, "The Steady State Universe," *The Universe* [New York, 1957], pp. 80–81).

an explanation for the very existence of things became imperative, or, I should say, was conceived at all.

Greek philosophy took its starting point from Greek religion or theology when it conceived the universe as some basic stuff or chaos progressively organized by a variety of processes to achieve the present organization or structure, but with no notion of a philosophical principle which was a being and could cause the universe of beings. Similarly, Judaeo-Christian tradition offered the philosophers — and we are here linking Maimonides with St. Thomas Aquinas, as well as St. Augustine before them — the notion of creation, or, as it was crystallized in St. Augustine, a philosophical principle which was at the same time a real being, God, who produced the universe of beings out of nothing. This *creatio ex nihilo* was to explain the fact that things are, because the existence of things is not a self-evident and self-explanatory phenomenon. That something should exist which does not carry within itself its own reason for being, that something which comes to be and loses its being should exist at all, is beyond comprehension unless there is a being which contains within itself its own reason for being and can therefore be both explanation in the Greek sense and cause in the Christian sense for the being of other existents.

§ 5. THE ORIGIN OF BEING

Creation tells us that once things were not, and now they are. Therefore, the most important aspect of a thing is that by which it is set apart from nothing and placed outside its causes.

We have not time and this is not the place for a detailed analysis of being, but let us say only that by being we mean that which is most fundamental in anything and, at the same time, that which includes all the perfections of a thing. If we take a piece of chalk, for instance, we know that below and beneath its superficial accidents lies its being. After we have spoken of its whiteness, its smoothness, its cylindrical shape, the last thing we can say about it is that it is, and beyond that the mind hesitates and moves in fumbling, stumbling fashion.

Of all human experiences on the commonsense level I think that the fact of death makes us most aware of what we mean by being or existence. (One who has walked after a funeral through the house of a relative or friend who has just passed away, through rooms recently so full of a presence and now so empty, has an inchoate intuition of being. One who has tenderly folded away for the last time the garments of a loved one knows in a commonsense way what it means to *be*, knows what *existence* is as opposed to *nothingness*.)

§ 6. COSMOLOGY AS THE ORGANIZATION OF A PREEXISTING BEING

It is this aspect of things, that by which they are at all, their existence, with which creation is concerned, and not primarily with why they are of this kind or that, why they have this organization or that structure. The latter lies in the order of essence rather than existence. But this is exactly what Gamow means by a beginning: how the primordial matter or "ylem" was organized into the present universe of sun, planets, stars, galaxies, and island universes. What he is claiming, against Hoyle, is that our universe was not always of the same structure or kind as it is now. He is not talking of the origin of being, but of the organization of an already existing being into further stages and progressive modes of being.[7] That is why scientific theory is provisional. It tells us what could have happened. It describes a possible series of events, and it does not have any means of verifying which of two conflicting theories is true because it deals with the pure possibility of abstract essence. Science needs to be supplemented by a metaphysic to judge which was ontological or — to use that old-fashioned and much maligned word — true. These astronomical events could have happened in either of these ways, or both of these ways — there is much conjecture, but little evidence that they actually did so.

§ 7. ATOMIC THEORY AND THE PHILOSOPHIC THEORY OF INDEFINITE DIVISIBILITY OF BODIES

Contemporary thinkers have been much involved in the nature and methodology of the physical sciences. Physical theory has achieved a prominent place among the disciplines of the human intellect as the type of ideal knowledge. But the same can hardly be said for current philosophical interpretations of recent theoretical formulations of experimental findings. The concept of antimatter is a case in point. The notion of antimatter and mirror-image properties of particles is a valid experimental one. After all, the primary subatomic particles have been, as it were, canonized by modern theoretical physics. Whenever matter is broken down, the term of this disintegration has been particles of certain masses and charges. But now experimental findings, for example, indi-

---

[7] "In view of the objections raised by some reviewers concerning the use of the word 'creation' it should be explained that the author understands this term, not in the sense of 'making something out of nothing,' but rather as making something shapely out of shapelessness, as for example, in the phrase 'the latest creation of Parisian fashion'" (Gamow, *op. cit.*, p. vii). This seems to be formal causality, the progressive specification of an undifferentiated matter.

cate particles of the same mass as the electron but with a different charge, positive instead of negative; also, a particle of the mass of the proton but with a negative charge can be produced in the new reactors.

On the basis of these experimental findings speculation has run rampant even to the assertion of the possibility of new worlds and individuals, the mirror-images of each other. Do such apparently fantastic deductions have any real scientific basis or are they pure figments of poetic or artistic license? It would seem that they are extrapolations and valid scientific ones, but ones which embody faulty philosophical assumptions.

Atomic theory, as classically formulated, looks upon the primary subatomic particles as building blocks in the construction of the universe. All these different kinds of things have been the result of the collision and union of the primary particles — the electron, the proton, the neutron. But with the passage of time more particles of different masses and charges have been discovered, about ninety-seven hypothetical and about thirty-five verified — at last reading. This has been the reason for the breakdown of atomic theory in its original mechanistic phase and the re-ordering of these "building-block" particles into "classes of particles." Among the multiplication of particles were found the peculiar ones we discussed above and which have given rise to the notion of antimatter, that weird progenitor of mirror-image twins — planets, people, and universes.[8]

The initial philosophical error which resulted in these flights of speculation about antimatter and mirror-image twins was the consideration of the atomic theory as the theory of the *construction of matter* rather than the theory of the *destruction* or *disintegration of matter*. The atomic theory is not so much the way things can be put together as the way things can be taken apart. For example, as the atomic theory is all too often taught, one would think that bodies, even living bodies, are formed or constructed by the addition of these subatomic particles which somehow or other unite to produce lead, gold, sodium, plants, brutes, and even human beings in their proper constitutive powers. This after all is what is meant by mechanism as the reduction of the processes of living beings to physicochemical reactions.

But if we look on the atomic theory as the laws of the destruction of matter, the way in which matter and bodies may be taken apart, then we circumvent all such problems.

If we begin with the doctrine of the philosophy of nature of the

---

8 M. Duquesne, *Matter and Antimatter*, pp. 118–123.

indefinite divisibility of matter or bodies, then the atomic theory makes sense. If we consider that these particles are stages into which bodies may be corrupted, the whole theory falls into place. Let us use as a metaphor the image of a log being struck by an ax. When the ax strikes the log at a certain angle, with a certain force, a certain-sized chip is produced. This is what happened in the initial reactors and accelerators: the use of simple substances smashed against each other at certain designated speeds. But if we vary the angle of the cut, the speed of the ax, and the force of the blow we get a different-sized chip. In fact we can get an indefinite number of different-sized chips depending on the variation of these factors so enumerated.[9] The same is true of the cyclotron, bevatron, and the atomic piles. They have vastly improved and can now break up matter into an almost indefinite number of subatomic particles. These are the particles into which we can break down macroscopic bodies or elements. But are these the stages by which the living body or any element is produced? There is not nearly so much evidence in support of that side of the theory.

To come back to our problem of antimatter and mirror-image universes, they are based on this faulty view of the atomic theory as the law of the synthesis of macroscopic bodies. If the primary subatomic particles were not looked on as the ultimate constituents of matter, just as molecules and atoms had been before them, this situation would not have arisen. If they were not considered to be the *ultimate particles* out of which the whole universe is produced, rather than stages or *phases* in the corruption of matter which enable the mind tracing this pattern to predict what substances will combine in what mathematical proportions, this fantastic extrapolation would not have occurred. The presence of a particle with the mass of the electron but a positive charge, or the existence of a particle with the mass of the proton but a negative charge, would not have been so baffling and would not have needed so fantastic

---

[9] "We have seen how the theory of holes, by giving a definite meaning to electrons of negative energy, was able to predict the existence of new particles and to give a precise definition of their properties. Particle and anti-particle only differ in the signs of their charge and of their magnetic moment.

"Theoretically predicted in 1930, anti-particles were soon to be demonstrated experimentally. The first to be detected was the anti-electron, or positive electron. Further progress had to await the construction of giant accelerators, when $\pi-$ and $\pi+$ mesons could be produced in the synchro-cyclotron, and anti-protons and anti-neutrons in the bevatron.

"More recently still, atomic piles have been used to prove the existence of the neutrino and the anti-neutrino, and by the end of 1956, all the anti-particles necessary for building a model of anti-matter had been observed" (Duquesne, *op. cit.,* p. 119).

a system of speculations by reputable scientists to explain them. They are the inevitable productions of an indefinitely divisible matter as the instruments of division become more and more refined.

The whole point of just such an analysis is that any ultimate explanation of the structure of matter depends more on *form*, on principles of organization, than it does on material particles.

CHAPTER IX. / PSYCHOANALYTIC THEORY AND PHILOSOPHY

THE fundamental operations of knowledge and love in man can be approached in a variety of ways. One valid method of approach is that of natural science. Scientists do contemplate their own mental operations and at times even seem to be poaching on the preserves of the poet.

Who has not experienced the mysterious thrill of spring time in a forest, with sunbeams flickering through the foliage, and the low humming of insect life? It is the feeling of unity with nature, which is the counterpart of the attitude of the scientist, analysing the sunbeams into light quanta and the soft rustlings of the dragonfly into condensations and rarefactions of the air. But what is lost in fleeting sentiment is more than regained in the feeling of intellectual security afforded by the scientific attitude, which may grow into a trusting devotion, challenging the peace of the religious mystic. For in the majestic growth of science, analytical in its experimental groping for detail, synthetic in its sweeping generalization, we are watching at least one aspect of the human mind which may be believed to have a future of dizzy heights and nearly unlimited perfectibility.[1]

§ 1. THE PHYSIOLOGICAL APPROACH TO PSYCHOLOGICAL PHENOMENA

Natural science does give us many basic facts about knowledge and

---

[1] Svein Rosseland, *Theoretical Astrophysics,* Introduction; quoted by Cecilia Payne-Gaposchkin, *Introduction to Astronomy,* p. 1.

appetite. For instance the neurophysiological analysis has been able to marshal a multitude of facts into two major theories of the higher processes in man: the "general cortex" theory often identified with Sherrington and the current "reticular formation" theory outlined by Magoun and others, which is based on the pattern of progressive, electrically stimulated centers in the brain. Such a theory is physiological rather than anatomical. But apart from tracing the electrical patterns of nerve impulses there is actually very little about the human operation of thought that can be extracted. The inability of physiology to explain thought is evident in paragraphs such as this from the great formulator of the "conditioned reflex," Ivan Pavlov.

> If we could look through the skull into the brain of a consciously thinking person, and if the place of optimal excitability were luminous, then we should see playing over the cerebral surface a bright spot with fantastic, waving borders, constantly fluctuating in size and form, surrounded by a darkness more or less deep, covering the rest of the hemispheres.[2]

Even the valuable work on the localization of function according to brain areas in animals does not throw much illumination on the nature of the human brain in its specifically human functions.[3]

Arthus sums up our conclusions very well. Physiology has very little to tell us about the higher processes, about the immaterial operations of thought.

> Physiology is still incomplete and imperfect. Many points are still dark, many hypotheses still have to be justified. And yet the well observed and well established physiological facts are sufficiently numerous to provide medicine and hygiene with a solid foundation upon which these two sciences may build safely; and sufficiently numerous to provide a scientific philosophy with general views on the conditions and mechanisms of life. Strongly impressed by the great results obtained, some people have thought that all manifestations of life, even the most immaterial, should belong to the realm of physiology. We believe this to be a mistake and think that it is important to separate clearly the material or physiological facts from the immaterial or

---

[2] Ivan P. Pavlov, *Lectures on Conditioned Reflexes* (trans. W. Horsley Gantt).

[3] "Organization, localization and interconnection of centres in animals are not identical with the human brain" (G. Mitchell, *Anatomy of the Autonomic Nervous System*, pp. 65–66).

"These maps are not unmixed blessings as they suggest a false degree of rigid compartition in the anatomical and functional organization of the brain, whereas, with few exceptions, adjacent cortical areas merge into each other with no distinct lines of cellular or fibre-layer demarcation: and despite the assumption of certain writers, many are not convinced that cytoarchitectural features alone are conclusive evidence when deciding homologies between various areas in human and animal brains" (*ibid.*, p. 64).

psychological ones. This undoubtedly will reduce the field of physiology but it will remain vast enough and there will be enough virgin soil left to provide work to honest researchers for years and perhaps centuries.[4]

Likewise, in regard to appetition, the combination of drugs and motivation studies gives us some very real knowledge of appetite. As an illustration, we know from experimental methods that a ventral lesion of the hypothalamus leads to obesity. In one study, for example, animals whose hypothalamus had been operated on had voracious appetites, but when they were fed food made bitter with quinine they ate less than the control animals which had not undergone the same operation. These control animals ate less than the surgically modified animals whose food had no quinine but more than those whose food was mixed with quinine. This seemed to indicate to Dr. Miller (1958) that the aspect of hunger involved in such a ventral lesion of the hypothalamus was not plain hunger or pure consumption of calories, but a *residual hunger*, the last bit of appetite that keeps an animal nibbling when others are filled. Thus hunger is not simple, but complex.

Another illustration: If an animal is fed by a fistula directly into the stomach with the source of food supply in its control through a lever it can press, it will consume a very large amount of saline solution and a smaller amount of milk. This seems fitting because of the nutritional content of the latter. But if the animal takes milk by mouth it will not consume as much milk as it will if it takes it directly into the stomach. This seems to be clear experimental evidence of the role of the mouth as well as of the stomach in regulating the food intake in hunger.

§ 2. THE PSYCHOANALYTIC APPROACH TO PSYCHOLOGICAL PHENOMENA

Contributions such as these and many more important ones could be suggested by any scientist working in animal behavior, but natural science is not adequate to explain certain other realities of behavior; for example, the phenomena of anxiety, elation, and extreme anxiety have the same physiological pattern. They are physiologically identical. Consequently some *psychological determinant* is involved.

Examples of the inadequacy of natural science in the face of certain aspects of behavior could be multiplied: for instance, the work of the American physiologist Cannon, who collected the documentation on "Voodoo death" by social isolation. Another illustration is that of wild

---

[4] Maurice Arthus, *Philosophy of Scientific Investigation*, p. 7.

Norway rats placed in a tank of water with a stream of water of great force playing upon them from above. Ordinarily they will fight for hours before drowning, but if the ends of their whiskers are cut off they are dead within a minute — of cardiac failure, not drowning. They apparently die of fear.

It is in this area of activity, then, that we would locate the proper work of psychoanalysis. *Psychotherapy and, in general, psychoanalysis, are to a certain extent the application of a qualitative way of looking at the world in opposition to the mechanical concepts dominant in the natural sciences since Descartes and the quantitative methods that have ruled arbitrarily since Von Helmholtz.*

Freud did not work in an experimental, scientific way. One can search through his writings in vain for the concrete data from which, by a strict induction remaining ever close to the facts, he arrived at his major analytical concepts. His cases are actually illustrations; his method was intuitive. He was a poet and dealt in myth and symbol. Concerned with concrete individual reality, he had a kind of connatural sympathy with it. The lesson that psychoanalysis has to teach us, as a reaction against seventeenth-century Cartesian rationalism, is that the rational, logical analysis of reality is inadequate. The human being needs communion with the concrete real as well as the abstract general.

Freudianism has had a real vogue in modern times as a reaction against the liberalism of the eighteenth and nineteenth centuries. Man was good, an angel; if he were left alone with the minimum of restraint in politics and economics, the greatest good for all would result.

But instead we discovered the unpleasant truth that when man was completely unrestricted in his actions, he invariably ended by abusing his fellowman. To account for this phenomenon man had to admit that he was not an angel. But then, predictably, the pendulum swung to the other extreme. Instead of making the candid admission that there were certain elements in human nature of which man was not proud, people found a strange sort of solace in being told that they were not responsible for these aberrations of behavior. Man is rotten to the core anyway. There is a certain freedom, of a specious kind, in a theory of this sort. One is not shackled by the dictatorial demands of an outmoded morality that contradicts and seems to take particular delight in frustrating the most powerful urges and the most compelling drives of this body of ours. This was the perfect setting for the Freudian doctrine and, perhaps, the strongest reason for its popularity.

Granted the fundamentally rotten nature of man, rotten in terms of current religious and moral prejudices, that is, we can go on to construct the psychological nature of man. *The source of Freud's systematic theory is, of course, the existence of mental and emotional ills with no apparent physical cause.* These psychological aberrations, neuroses for example, can be aided by proper treatment.

It was in the attempt to cure sick people that Freud's theory was formulated. First of all he tried to explain the origin of mental diseases such as hysteria and compulsion. In order to do this in a systematic way he found that he had to construct a psychology.

§ 3. PSYCHOANALYSIS AS PSYCHOLOGICAL SCIENCE

The psychological nature of man includes three levels, the ego, the superego, and the id. They are so-called scientific Latin words for common psychological phenomena. The ego is the ordinary mental life of a man, the mind or consciousness in other words; the superego is a complexus of a man's ideals, ambitions, noble religious sentiments, and moral standards. This is supposed to be an arbitrary ideal self impressed on the ego by education and training. *The id is perhaps the most fundamental and important stage in man's psychological structure.* It is the cesspool of his nature out of which arise the dank smells of all the lowest appetites. The basic drive on this level is the sex drive. This is the real core of personality and all psychological diseases and neuroses find their origin here.

The ego has been taught that certain things are wrong — certain movements of the id. When these rise up in consciousness there is a sharp conflict with the superego. Dutifully the ego rejects these degraded drives and pushes them back into the unconscious movements of the appetite from whence they came. This is where trouble begins. These sexual appetites, once rejected, still exert their power. These unfulfilled hungers cease their clamoring to be filled, but they still pursue their end in a more subtle way, exerting pressure on the conscious ego. It is in this conflict of unfulfilled sexual desires that all psychosomatic aberrations begin. Fear, guilt, and anxiety that cripple the human mechanism and interfere with its proper operations are the result.

§ 4. PSYCHOANALYSIS AS PSYCHOLOGICAL THERAPY

The therapy or treatment for this sad situation is psychoanalysis, that system of free association, in a broad sense, whose purpose it is to discover the particular sex pressures or desires that are causing the trouble.

One who has an obsession for snakes, for example, becomes a ready object of diagnosis. The emotionally packed image lurks in the very forefront of consciousness ready to communicate itself in any and every similarity, so that the patient will see a serpent in the crack of a sidewalk and in the drop of a light cord. Even the very technical and effective Rohrschach ink-blot test utilizes this principle of free association.

Once the patient gets to know the reason for his aberrations, it is claimed, he is more than half cured. But this is not nearly as certain as one could wish. Many unconscious operations are best left unconscious and undisturbed. When one makes them conscious he interferes with them — the beat of the heart and breathing are two instances. It is often better that a man remain unaware of the enmities and murderous impulses he harbors for a member of his family, a superior, or a friend. *Most unconscious operations are best left unconscious.*

§ 5. THE ARTICULATIONS OF PSYCHOANALYSIS AND PHILOSOPHY

Psychoanalysis is a *valid method* of treatment, but the *philosophy* of Freud leaves much to be desired. What is the basis of truth in Freud? When we compare his structure to the Christian universe into which he was born we find a parallel interpretation of the facts of the psychological life of man that he discussed. First of all, the notion that man basically is not an angel is nothing new, despite its modern vogue. In the ancient tradition of Christianity human nature is tainted, not rotten, but sullied to the extent that one must be on guard against certain inclinations in his neighbor and in himself. That, we think, meets the facts of the situation in more adequate fashion than Freudian concepts. The human being is not completely corrupt. He can descend into the pits of degradation, but he can also rise to the nobility of the stars.

The ego is of course the intellect, the common exercise of consciousness. Using the Latin word *ego* does not make it more or less scientific. The id is reducible to what we call the physical, as opposed to the psychical, elements in man, the vegetative and animal operations and powers of the soul, basically good in themselves but independent of man's consciousness. Sex is only one of these functions; breathing, digesting, the pumping of the heart, and so forth, are but a few of the others.

The *superego* is the end and purpose of an intellectual or spiritual soul attempting to find its moral and religious perfection. Far from being a basic conflict in the order of nature, it is actually a cooperation. One could not achieve moral perfection if one were not born or alive. The modifications in our soul, on the other hand, are formed by the virtues, the perfection of man according to his nature, whole and entire, body and spirit.

There is a danger of sex's becoming an obsession by the very fact of the Freudian analyst's intense concentration upon it. Every physical action, the action and passion in every change or movement, can acquire sexual significance to the Freudian. Sex is so powerful a drive (it was made that way for the preservation and continuation of the species) that an overlong preoccupation with it can become obsessive. The analyst who must deal so intimately with these problems must be a profoundly spiritual and disciplined man if he is not to become obsessed.[5]

---

[5] "I was once sitting on a summer day in a meadow in Kent under the shadow of a little village church, with a rather curious companion with whom I had just been walking through the woods. He was one of a group of eccentrics I had come across in my wanderings who had a new religion called Higher Thought; in which I had been so far initiated as to realize a general atmosphere of loftiness or height, and was hoping at some later and more esoteric stage to discover the beginnings of thought. My companion was the most amusing of them, for however he may have stood towards thought, he was at least very much their superior in experience, having travelled beyond the tropics while they were meditating in the suburbs: though he had been charged with excess in telling travellers' tales. In spite of anything against him, I preferred him to his companions and willingly went with him through the wood; where I could not but feel that his sunburnt face and fierce tufted eyebrows and pointed beard gave him something of the look of Pan. Then we sat down in the meadow and gazed idly at the tree-tops and the spire of the village church; while the warm afternoon began to mellow into early evening and the song of a speck of a bird was faint far up in the sky and no more than a whisper of breeze soothed rather than stirred the ancient orchards of the garden of England. Then my companion said to me: 'Do you know why the spire of that church goes up like that?' I expressed a respectable agnosticism, and he answered in an off-hand way, 'Oh, the same as the obelisks; the Phallic Worship of antiquity.' Then I looked across at him suddenly as he lay there leering above his goatlike beard; and for the moment I thought he was not Pan but the Devil. No mortal words can express the immense, the insane incongruity and unnatural perversion of thought involved in saying such a thing at such a moment and in such a place. For one moment I was in the mood in which men burned witches; and then a sense of absurdity equally enormous seemed to open about me like the dawn. 'Why of course,' I said after a moment's reflection, 'If it hadn't been for phallic worship, they would have built the spire pointing downwards and standing on its own apex.' I could have sat in that field and laughed for an hour. My friend did not seem offended, for indeed he was never thin-skinned about his scientific discoveries. I had only met him by chance and I never met him again, and I believe he is now dead; but though it has nothing to do with the argument, it may be worth while to mention the name of this adherent of Higher Thought and interpreter of primitive religious origins; or

The driving motive in human life is not the *libido* or the sexual force, but the movement of love whose terminus is happiness. Love between intellectual beings is basically spiritual. Sex is not supreme. Sex is incidental in the life of the average human being.

The Freudians are well aware of the importance of a *Weltanschauung*. They take two years to indoctrinate just such a perspective, utilizing intensive methods of propagandizing. When the actress, for instance, comes to the Freudian analyst, she is disoriented, unable to handle the wealth, friends, and situations into which her success has catapulted her, or failure has crushed her, torn by the emotions she has learned to turn on and off like a faucet, with the consequence that emotions have commenced to come and go with an autonomy of their own, apart from her volition, in violent disproportion to occasion and importance. When such a young lady comes to the Freudian analyst, all this is explained to her. She is told that this is the situation in which she is living, these are the pressures exerted on her by money, friends, mother, morals. These are her very normal and natural desires, circumvented, and resulting in frustrations. In other words she is able to locate herself within a psychology: this is the world in which she is living and this is what is happening to her. She is given a perspective, a *Weltanschauung,* an orientation to explain, and then modify, what is happening to her. This type of integration is most important to the personality and its health.

Paranoia, although relatively rare, provides raw material of systematic behavior patterns that helps to throw light on normal behavior. The paranoid presents an integrated personality because of his highly organized or systematized delusion. He can mask his illness even while normal personalities around him are crumbling as the result of constant contact with him. The very organization and systematization of his delusion aid him, but once it is exposed his personality disintegrates.

His role in life reflects an individual's philosophy or *Weltanschauung* which he must have in order to understand what is expected of him. It also helps to establish identification because goal-directed behavior makes no sense unless it is located within the intelligible framework of a *Weltanschauung*.

If the perfect life is the fulfillment of the ends of love in proper

---

at any rate the name by which he was known. It was Louis de Rougemont. That insane image of the Kentish church standing on the point of its spire, as in some old rustic topsy-turvy tale, always comes back into my imagination when I hear these things said about pagan origins; and calls to my aid the laughter of the giants" (G. K. Chesterton, "The Everlasting Man," in *The Man Who Was Chesterton,* pp. 357–358).

order by the formation of good habits or virtues, then the best therapy is to set up good habits and to give human beings the motives to begin to establish the virtues. The person who has spent his life in appropriating these principles and weaving them into the very texture of his personality knows the stability, the calm, luminous vision that wisdom affords its devotees. Many psychiatric, psychoanalytic, and psychological theories in current vogue base their procedures on the treatment of certain superficial concomitants, psychological resonances or emotional results of a personality really warped by a faulty view of itself and its relations to the world about it.

Does a philosophy have any clinical importance? Is there any way of perceiving philosophical principles at work, operative in the practical order? Is there any way of checking to see, in a concrete practical situation, the dynamism of an ultimate system of values, the influence that the whole combination of religious beliefs, commonsense conclusions, and philosophic insight into causes has on a man's behavior?[6]

His *Weltanschauung* does affect his behavior, but usually not immediately. However his notions of human nature, his moral standards, no matter how crude and amorphous in formulation they may be, certainly show up over the space of a lifetime. A man's choice of career and his performance in it, his relations with others, his marriage and what becomes of it — all these events reveal the raw stuff of an inductive experience modified by his basic conceptions of life and the world in which he lives. A philosophy does have a clinical importance and *a verifiable one, but not immediately.*

---

6 "In the preface to that admirable collection of essays of his called 'Heretics,' Mr. Chesterton writes these words: 'There are some people — and I am one of them — who think that the most practical and important thing about a man is still his view of the universe. We think that for a landlady considering a lodger it is important to know his income, but still more important to know his philosophy. We think that for a general about to fight an enemy it is important to know the enemy's numbers, but still more important to know the enemy's philosophy. We think the question is not whether the theory of the cosmos affects matters, but whether in the long run anything else affects them.' I think with Mr. Chesterton in this matter. I know that you, ladies and gentlemen, have a philosophy, each and all of you, and that the most interesting and important thing about you is the way in which it determines the perspective in your several worlds" (William James, *Pragmatism*, 1907, Lecture One, p. 1).

"The most important emotional factors which motivate or disturb men are those which are sustained or actually engendered by complicated conceptual thought processes," Prof. Silvano Arieti, professor of clinical psychiatry, New York Medical College, told the American Association for the Advancement of Science annual meeting in Montreal in 1965.

Such conditions as severe anxiety reactions, schizophrenia, and paranoid states have very little to do with hunger, thirst, and sex as such, but very much to do with the complicated conceptual world of man, Dr. Arieti said (Montreal Science Service).

In our analysis of behavior the raw material of investigation could well be the neurotic. For in this case we see the divagations of normal activity worked by a *Weltanschauung*. The psychotic situation has already resulted in so many profound organic changes, that often the possible mental causes are lost to view. In the neurotic the physical effect is still rather closely connected to the mental state which caused it. We do not mean to imply that philosophical therapeutics is the only or the whole method of psychoneurotic treatment, but that the intellectual and religious perspectives play an important part in the development and the relief of neuroses. Many specialists are required for the solution of such complex personality problems.

CHAPTER X. / PHILOSOPHY AS A
PRINCIPLE OF UNIFICATION
AND UNITY

METHODOLOGY is, properly, the study of scientific methods. There is no universal agreement on the nature of scientific methodology, just as there is no agreement on the nature of any particular scientific method. The movement toward specialization in the sciences, toward finer and ever more detailed knowledge, is away from the direction of interest in the general or common characteristics which all the physical sciences seem to possess in common.

Some thinkers, following Descartes, have held for a single, homogeneous, universal method, basically mathematical. In this view the deductive method is the scientific ideal. Bacon, too, proposed a single method, one fundamentally experimental. This view was later reinforced by empiricism, a reaction against the mathematical ideal of Cartesian scientific method. Bacon's method is primarily an elaborate induction, in opposition to Aristotle's "simple enumeration."

§ 1. SCIENTIFIC METHODOLOGY

The methodology of the physical sciences, however, is not a universal method for all the sciences, but a collection of disparate yet complementary methods having in common the general laws of logic but specified by their proper objects.[1]

Methodology is also the search for a unity among scientific methods. For this reason much of methodology lies outside of the particular sciences and has been to a large extent the concern of the philosopher and the logician, or the natural scientist turned philosopher, rather than the professional scientist in his proper work. For scientific methodology is not necessary for scientific work. The scientist uses his methods with the same instinctive ease of experience as the exercise of common sense and of habits developed by repeated acts. Once he has formulated his scientific laws founded in observation and confirmed in experiment, he reflects on his completed work. It is only at this point that methodology arises, due to reflection on scientific methods, the initial exercise of which is in large part instinctive and unconscious although deliberative and intellectual.

Methodology, then, is located on the frontiers of science and philosophy. The scientist steps over into philosophy. This is simply because no science judges its own first principles but always takes them from a higher science. In this case the scientist utilizes philosophy.

Actually, there is more than one scientific methodology. Methodology must make room for more than one scientific method. For some thinkers the essentials of methodology are to be found in a combination of logic and epistemology. The attempt to reduce scientific methodology to logic or linguistics has been a common failing of our day. For these thinkers methodology is only a subdivision of logic. But the reduction of methodology to logic has resulted in a view of scientific method so formal that scientific laws are interpreted as tautologies to account for their necessity and certainty. It is possible to define physical concepts such as energy and temperature so that the laws of thermodynamics appear to be the result of a "vicious circle" in argumentation. In fact, Eddington does at one point suggest that Newtonian mechanics could be viewed as "one vast tautology." Only the validity of practical results militates against such a reduction of methodology to logic.

---

[1] "It is of utmost importance that the expressions peculiar to a science will possess meanings that are fixed by its *own* procedures, and are therefore intelligible in terms of its own rules of usage whether or not the science has been, or will be [explained in terms of] some other discipline" (Ernest Nagel, "The Meaning of Reduction in the Natural Sciences," *Philosophy of Science*, A. C. Danto and S. Morgenbeiser, eds. [New York: Meridian Books, 1960], p. 301).

§ 2. PHILOSOPHY AND METHODOLOGY

But the methods of the physical sciences do have some characteristics in common over and above the general principles of logic, by reason of the fact that their different subjects are drawn from a definite class of reality and their objects determine a certain methodic perspective. In fact we could conclude that the formation of metalanguages, metalogics, and metamathematics are all recognitions that some broader and more synthetic basis for the organization and analysis of scientific methods is necessary and is more pressing than the intrinsic data of the particular sciences themselves. But a logic by itself is insufficient to account for these variable and often conflicting scientific data. For scholastic thinkers, the function of a metalanguage of Wittgenstein, a metalogic of Tarski, or a metamathematics of Hilbert was considered to be one of the functions of philosophy in general and metaphysics in particular.

No science judges its own nature or its own first principles, but it receives them from a higher science, as optics takes its principles from the physics of light. The mathematician does not set his own first principles, e.g., the whole is greater than any of its parts, nor does he ask what a number is, what of reality does a number seize. He simply proceeds to use these principles. The quantitative unity which is at the basis of number finds its ultimate explanation in the metaphysical unity of substance and ultimately of being. Thus in the nature and classification of the sciences philosophy is employed to explain to science its own proper nature.

As we stated above, one would barely suspect that the different sciences are speaking of the same world, their languages are so different. The mutual unintelligibility and incommunicability between physics and biology, for instance, must be dissolved if full use is to be made of intellectual work and if the significant achievements of one science are to be made available for the others. This is one of the fundamental roles of methodology, the integration of the sciences. Whether we use logical positivism, empiricism, idealism, linguistic analysis, or scholastic metaphysical realism, some philosophical concepts are necessary to construct a methodology of the physical sciences.

Science does not have an artificial starting point. Its origins are to be found in commonsense knowledge. It starts with the knowledge of everyday life and then attempts to go deeper in understanding, to find a more fundamental explanation.

Since science is properly a knowledge of causes, as we have seen, the different sciences will vary by reason of the kind of causes they seek. The subject matter of the science determines its methodology. We cannot talk about scientific method as if it were a Kantian logic, a series of mental forms independent of content.

§ 3. HYBRID SCIENCES

When two or more sciences have the same subject matter but different objects, that is, different perspectives or "cross-sections" of the same subject, it is possible to use the object of the more abstract science on the subject matter of the other, and to consider the consequent theoretical formulations as explanations of the less abstract science instead of explanations of the same subject matter from the object or particular point of view of the original and more abstract science. Mathematical physics and biochemistry are just such "hybrid sciences."

In order to make a set of empirical facts scientific, a demonstrative science must be utilized. Demonstration depends on the inherent organization or systematization already existent in the set of empirical facts. Somehow or other these receive a unity from the quantitative relations inherent in their physical structure as amenable to a dimensional geometry. But some demonstrative science must project this unity and intensify it. Then, and only thus transmuted and transformed, can a set of empirical facts become a science. The philosophy of nature once did this, but now mathematics performs this function. We know from physics that a body has three and only three dimensions. But this knowledge can become explanatory and demonstrative only through geometry. We can prove that through one and the same point three and only three perpendicular lines can be drawn. For another example, the explanation of genetic behavior in terms of DNA is a chemical answer to a chemical problem and of tremendous interest to the chemist, but it is not a biological solution to the biological problem of genetics. It can be a practical instrument of experimentation but not of understanding or explanation in biological terms, although it does serve to indicate the ultimate unitary basis of all knowledge.

Although the different natural sciences achieve a partial view of a very complex reality, the natural unity for such knowledges is within a discipline which views reality as a totality, which looks on things as natural wholes rather than as parts, or formal, intelligible aspects. The doctrine of the soul provides a principle of total organization, within the framework of which partial principles and mechanisms of organization can be developed.

It is a current convention that cosmic teleology should be kept out of the laboratory because it interferes with the work at hand. There is, of course, a certain historical and technical validity to such an assumption; it is, in part, the fruit of a bitter intellectual struggle. But it still remains true, as very eminent embryologists testify, that the striking fact about the embryo is, of course, its purposeful development. A restatement of teleology in the more sophisticated terms of organismic biology may be reconciled with biological phenomena, especially with experimental developmental embryology, where there is progression toward maturity. The notions of *prospective fate* and *potential end* fairly shout for some sort of philosophical foundation.

The teleological process is not merely a shorthand form of description; it reaches the primary level of the facts of development, for example, of transplantation, as we have already seen.

§ 4. VERIFICATION

What do we mean when we say that philosophy in its analysis of essence can set the bounds of possibility? How do we choose among possible scientific theories? As we have seen, the present state of the stellar universe could have resulted from an initial explosion. Man could have evolved from some lower form, some primordial jellyfish. Mechanically speaking, things could be constructed of atomic and subatomic particles. There are a number of theories of general organization of the embryo. One way of explaining human behavior is by the pressure of unconscious forces, so that man only superficially appears to be free. All these are possible modes of being. Things could exist in this way. Events might have happened in this fashion. Whether they did so or not seems to be outside the scientific provenance, outside the two modes of scientific verification as currently conceived. One is *sensation*, the other is *mathematical demonstration*. But natural science, since Descartes, has grown wary of the senses and the spontaneous certitudes of common sense so intimately interwoven with them. Like friends who have deceived us once, we can never completely trust them again. A sensible verification seems to be only as accurate as the theoretical framework within which it becomes significant.[2] There are no "pure observations," as Popper has shown.

---

[2] A. N. Whitehead claims "there are no brute, self-contained matters of fact, capable of being understood apart from interpretation as an element in a system. . . . Thus the understanding of the immediate brute fact requires its metaphysical interpreta-

Mathematical demonstration is verified by reduction to primary axioms. But axioms seem to be arbitrary assumptions, still requiring validation by a further scientific deduction, a monstrous tautology a la Wittgenstein and Russell. To a theoretician of this persuasion, Maxwell's differential equations have no true correspondence to the experimental facts of Faraday. This leaves theory floating peacefully in some abstract Platonic heaven. It does not explain reality, and consequently it cannot explain even its own predictive power. To root mathematical axioms in reality demands a metaphysical reduction of these mathematical axioms to ontological principles, to nature, and finally to *being* as existence.

Perhaps the most important conclusion of scientific methodology is that there is not one supreme and sole science, but all the sciences are complementary and supplementary modes of knowledge, affording together a total view of the universe.

---

tion as an item in a world with some systematic relation to it" (*Process and Reality,* pp. 21–22).

"Even from this point of view science is no more closely connected with 'our experience' than other instruments or means of production. And even if we look at it as gratifying our intellectual needs, its connection with our experiences does not differ in principle from that of any other objective structure. Admittedly it is not incorrect to say that science is '. . . an instrument' whose purpose is 'to predict from immediate or given experiences later experiences, and even as far as possible to control them.' But I do not think that this talk about experiences contributes to clarity. It has hardly more point than, say, the not incorrect characterization of an oil derrick by the assertion that its purpose is to give us certain experiences: not oil, but rather the sight and smell of oil; not money, but rather the feeling of having money" (Karl Popper, *The Logic of Scientific Discovery,* p. 100).

"Empiricism and verification by sense experience makes sense only if there is a reality which sense perception grasps and thus it may serve as a brake on the constructive and hypothesizing tendencies of the intellect. If sense knowledge does grasp existence in a way and on a level denied to conceptual knowledge or ideas, then within such a metaphysical realism empiricism does make sense.

"Much of contemporary empiricism is the unreasonable end result of this philosophical spring cleaning. It is a *fragment* that cannot stand on its own feet. Once, when metaphysics was still a respectable enterprise, the reference to observation made excellent sense. Today it is hardly more than an article of faith" (Paul Feyerabend, "Problems of Empiricism," p. 148).

PART THREE
PRACTICAL PHILOSOPHY

KNOWLEDGE for its own sake, for the sheer joy of its possession, is called *speculative*. It is the highest type of knowledge because it is a good in itself, satisfying the natural appetite of one of our spiritual faculties, the intellect. Moreover, all knowledge has its speculative side. One first has to know something about swimming before he can practice, just as one must first learn about physiology and medicine before one can put that knowledge to use as a nurse or doctor.

This leads us to the second type of knowledge, which is for the sake of making or doing something, and which is called *practical*. In this case, the intellectual interest is awakened and sustained only until the object desired is possessed. Therefore, the mind works under the stimulus of another appetite. For example, you may be stimulated to study so that you won't be embarrassed in class, or to learn about budgeting so that you won't starve to death.

Practical knowledge is of two types. Knowledge for the sake of making a thing well is called *art*. Performance on a diving board, for example, is an art; it shows form and proportion. Knowledge for the sake of doing a thing in the right way is called *prudence*. It would be prudent, for example, to learn how to swim. It might have been prudent for a man to send his family away for a vacation although an unforeseen accident occurred and all were killed. Prudence, as we can see, like art, involves practical judgments in individual cases.

CHAPTER XI. / POLITICS
AND ETHICS

§ 1. IDEAS AS HISTORICAL DETERMINANTS

WHAT has philosophy, the so-called abstract science, to contribute to politics? Whether we realize it or not, ideas are among the most potent historical determinants, and the intellectual conclusions of one generation become the convictions and prejudices of the next. We are prone to overlook this fact because we are living within a specific culture which has been shaped by a certain set of ideas. The very atmosphere we breathe has been permeated by them, so much so that the tendency is to consider as part of an immutable reality what are merely the perspectives from which we view that reality. But a man cannot see the shape of the continent upon which he walks. It is too big. One has to get outside of it to view it properly, whether by sight or science.[1]

We should like to discuss the relations of a philosophy to everyday life, a philosophy whose premises and conclusions are coincident with Christian principles. Since political problems have taken on such unparalleled urgency and their solution or nonsolution will have such tremendous repercussions in every walk of life, we choose these politi-

---

[1] One of the reasons for studying the history of political ideas is precisely to avoid wasting our time over problems which others have already solved. Cf. Aristotle, *Politics*, II, 1.

cal questions as an ideal illustration of the need for such a Christian philosophy.

The role that philosophy plays in politics is not a new one, for it goes back to the fourth century before Christ. Greek philosophers were very much concerned with the political order, as philosophers have been ever since. "The history of philosophy is a series of footnotes to Plato," said Whitehead, and this surely holds true for political thinking. For it was in Plato's personal experience that the relations between philosophy and politics were first delineated. Plato was an amazing man, and he would have been an amazing man in any age. He came from a wealthy Athenian family whose members had always held positions of power in the government of Athens. In fact, the famous Critias, ruler of Athens during the wars with Sparta, was his uncle. The family was so much a part of politics that, while Plato was still a boy, two of his uncles became embroiled in a scandal over the misuse of public funds — but they were too wealthy and powerful to be punished. Plato had the personal gifts so valuable to public life. Xenophon, the author of the *Anabasis*, who was also a disciple of Socrates, tells us that Plato was renowned for his beauty, being the second handsomest man in Athens. The handsomest, according to Xenophon, was Alcibiades, the Greek Benedict Arnold who almost succeeded in betraying Athens to her enemies. Plato was also a famous athlete. That is the reason for the name "Plato"; it was not a family name. "Plato" in Greek means broad, and he acquired the name because of the breadth of his shoulders. When we couple all this with an intellectual and artistic genius that has made his name a byword twenty-five centuries after his death, we can arrive at some idea of the manner of man he was.

§ 2. PLATO AND THE GENESIS OF POLITICAL PHILOSOPHY

This sensitive, ambitious young man, like so many others of his day, became disillusioned with the corruption of Athenian politics. Mob rule and oppressive taxation dismayed him. From half to two-thirds of the population of ancient Athens were slaves so that the burden of taxation fell on a minority. The petty bickerings of politicians resulted in more than thirty long years of warfare sustained only by a national system of conscription and universal military training. Plato had been a soldier, and even though he distinguished himself in battle he was filled with a sense of its futility. As a consequence he decided to do something about it. Like many an ambitious young man since, he wanted to enter public life to reform it from within. He ran for some minor office but was severely defeated — smeared because of the scandal in which his uncles were involved. We can imagine the hurt and frustration of it, but out of this personal injury came an incalculable good.[2] For Plato decided to go ahead with his crusade anyway. The results, however, were completely unexpected. When he had fully examined the existing political structure, he found it a good one. It was a democracy of sorts, efficient in its fashion, perhaps an ideal political structure considering the day and age. The difficulty, however, went deeper than the political structure; it concerned more properly the character of the men who occupied the office. Plato was the first thinker to spell out systematically that certain political problems were not solvable in the political order, in other words, that "politics demands an ethics." It was the political ethics of his day which resulted in the corruption of government, not the structure of government itself.

But this was only the starting point. From this initial insight Plato was to develop, for the first time in history, the whole of philosophy. For he saw that to construct an ethics, moral values must have a foundation. They must be grounded on a philosophy of nature. Instead of being conventional, artificial laws, they must be rooted in nature, so that men will realize that it is natural to be virtuous.[3] Finally, in

---

[2] "Finally, in a democratic state the view that makes morality consist in the performance of the public duties prescribed by the customs of the tribe develops very easily into a belief that the highest form of human activity consists in a political life and activities and in the work of the state. 'We alone,' says Pericles of the Athenians in the great funeral speech reported by Thucidides, 'regard the man who takes no part in public affairs not as harmless but as a useless person.' And the whole movement towards Democracy is an indication of the feeling, however vague, that political and public work is the best field for the development and exercise of the highest human qualities, and that an opportunity to take part in such work is an essential condition of the 'good life'" (Guy Field, *Plato and His Contemporaries*, 2d. ed. [London, 1948], pp. 82–83).

[3] Cal. "Quite so, Socrates; and they are really fools, for how can a man be happy who is the servant of anything? On the contrary, I plainly assert that he who would truly live ought to allow his desires to wax to the uttermost, and not to chastize them; but when they have grown to their greatest he should have courage and intelligence to minister to them and to satisfy all his longings. And this I affirm to be natural justice and nobility. To this, however, the many cannot attain, and they blame the strong man because they are ashamed of their own weakness which they desire to conceal, and hence they say that intemperance is base. As I have remarked already, they enslave the nobler natures, and being unable to satisfy their own pleasures, they praise temperance and justice out of their own cowardice. For if a man had been originally the son of a king or had a nature capable of acquiring an empire or a tyranny or a sovereignty, what could be more truly base or evil than temperance — to a man like this, I say, who might freely be enjoying every good, and has no one to stand in his way, and yet has admitted custom and reason and the opinion of other men to be lords over him? Must not he be in a miserable plight whom the reputation of justice and temperance hinders from giving more to his friends than to his enemies, even though he be a ruler in his city? Nay, Socrates, for you profess to be a votary of the truth, and the truth is this: — that

recognizing the virtuous man as the complete realization of his essence (what he should be), Plato, genius that he was, created the first metaphysics, the ultimate explanation of the natural order. It is no mere coincidence that philosophy was born in answer to the problems of politics. The chronological order of Plato's dialogues falls into this very pattern. The earlier works are an attempt to establish an ethics in answer to political problems. The *Gorgias* is a good example of this.[4] The second stage is the foundation of an ethics in a philosophy of nature, whose sketch is found in the *Phaedrus,* where Plato discusses the nature of the soul and its destiny, and also in the *Republic.* Finally he is forced by his preoccupation with psychological problems to construct a metaphysics, a task which he attempts in the *Parmenides* and the *Sophist.*

In his scientific analysis of the political order, Plato attempted to provide principles in the light of which such problems could be delineated. Fluid and amorphous commonsense notions, lacking the rigor and intellectual precision of principles, were inadequate for problems of this kind. It is not that philosophical principles of politics could be of direct help, then or now, in the practical problems of concrete

---

luxury and intemperance and license, if they be provided with means, are virtue and happiness — all the rest is a mere bauble, agreements contrary to nature, foolish talk of men, nothing worth" (Plato, *Gorgias,* 483 e ff.). This argument holds that it is natural to be vicious, the precise issue.

4 In the most important of his earlier dialogues, Plato handles this problem. The title of this work is the *Gorgias* whose protagonist was perhaps the most famous teacher of the day. There is a story in a fragment of Aristotle of a Corinthian farmer who read the *Gorgias* and was so moved by it that he sold his property and came to Athens to join the Academy. Now Gorgias claimed to teach wealthy young men how to succeed in public life through mastery of law and rhetoric. Socrates, who is the hero of the play, asks Gorgias just how he prepares young men for success in the political arena. Gorgias replies: "What a marvelous thing rhetoric is, Socrates. Let me offer you a striking example of this. On several occasions I have been with my brother Herodicus, a physician, to see one of his patients who would not allow the physician to give him medicine or apply the knife or hot iron to him. And I have persuaded him to do for me what he would not do for the physician, just by the use of rhetoric. And I say that if a physician and a rhetorician were to go to any city and had there to argue in the assembly as to which of them should be elected state-physician, the physician would have no chance, the rhetorician would win easily. And in a contest with a man of any other profession the rhetorician could get himself elected or chosen, for he can speak more persuasively to the multitude than any of them, and on any subject. Such is the marvelous nature and power of rhetoric." To this panegyric Socrates answers: "That is all very wonderful but is there not something very dangerous about putting the power to be elected to public office in the hands of men? Is there not something intrinsically wrong about a man who is trained to win office without the proper qualifications and against the man with those qualifications? Is the ability to win votes unjustly a good thing, after all?" (Plato, *Gorgias,* 455a–457c.)

civic life on every level. They are of no help in urban redevelopment, in proper balancing of the tax burden between commercial and residential contributions to government, or in zoning problems in the face of a shifting racial population. Principles do not supply facile solutions. They are the guides according to which problems can be solved on the practical level by painful, prudential judgments. They provide light for reason, warmth for the ideals of the heart, direction for the wavering spirit.

§ 3. POLITICS, ETHICS, AND PRACTICAL KNOWLEDGE

But in the investigation of one reality, there are different levels of ideas, such as the theological, the philosophical, and the political. These levels are cross sections of reality glimpsed by the mind. A total unified view demands the articulation of all intellectual perspectives. Where does ethics end and politics begin? The answer is that actually they are continuous. Ethics permeates every area of human action, and thus the whole of politics, providing a framework for its development, if only indirectly. For the political order has its own knowledges, supreme in their own sphere, yet dependent upon knowledges of other areas of human existence. Knowledge moves from the speculative to the practical in any system of related knowledges; for example, the physicist, engineer, machinist, and laborer each depends, in turn, on the preceding knowledge for his proper function. Likewise in the business world knowledge moves from the economist, through the manager and the technician, to the worker.

So too in the political order, each knowledge has its own nature and prerogatives as well as its dependency and limitations. The political philosopher is concerned with the nature of political life in general, its origins and location in the total picture of reality. The political scientist, cognizant of the nature of the political order, constructs the possible ways in which this nature has been and can be realized. The different types of government, their relations and modifications, values and defects, are his domain. Society, as a human construction, can be refashioned upon any plan that has ever been devised. The statesman constructs the constitution that is, here and now, best for this people at this precise point in their historical development. The politician is equipped for skillful operation of the offices that constitute the political structure. Although the statesman and the manager are working on the same level as the engineer, their modes of operation are different. The engineer has a speculative knowledge and he is aware of its laws, at least as conclusions. But economics and politics are, for the most part, attempts to organize a unified body of knowledge on the level of practical intellection without an antecedent science to rely upon for proximate principles. This is the role that political philosophy should serve. The formation of the statesman and of the politician must follow upon the laws of experience and the development of habits. They learn primarily by doing, with a consequent reflection upon what has been done, although there must be some sort of construction of organized theoretical knowledge to systematize and order their work. Unlike the engineer with a speculative knowledge to apply, the statesman and the politician cannot depend on political science to the same extent. Their decisions must be, in large measure, the results of what they are or have become. The nucleus of such knowledges is a practical, prudential judgment of experience in dealing with concrete individual circumstances. The statesman must, and sometimes does, make the best of a bad constitution and of bad legislation.[5] However, political philosophy can provide the political scientist, the statesman, and the politician (without intruding upon their proper functions), with a general framework of the particular intelligible structure of the political order and provide justification for the basic human values that no political mind can ignore.

The plan of a political philosophy is to map the political order, not in its present distortion, but as it should be. To quote Lord Acton: "The great question is to discover, not what governments prescribe, but what they ought to prescribe; for no prescription is valid against the conscience of mankind."[6] Our purpose is to present the everyday concepts of society, government, law, authority, the common good, and similar notions, in an integral, cohesive, systematic whole. There is so much confusion concerning these fundamental, all-important conceptions, it is no wonder that both domestic and foreign issues seem to be entirely beyond our control.

§ 4. DEFINITION OF THE STATE

What then is the state? For a scientific definition we must give the causes of a thing. That type of knowledge which we call science, as we have seen, is distinguished from the knowledge of common sense, the knowledge of the man in the street, inasmuch as it deals with causes, while the knowledge of common sense is concerned with effects, results, and conclusions. To have scientific knowledge, we have to

---

[5] Aristotle, *Politics*, IV, 1.
[6] John Acton, *History of Freedom*, London, 1909, p. 24.

know the causes of a thing, that is, the reasons why it is what it is. In the natural sciences, like physics and biology, we study the proximate causes of things. In philosophy we study the ultimate, the most fundamental causes of why things are what they are.[7]

What then is the state? For a scientific definition, we must give the causes of the thing; for a philosophical definition, we must give the ultimate causes of the thing.[8] Aristotle, you will remember, classified all causes, or reasons of things, into four possible genera or types.

For instance, really to know what man is, in his ultimate nature, we must measure him by these four causes. The efficient cause of man is God, who made him. The material cause is matter, or in a general sense, body. His formal cause is an immaterial soul, which makes man to be what he is and places an incalculable price on his person. Man's final cause is also God himself, possessed in eternal happiness which is called beatitude by the theologians. We cannot enter into proof of these things now; however, Christians can agree on these fundamentals by reason of the faith they possess. With this definition of man then in mind, we can turn to the definition of the state.

§ 5. REPARATIONS

It is important to know just what man is, and what society is. Society is properly a collection of men, not a physical being in its own right, according to Thomas Aquinas. This sounds so eminently sensible, as all of Thomas Aquinas is when dissected from necessary technical formulations, that we are liable to accept it as the common opinion of mankind. But in terms of political philosophy it is really novel. Take, for instance, the question of reparations today. Every nation in the world without exception accepts the principle that national reparations are moral and valid. It seems logical that a nation that has sinned should be punished. But why? Is it because a nation is the leviathan of Hobbes, or the physical being of Rousseau? It is a being which acts, and thus if it transgresses the moral order, it must be punished. But this position is contradictory to Christian principles, for "The state is an artificial

---

[7] Cf. William Carlo, "Freedom and Human Knowledge," *The Concept of Freedom,* Carl Grindel, C.M., ed. (Chicago, 1955).

[8] "The application of principles is analogical — the more transcendent the principles the more analogical is the application — and this application takes various typical forms in reference to the historical climates or historical constellations through which the development of mankind is passing; in such a manner that the same immutable principles are to be applied or realized in the course of time according to typically different patterns" (Jacques Maritain, *Man and the State* [Chicago, 1951], p. 156).

being, an *opus rationis*," according to Thomas Aquinas. And it is only the natural individual human being who is capable of acting, who is the source of moral operations. Therefore, it is only individuals in the state who act for the right or the wrong, not the state as such. This position is not simply an antique curiosity; in fact this opinion has been recorded by modern political scientists.

> The will of the state, in short, is the will which is adopted out of the conflict of myriad wills which contend with each other for the mastery of social forces. It is never deliberate in the sense that it is always determined by national considerations. It is never single, in the sense that it derives from a unanimous agreement of those to whom it applies. . . . Still less than the notion of a common will can we accept the doctrine that it finds embodiment within the state. It is argued, to use a phrase of Dr. Bosanquet, that all State-action is, at bottom, the exercise of the real will of society . . . nor are they based upon the effort of some unified will. What rather exists is an amazing welter of wills which press upon each other.[9]

If a state is composed entirely of individuals, and the individual alone is capable of a moral judgment, if in every state there is at least a minority which does not concur in the sentiments of the majority, then it is impossible for a state to be punished as a state. You cannot punish a nation as a nation, only the responsible individuals. You cannot burn the wheat with the cockle.[10]

It is directly in line with the tradition of the state as a huge physical person, a giant, stemming from Hobbes, that we today think the way we do on the question of reparations.[11] And this is not the only case. Freedom of speech, the role of the majority in a democracy, the legal system, and so many of our public institutions and business corpora-

---

[9] Harold Laski, *Grammar of Politics* (London, 1930), p. 31.

[10] Cf. I. Eschmann, "Studies on the Notion of Society in St. Thomas Aquinas," *Mediaeval Studies* (1946), pp. 1–42. This scholarly treatment of the problem of national reparations cannot be too highly recommended.

[11] "Art goes yet further, imitating that rational and most excellent work of nature, man. For by art is created that great *Leviathan* called a Commonwealth, or State, in Latin Civitas, which is but an artificial man; though of greater stature and strength than the natural, for whose protection and defense it was intended; and in which the sovereignty is an artificial soul, as giving life and motion to the whole body; the magistrates, and other officers of judicature and execution, artificial joints; reward and punishment, by which fastened to the seat of the sovereignty every joint and member is moved to perform his duty, are the nerves, that do the same in the body natural; the wealth and riches of all the particular members are the strength; *salus populi*, the people's safety, its business; counselors, by whom all things needful for it to know are suggested unto it, are the memory; equity and laws, an artificial reason and will; concord, health; sedition, sickness; body politic were at first made, set together, and united, resemble that *fiat*, or the *let us make man*, pronounced by God in the creation" (Thomas Hobbes, *Leviathan* [Cambridge, 1904], Introduction).

tions — all are saturated with, we might even say contaminated by, these political notions.

In examining the causes of the state then, we find that human life and activities are the so-called matter of the state. The formal cause is law, which orders and organizes the myriad of human activities and commerce into a whole. The efficient cause is government, which motivates society and impels it to its proper end and final cause, the common good.[12]

This, then, is the skeletal framework of a Thomistic *Civitas. (Material cause,* human life and activity; *formal cause,* law; *efficient cause,* government; and *final cause,* the common good).[13]

Now in Thomas Aquinas the notion of nature has the function of binding this skeleton together, of providing the sinews and muscles by means of which the bones may articulate in unison and act as a whole. What is nature? Nature is really the same principle which the scholastics also called form (not to be confused with shape, which is merely an accident of quantity). Where in the world about us do we find form? Consider, for example, a man, a dog, and a flower. Their ultimate physical and chemical constituents are practically identical — almost so in their organic composition and even more so in their inorganic constitution. Yet among a man, a dog, and a rose there are worlds of difference. Why do they differ so, when materially they are identical? This reason for difference we call form. It is the principle of organization, that which makes things to be *what* they are: the material of a man to be a man, the material of a dog to be a dog, the material of a rose to be a rose. Essence and nature are merely other names for this reality which we call form, something which we can neither weigh nor measure, but which must be present to account for the facts.

---

[12] "Leviathan Or The Matter, Form and Power of a Commonwealth, Ecclesiastical and Civil; To describe the nature of this artificial man, I will consider: First, the matter therefore, and the artificer; both of which is man. Secondly, how and by what covenants it is made; what are the rights and just power or authority of a sovereign; and what it is that preserveth or dissolveth it" *(ibid.).*

[13] "Ad secundum dicendum quod operationes quidem sunt in particularibus sed illa particularia referri possunt ad bonum commune, non quidem communitate generis vel speciei, sed communitate causae finalis, secundum quod bonum commune dicitur finis communis" (St. Thomas, *S.T.,* I–II, 90, 2, ad 2).

Cf. J. Maritain, *Degrees of Knowledge,* p. 260, also pp. 231–232.

Cf. also on this point, our method has precedents not only in Aristotle but in the method of Charles Cardinal Journet, our greatest contemporary theologian, in his profound analysis of the Church. ". . . in which I hope to explain the Church, from the standpoint of speculative theology, in terms of the four causes from which she results — efficient, material, formal, and final" (Charles Journet, *The Church of the Word Incarnate: An Essay in Speculative Theology,* trans. A. H. C. Downes [London: Sheed and Ward, 1955]).

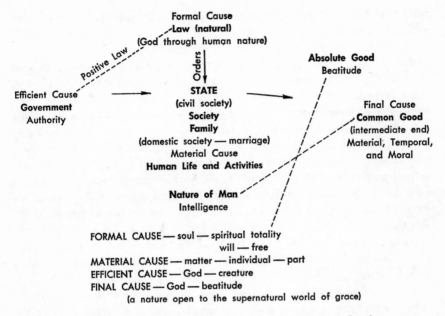

Formal Cause
Law (natural)
(God through human nature)

Positive Law

Orders

Efficient Cause
Government
Authority

STATE
(civil society)
Society
Family
(domestic society — marriage)
Material Cause
Human Life and Activities

Absolute Good
Beatitude

Final Cause
Common Good
(intermediate end)
Material, Temporal,
and Moral

Nature of Man
Intelligence

FORMAL CAUSE — soul — spiritual totality
will — free
MATERIAL CAUSE — matter — individual — part
EFFICIENT CAUSE — God — creature
FINAL CAUSE — God — beatitude
(a nature open to the supernatural world of grace)

Human Nature Is the Cause of the State and Measures It in Its Every Function

The study of natures is the proper business of philosophy, for nature is the essence or form of a thing considered as the ultimate principle of its operations. Aristotle tells us that nature means maturity. What each being is when its development is complete, that is the nature of each, the complete perfection of a species. The word nature is also taken in the metaphysical sense of essence, involving a certain finality. Then, what is natural is that which answers the requirements and propensities of the essence, that which the nature needs.

It is upon this conception of nature that we shall erect a political order in accordance with the principles of Thomas Aquinas. If that activity is natural to man which is simply indispensable for human conservation and development, then, before we can judge what is natural, what belongs to man by the very fact of being a man, we must first know what man is. We must know first what man is before we treat him as a mere cog in a machine, or as the most precious component of creation.

The basic facts about man are that he is possessed of an intellect and free will, and is destined for immortal life. He is a person. And a person, according to Boethius, is simply an individual substance possessing a rational nature. Man, since he is defined as a rational animal, falls within the scope of personality. He has an intellect by means of which he can know all things, and, granted the special ontological basis of a Thomistic epistemology, in knowing all things, he, in a way, becomes all things and gives them existence in a mode other than that in which they are found in nature. Thus he is superior to the universe. Also, from this fact of knowledge, man is able to control and to determine his own relation to the things which he knows. This is simply freedom, freedom of the will, a faculty whose existence is necessitated by the fact of knowledge again. Man is a being, not merely an intellect, and it would be an anomaly for a being to know, to distinguish, and to compare other beings unless he did so for the purpose of attaining and using them. Since this is so, we find man again in a position superior to all nature. He is established at the very center of the universe. All things are ordered to him, all things are for his good. The world revolves around him like planets about the sun. It is for these reasons that Thomas Aquinas has said that the person is that which is noblest in all nature.

It is a unique position that we human beings occupy. In a sense, man is part of a whole, and as such completely subjected to the laws of the whole. A being with matter as a constituent, man is thus, of his nature, a part through the individuating power of matter. Individuality flows from matter, and as an individual, man is subject to the physical laws of a material universe. In another sense, however, man is himself a whole, because the degree of perfection of his immanency as an original center of spontaneous reactions and free decisions confers upon him an independence and a freedom unparalleled in creation.

Human society, properly speaking, is a collection of persons. Current political theory is, as a matter of fact, built not upon birth or property but upon the personality of man. Marx (though no respecter of human dignity) has shown the weakness of a state built upon the sandy foundation of a division into rich and poor.[14] Society comes into existence because it is a necessary good, simply an outgrowth of our human nature, and the necessary condition for a completely human life. Man needs society. Man, when cut off from association with his fellows, is no longer man, but either a beast or a god, because, according to Aristotle in his *Politics,* man is by nature a political animal. What does he mean by these words? Simply that man is so constituted that he needs society. Language is an indication of this. This notion of nature is a perennial one and valid even down to our own day.

---

14 Cf. Harold Laski, *op. cit.,* pp. 15–16.

Man finds himself, in the modern world, living under the authority
of governments; and the obligation to obey their orders arises from
the facts of his nature. For he is a community-building animal, driven
by inherited instinct to live with his fellows. Crusoe on his desert
island, or St. Simon Stylites upon his pillar, may defy the normal
impulses which make them men; but for the vast majority, to live
with others is the condition of a rational existence. Therein, at the
outset, is implied the necessity of government.[15]

Man cannot develop as man, he cannot achieve his own proper perfection without the help of his fellowmen. If what distinguishes man
from the brute is his intellect, if what is highest in man is his intellectual power, then his supreme natural perfection lies in cultivating these
powers. But this is impossible without education. Society is needed. It
is only by the banding together of men, each of whom performs some
proper function in the community, that each man can attain the most
human mode of living. The care of the sick and suffering, the security
of the individual against the criminal, the protection of the entire
group against mass aggression from without are all the proper functions
of society and are required for the accomplishment of human dignity.

Thus the role of the state is not (as some would have it) entirely or
primarily that of protection. Hobbes, the political philosopher, would
have the sole and primary purpose of the state that of the policeman —
to keep men from each other's throats. He slept with a gun within
easy reach so that he might do his part as a good citizen in helping the
state protect him against his fellow "wolves." But protection, of course,
is not the total reason for the existence of the state, but only a partial
one. The real reason is to enable man to develop and realize his deepest
perfection and highest destiny. Although peace and law and order are
necessary prerequisites, they are not exclusive.

The family and the state, then, are the only truly natural societies —
and they both minister only to the individual. The family is natural
because the individual needs it. The infant needs a considerable period
of care until he becomes self-sufficient. That is why we have families,
because the individual, by his intrinsic constitution, by what he is, in
other words, by his nature, needs it. That is one reason why divorce
is wrong. It is wrong to deprive a being of anything he needs for his
conservation and development. You might as well deprive an infant
of the air he breathes or the food he drinks as to deprive him of the
parents he needs. Thus the family is the first society. It is not merely
a unit of a greater society; it is a *societas*, the domestic society.

The state is necessary because the family, or domestic society, is

---

[15] *Ibid.*, p. 17.

limited and cannot cope with all the requirements of human perfection. It cannot produce a doctor, a lawyer, or a theologian. However the purpose of both of them, the family and the state, is to help us toward being more thoroughly men. That is why I must obey the state, because such is the condition of the humanity that is within me, that I cannot develop as a man unless I fall into my place as subject of some state.

Law which organizes, determines, and orders society is likewise measured by the nature of man. In fact the natural law is simply the dictates of the tendencies and propensities of the nature of man as perceived through reason. We see by the very nature that God has given us what is necessary for its conservation and development. The natural law, then, is simply the nature of man intelligibly illuminated by reason. Right is simply what is good for man as man; wrong is what is bad for man as man.

Since the natural law does not cover all the details of man's life, it demands the creation of civil law, out of which government is formed. Government, which is based upon an authority existing only for the protection and exercise of natural rights, supplies the needs of the person and provides opportunity for his physical, intellectual, moral, and social betterment. All this, taken *in toto,* may be called the common good, and it is this which is the purpose of the state — the expansion and development of the person in all his aspects.

§ 6. PERSON AND INDIVIDUAL

In brief, then, we can see that the causes or principles of the state are all measured and determined by the nature of man. This nature brings both society and the state into existence; and as a person, possessing intellect and will, man is superior, not only to the state which he has fathered, but indeed to the rest of the universe. However, it is also true that as an individual, man is part of the social whole, and as a result must be subordinate to the common good, as the part to the whole. Thus it is in the nature of things that man sacrifice his temporal goods, and if necessary his life itself, for the sake of the community, and that social life impose upon the life of the person taken as a whole many a constraint and many a sacrifice. But even here, as a person, he is superior to the state and uses these constraints and sacrifices to raise his spiritual level. Even in the act of giving his life he uses the community, for he accomplishes, through an act of such great virtue, the moral perfection which is his greatest good. Only God (not the state) is above the human person.

The organization of the political order around the human person, as we have developed it here, has been the object of controversy among certain contemporary thinkers of philosophical stature. They would prefer to reorganize society around the common good in its various levels culminating in the sovereign end, God himself. Charles de Koninck sees in the personalist doctrines a flattery of human persons rather than a correct evaluation of the true dignity of the human person. He maintains that such doctrine, under the pretext of glorifying the person, actually causes the atrophy of the person by depriving it of its proper divine goods.[16]

He goes on to tell us that modern Personalism is the speculative expression of the practical sin of the angels, a proud rejection of God. The aggrandizement of the person is a diabolical vengeance. Man can achieve his true dignity only by subordinating his every personal good to the common good. The personalist doctrine is "pernicious in the extreme."[17] It is one manifestation of hydra-headed Pelagianism rejecting not only the dependence of the creature on its Creator but also

---

16 "Il est temps plus que jamais, en effet, de crier casse-cou. Et de vouloir que les sociétés ne se réorganisent pas en fonction de la personne individuelle, mais en fonction du bien commun, à ses divers degrés, c'est-à-dire de la fin souveraine, c'est-à-dire en fonction de Dieu. L'auteur s'attaque ouvertement aux personnalistes, mais pour défendre vraiment la dignité de la personne humaine. Son étude insiste sur la grandeur de la personne sans flatter les personnes. Elle s'oppose à toute doctrine qui sous prétexte de la glorifier, diminue et atrophie la personne humaine et la prive de ses biens les plus divins" (Charles de Koninck, De la Primauté du Bien Commun [Quebec, 1943], p. xii).

17 "N'y aurait-il pas entre l'exaltation du bien tout personnel au-dessus de tout bien vraiment commun, et la négation de la dignité des personnes, quelque lien de conséquence très logique et mis en oeuvre au cours de l'histoire? Le péché des anges fut une erreur pratiquement personnaliste: ils ont préféré la dignité de leur propre personne dignité qui leur serait venue dans la subordination à un bien supérieur mais commun dans sa supériorité même. L'hérésie pélagienne, dit Jean de Saint Thomas, peut-être considérée comme une étincelle de ce péché des anges. Elle n'en est qu'une étincelle, car, alors que l'erreur des anges fut purement pratique, l'erreur des pélagiens était en même temps spéculative. Nous croyons que le personnalisme moderne n'est qu'une réflexion de cette étincelle, spéculativement encore plus faible. Il érige en doctrine spéculative une erreur qui fut à l'origine seulement pratique. L'asservissement de la personne au nom du bien commun est comme une vengeance diabolique à la fois remarquable et cruelle, une attaque sournoise contre la communauté du bien à laquelle le démon avait refusé de se soumattre. La négation de la dignité supérieure que l'homme reçoit dans la subordination de son bien tout personnel au bien commun assurerait la négation de toute dignité humaine. Nous n'entendons pas soutenir ici que l'erreur de tous ceux qui se disent aujourd'hui personnalistes est plus que spéculative. Qu'il n'y ait là-dessus aucune ambiguïté. Sans doute notre insistance pourra-t-elle blesser ceux des personnalistes qui ont identifié cette doctrine a leur personne. C'est la leur responsabilité très personnelle. Mais il y a aussi la nôtre — nous jugeons cette doctrine pernicieuse à l'extreme" (ibid., p. 4).

the necessity of grace to save man from sin, for the person is "nothing but an imitation of God."[18]

Actually the real issue in this controversy is the question of the autonomy of natures. Is there a principle of organization in each thing by reason of which it is what it is, or does anything which belongs to creatures in their natures (any proper possession of creatures), somehow lessen their dependence on their Creator? Is the assertion of the autonomy of natures a Promethean rebellion against the Deity?

The emphasis on the common good is due to the inability to perceive a formal cause as other than the mere action of an efficient cause, even though an effect always exists in the independence proper to it, or perhaps it is due to the absence of efficient causality altogether, with its function fulfilled by a formal cause alone. The nature is basically a construct and achieved by a constructural operation. Such a procedure is typically Augustinian. The thing is *nothing else* but a reflection of the divine nature. Such thinkers do not know how to root essences in an absolute, which as a consequence must devour the proper being of each and every thing. Idealism, as an extreme expression of the same doctrine, gets rid of God by eliminating possible ontological loci of his causal power. Things (beings in their existential status) rear up as stark, brutal reminders of a cause that explains their own existence. Idealism has done a great disservice in attempting to make existence and being meaningless to the human mind by removing existential attributes from the purview of human thought.

The difference between what we might call an Augustinian Politic and a Thomistic Politic is precisely that they are alternate ways of applying immutable principles. What we might call the Augustinian method is to apply them univocally. Since, for Augustine, there are no natures in things, there cannot be a science of anything but God. Man, as simply a vessel for grace, is not the proper object of scientific examination, because he has no nature. This applies even to politics. There can be no such thing as an autonomous state. This doctrine is well expressed in the medieval theory of the empire existing within the Church.

For Thomas Aquinas, on the other hand, the state does have an

---

[18] "Nous devons nous attendre à un retour plus veilè des doctrines les plus néfastes du passé. Il n'est peut-être pas de doctrines qui aient eu plus de renaissances que ce monstre polycéphale qu'est le pélagianisme. Raison de plus pour les chrétiens de crier la necessité de la grâce pour sauver l'homme de péché et le guérir de ses blessures, de proclamer que la personne n'est rien sinon en tant qu'imitation de Dieu, participation de l'Être incréé, par son ordination au divin bien commun, par sa vocation surnaturelle à partager la vie et la spleudeur du Seigneur" (*ibid.*, p. xxii).

autonomy within its own sphere. It has its own duties and its own powers. Just as Thomas Aquinas is unique in the modernity of his doctrine of natures which remains Christian against the charges of Latin Averroism, so he is unique in the modernity of his political philosophy among his Christian contemporaries. Just as he had the opportunity to see Aristotle, the first thinker of his age, in the original, so he had the chance to observe the first national state in action, to note its virtues and vices, in the example of the Kingdom of Sicily under Frederick II, the first modern state.

§ 7. TOTALITARIANISM

Professor de Koninck sees in the autonomy of an insufficient nature and the doctrine of Personalism founded on it, the tyranny of liberalism identified with bourgeoisie imperialism where each person places his private good above the common good. The result is a society of tyrants in which one dominates the other by force. The chief eventuality is that the subjects themselves are only frustrated tyrants.[19] Of course even the doctrine of the common good can be perverted by the totalitarian regimes that seize on this doctrine as a pretext for imposing on citizens an ignoble subjection to the state. Even the doctrine of the primacy of the common good can be converted to the ends of totalitarianism.[20]

Today, we are dreaming in a world of giants. It is the giants, the colossal nations, which are important, while we pygmies are insignificant. It is the state which is everything. It is time we awakened from the illusions that shackle us. We are not for the state, but the state is for us. It has no reason to exist except for the good of man. We are not food for Leviathan nor cannon fodder for his gaping maw. He is a great hulking servant, not a master. He must serve you, not oppress you. It is interesting to note that historically, nationalism and the political philosophies expressing it began with the breakdown of a common theology and the beginnings of secularism. Western culture, turning its back

---

[19] "Une société constituée de personnes qui aiment leur bien privé au-dessus du bien commun, ou qui identifient le bien commun au bien privé, c'est une société, non pas d'hommes libres, mais de tyrans, qui se mèneront les uns les autres par la force, et où le chef éventuel n'est que le plus astucieux et le plus fort parmi les tyrans, les sujets eux-mêmes n'étant que des tyrans frustrés" (ibid., p. xvii).

[20] "On peut à la fois affirmer la dignité de la personne et être en fort mauvaise compagnie. Suffrait-il d'exalter la primauté de bien commun? Non plus. Les régimes totalitaires saisissent le bien commun comme prétexte pour asservir les personnes de la façon la plus ignoble. Comparée à l'esclavage où ils menacent de nous soumettre, la servitude des bêtes est liberté. Commettrons-nous la lâcheté de concéder au totalitarisme le pervertissement du bien commun et de sa primauté?" (ibid., p. 3.)

upon God, but still reminded of him at every heartbeat, needing him
in every fiber of its being, proceeded to make unto itself a graven image,
a Moloch it might adore — and today he is devouring us. We have substituted for God, the state, and for the saint, the citizen.

We are now in a transitional stage from the time when the common
good was the good of a nation to that glorious day when the common
good will be the good of all mankind. So much of our problem today
results from the tugs on the human heart of both national and supra-
national ideals and values.

§ 8. SPIRITUAL END OF MAN

Actually the state exists for each man and is subordinate to him.
For there is in each human person a transcendent end to which society
itself, and its common good, must be subordinated.[21] To put it more
simply, man is made for happiness, not just this particular happiness,
but absolute happiness. There is nothing we poor human beings want
more than to be perfectly, completely happy. The animal in the
management of his appetites, for instance, eats and drinks until he
is satisfied, and then stops. The animal uses all his appetites normally
and naturally and does not usually abuse them. But man, who is so
superior to the brute, mishandles his appetites. Man will eat until he
is filled, and then continue to eat. Man does not stop drinking simply
because he has had enough. There seems to be in human behavior
an almost gravitational inclination to perversion. Man tries to wring
the last drop of pleasure out of a sense organ that has become jaded
and incapable of performing its natural function. Why does man do
this, he who is much nobler than the brute? Why does he have to
keep a severe control upon his appetites in order to escape perversion?
Why does he take each sensory faculty and stretch it to the limit of
its capacity, and still further, even when, like a wire, it has already
reached its limit of stress and strain, so that the amount of happiness
derived diminishes in inverse proportion to effort and desire? The
animal does not do this. Any perversion of the brute is due to the
abnormal conditions in which he has been placed by man who is,
therefore, responsible. But the only reason that makes such behavior
on the part of man intelligible is his desire for perfect happiness. He
is attempting to squeeze from one limited organ, or from a collection
of them, perfect happiness. He is trying to get from finite instruments

---

[21] Justice is not the will of the majority or of the wealthier, but that course of
action which the moral aim of the state requires. Aristotle, *Politics*, III, 10.

the infinite happiness for which his nature craves. This happiness is not simply a pleasure or any sum of pleasures. This is obvious when we examine the processes of appetite. The only purpose of pleasure is to insure the satisfaction of the needs of a nature. It is the guarantee that the demands of a nature will be fulfilled, namely that some being or thing which a person needs will be supplied it. We can see that it is a being or a thing which is the object of appetite, and not simply pleasure, because pleasure always vanishes when the thing has been attained. Once you have quenched your thirst, there is less and less pleasure in drinking, until finally it becomes a pain. So it is with all the appetites that, when the thing needed has been acquired, the pleasure ceases, proving that it is a thing or a being which is the object of happiness. Perfect happiness will thus demand a perfect being. Human behavior, even in sin, bears witness to the fact of the existence of God and to man's abysmal need of God, a need which goes down to the very roots of man's animal nature, and is much more obvious in his intellectual nature. Man's proper end is one that cannot be satisfied in this life. It is nothing less than absolute good, God himself, and this has tremendous implications in his relations to society and its social institutions.

Since, then, the continuity of human existence is unbroken by death, and since there is an extension of the specifically human life in a sphere other than the temporal, the good of man is not merely this material, temporal good but an absolute eternal good.[22] And society, if it is to fulfill its proper function, must recognize that the good of man is not restricted to this world. Society must thus remove as many obstacles as possible to man's final end and provide as much aid as it can for the achievement of that end.[23]

---

[22] "Now the Christian knows that there is a supernatural order, and that the ultimate end — the absolute ultimate end — of the human person is God causing His own personal life and eternal bliss to be participated in by man. The direct ordination of the human person to God transcends every created common good — both the common good of political society and the intrinsic common good of the universe. Here is the rock of the dignity of the human person as well as of the unshakeable requirements of the Christian message. Thus the indirect subordination of the body politic — not as a mere means, but as an end worthy in itself yet of lesser dignity — to the supratemporal values to which human life is appendent, refers first and foremost, as matter of fact, to the supernatural end to which the human person is directly ordained. To sum up all this in one single expression, let us say that the law we are faced with here is the law of the *primacy of the spiritual*" (Maritain, *Man and the State*, pp. 149–150).

[23] "There is no distinction without an order of values. If the things that are God's are distinct from the things that are Caesar's, that means that they are better. The said distinction, developing its virtualities in the course of human history, has resulted in the notion of the intrinsically *lay* or *secular* nature of the body politic. I do not

Therefore, in making our own spiritual progress our very first aim in life, and other ambitions secondary, we are helping society to achieve its goal, the ultimate purpose to which it is ordained. Thus we become better citizens in fulfilling our moral and religious duties. For the ultimate end to which society is ordered is our growth in virtue.

We are prone to forget this fact in social and political reforms. Without it there can be no true reform. When we examine the great Christian movements of history, we find that the driving energies that motivated them were not deliberately premeditated. No man says, "I shall reform the world," and then simply goes out and does it. Things do not work that way. The roles that men play in these Christian upheavals are thrust upon them when, and only when, they are prepared for them spiritually. It is the Holy Spirit who uses our spiritual energies to guide historical movements. The initiative of man has only a secondary role.

---

say that the body politic is by nature irreligious or indifferent to religion ('lay' and 'laicized,' 'secular' and 'secularized' are two quite different things); I say that by nature the body politic, which belongs strictly to the natural order, is only concerned with the temporal life of men and their temporal common good. In that temporal realm the body politic, as Pope Leo XIII has insisted, is fully autonomous (cf. encyclicals *Immortale Dei*, 'utraque potestas est, in suo genere, maxima,' and *Sapientiae Christianae*); the State, the modern State, is under the command of no superior authority in its own order. But the order of eternal life is superior in itself to the order of temporal life" (C. Journet, *Exigences Chrétiennes en politique* [Paris, 1944], Chap. 2; cf. Maritain, *Man and the State*, p. 153).

CHAPTER XII. / SUFFERING AND EVIL

SUFFERING is one of those blind, brutal facts of existence that cannot be ignored or explained away. It must be confronted, understood, and mastered. Too many human beings, wounded by life, spend the remainder of their alloted years nursing their resentment rather than healing their hurts. The experience of pain too often embitters and cramps the personality it should enoble and expand.

A typical case history is the experience of a little Jewish boy born in Poland. He attended rabbinical school there; he studied and memorized for long hours every day. He was very religious and probably possessed a better religious background at his age than any of us. He learned to read Scripture in the original Hebrew. Yet he became an atheist. He came to this country with his family looking for a better way of life, as so many of our own families have. They found it, but not immediately. At first they were able to maintain only the barest existence. Their income amounted to no more than seven or eight dollars a week. Many a time there was no food on the table, no money for rent. But during this trying period they did have a good friend, a watchmaker by trade. When he visited them he invariably brought a bag of groceries with him. The boy dates the most significant event of his life to the day when he overheard a conversation between his father and this friend. The friend said to his father, a good orthodox Jew:

"How can you possibly believe in God? Look at your children starving. You wouldn't let them starve. But this God whom you claim is so good could do something about it. Yet he doesn't! There is no God and if there were, so cruel a person should receive no devotion." The boy tells us that from that day he lost his belief in God.

The boy grew up, as so many poor boys have done, with more than his share of intelligence. He became a professor at a large eastern university and taught thousands of students over a lifetime. Of them he has this to say. "When they first came to me they hated me because I was stripping from them their precious bauble of faith, but later they came to love me because they saw I was freeing them from the shackles of ignorance and superstition!" During his teaching career thousands of students passed through his hands and I doubt if many of them remained the same afterwards. He was a very gifted man.

§ 1. THE PROBLEM OF PAIN

The question I am especially concerned with here is what do you say to a man like this professor? What about this problem? What about the evil, the pain, the suffering which somehow seem to be beaten right into the structure of the universe by a good God?[1] God could have made a different type of world. If you could make the world different, wouldn't you?

Consider the example of a little dog hit by a truck. Looking down at that broken body, this thought could arise in the mind: What a stupid waste! Why did it have to be? What sense does it make? Obviously the owner of the dog would feel it most keenly! Let us consider another example. If you have ever seen the serpents being fed at the zoo, you know that they will not touch dead animals so they must be fed live animals. One of the scenes that perhaps could sear itself into the brain is the picture of the rabbit crouched in a corner of the cage, huddled up against the glass as if it would push its way through — a picture of total physical collapse from fear, while the huge snake slithers toward him. One could wonder: Why is it? Why is it that suffering and evil seem to be built right into the structure of the universe, if there is a good God?

This is part of the evidence upon which certain thinkers claim that the "First Principle" of reality must be evil. He must be cruel. When one examines the world about him, that is precisely the way it has

---

[1] Cf. C. Journet, *The Meaning of Evil*, trans. Michael Barry (New York: P. J. Kenedy & Sons, 1963).

been put together. The life of one animal is nourished only by the pain and agony of another; the hawk prospers at the expense of the songbird impaled on its talons; the lion finds life in the warm blood that rushes from the throat of the antelope; the price of health and nourishment is always the pain and destruction of another thing. Why was the universe constructed that way if it was built by a being who is good, by someone who is omniscient enough to have done it differently, by someone omnipotent enough to have been able to do whatever he conceived? If you had those powers would you have acted in the same fashion? Our protagonist caught the tail of a terrible problem and could not let it go.

§ 2. SUFFERING IN ANIMALS

What we would like to do is to sketch some of the answers we might give a man such as the one above. For instance, the problem of suffering or pain in animals is a much more difficult problem than in human beings. One can always have recourse to the catechism for a religious answer as far as human beings are concerned. When a man suffers, his misfortunes may be explained in one of two ways. Either he is paying for past sins, or alternatively, he will be rewarded in the next life. That is direct and simple enough for anyone to understand. But the case of animals is more complex. First of all, animals cannot sin. That is out of the question. Second, there is no heaven for animals, they have no spiritual soul and therefore they have no immortality. Consequently suffering for animals seems to make no sense at all. How inexplicable the destiny of the animal that is cut off in its life after only a week of existence — the puppy under the wheels of the truck! How does one explain that?

We shall divide the problem into two parts. First, let us consider *animals as a species*. Let us try to see how the species of animals looks to God. Can we say that whoever produced animals as a species did a good thing or do we have to say there must be something perverse, there must be something sadistic about whatever intelligence there was that planned animals and constructed the universe in this precise way? Second, we would like to consider the case of *individual animals* whose brief lives are so pathetic and tragic that it would seem that they should never have been born. Finally we shall briefly discuss the situation of human beings.[2]

---

[2] "Fundamentally, what accounts for the presence of suffering in animals is precisely the perfection and delicacy of their organic constitution. Suffering is the price they

§ 3. DELIGHTS OF SENSATION

If we look closely at the nature and structure of animal life we can see the general design of a certain intelligible plan. What does it mean to be an animal in terms of pleasure and pain? The first thing to catch our attention is the very real pleasure of virginal sensations unhampered by the complex ambitions and drives of intelligence.

When we direct our attention to animals, to the very structure of their existence, we notice their powers of sensation. It is good to eat, it is good to drink. We easily recognize that fact. The fundamental appetites give human beings a great deal of pleasure; they are part and parcel of most affairs that human beings attend. But animals' powers of sensation are much more sensitive than those of man. A piece of raw steak to a dog gives, as far as we can ascertain, much more pleasure than a turkey dinner to a human being. For the child, the senses still have a certain newness, a certain unjadedness, a pristine freshness; we can remember, as children, how an ice-cream cone tasted

---

have to pay for their sensitivity. A camera does not suffer, but then it cannot see.

"To do away with the vulnerability of an animal's organs would be to do away with the animal itself; and that would be to deprive the universe of this immense reach of life, incomparably rich and variegated, which stretches from the lower world of minerals and plants to that of man.

"Doubtless all this will be granted without any difficulty — as, also, that to ask God constantly to intervene with miracles to remove the suffering of animals would be to reject the world of independent beings that he has made and to require him to create some other universe.

"But, it may be said, granted the existence of our animal world, and hence of suffering, could not the sum of suffering be less? The only answer, of course, is that it could be less. And also it could be greater. Here again we must avoid the perpetual trap, in which Leibniz was caught, of a God bound by his infinite goodness to create one particular better world rather than any other one, and bound ultimately to create the best of all possible worlds. In virtue of his infinite goodness God is bound, not to create an infinitely good world, which would be a pure contradiction, but to create a world which is by and large good.

"Suffering, in an animal, is the perception of a disorder coming about in its organism or in its usual environment. It may, therefore, in certain cases — and this is one of its secondary aspects — play the beneficial role of a warning, and cause the animal to regulate its behaviour accordingly.

"But here again it seems that nature has proceeded by groping and approximation rather than by aiming at anything absolute or rigorous. Biologists affirm that 'the pain which after being felt makes us avoid traumatisms is ill regulated; exaggerated in certain cases (toothache, neuralgia), it does not appear at all in some other dangerous ones (nephritis, pulmonary tuberculosis, incipient cancer).' From the philosophical point of view, it is not a question of knowing whether better adjustments might be possible — this will be agreed without difficulty — but of knowing whether this world of nature, put together by God himself, but with a free rein given to his creatures' activities, is by and large a good world, in which life prevails over death, good over evil, and existence over nothingness" (*ibid.*, pp. 139–140).

on a hot summer's afternoon. Very few things taste like that to us now! Animals seem to have that kind of experience in an intense fashion — the powers of taste, the whole world of smell. There is a certain delight in perfumes, often dependent on who wears them. There is a whole world of sensible titillation of the nostrils which almost every animal has, which is closed to human beings simply because we have an inhibiting intelligence. We just ignore it. Even reproduction, which is strong enough in human beings, seems to be much more intense in animals. A biologist can saw off the hind legs of a frog in the act of copulation and it does not appear to know it. When one considers all these sensations extended to their limit, it would seem that an animal, on a sensible level, gets a more intense delight out of life. The animal with his stronger basic sensory equipment, and his greater immersion in the life of the senses, derives far greater pleasure from them than man does.

§ 4. DELIGHTS OF PHYSICAL MOVEMENT

Second, there is a certain exhilaration, a certain delight that comes with physical movement in the proper exercise of the body. Those who participate in sports are well aware of this. Diving is one example, sprinting is another — the very real delights in bodily movement. Imagine what it must be like to be in the body of a hawk plummeting down on its prey, to be in the body of the lion charging with the speed of an express train on its victim. It would be like sitting at the wheel of a high-powered convertible going ninety miles an hour — except that it is not a machine, it is one's own sinews and nerves and muscles which are moving with a physical power and strength that no human being has ever experienced. Pound for pound, of all the animals man is the puniest and the weakest. A fifty-five- or sixty-five-pound orangutan is five times stronger than a man, and insects are powerful out of all proportion to their size.

§ 5. LACK OF INTELLECTUAL KNOWLEDGE

Over and above sensation and physical exhilaration, having an intellect is a good thing; it certainly is an advantage, but as anyone who has been to school knows, there are disadvantages to having an intellect. There is no labor quite so hard as mental work. Consider the now outmoded picture of the southern gentleman sitting under a magnolia tree, with a cool mint julep. The atmosphere of such a scene has a tremendous attraction to the human being. To be an aggressive, driving career man is to miss something. At some time or other everyone recognizes that. There is a certain perversion in being too ambitious. Animals have no ambition, they are not driven by envy for others, by fear of being left, or of not being able to support their families. Without an intellect worry is eliminated. Immediately one would cut out three quarters of the anguish, the most intense anguish that the human race experiences, if one could get rid of worry. The most terrible things human beings do, they usually do for mental reasons. Suicide and utterly extreme measures of that type usually flow from mental causes such as loneliness and fear, rather than from actual physical pain. In the long run, in an operation, for example, the greatest anxiety, the greatest pain, the worst part of the ordeal comes in thinking of it beforehand. During the operation one is unconscious, he does not feel a thing. An animal, not having an intellect which can span the future and the past, lives only in the moment, lives only in the single instant he is living. He cannot look forward to a lifetime of pain with cancer — and from that fear take his own life. It just doesn't exist for him. When one considers the basic structure of animal life, one can say for very good reason that it was good, as a species, that animals were made. Remember, God also looks at the group, at the species, as well as the individual. "Wherever two or three are gathered together in my name, there I am in the midst of them."

What about those *individuals* such as the rabbit and the puppy under the wheels of the truck? Do their fates make sense? Consider what it means to be a living thing, instead of a dead clod of earth — to be a living, pulsating, feeling, sensitive being. Imagine what it means actually to be *alive,* as compared to being *nothing,* even for a short time. There is drama in being an actual existing human being or any living thing as opposed to being a dead piece of earth, a tremendous value placed on being one as opposed to the other. Despite a period of searing pain, we think we can still say, "Yes, if I had to choose even to die that way, I would still choose to have lived, just to know what it is all about, just to experience." We think one can say that God is still good and that the puppy still has the best of the bargain despite the way he ends.

§ 6. SUFFERING IN HUMAN BEINGS

Of course, the whole structure of suffering depends on another factor. God did not put suffering in the universe just for animals. One can say, as some very good religious people have said, "The reason we have pain and suffering in life is because Adam ate the apple. Man is responsible for suffering. Why? Because he disobeyed God." It is within that general framework that one can account for the way that suffering is built into the very structure of the universe, that the lion could not live thirty-six hours on grass, that one needs a double or triple stomach in order to digest grass. One glance at the teeth and claws of the lion and one knows immediately that he was designed to kill and to eat flesh. The very structure of the universe is designed that way. Compare human bones and rocks. When one drops a rock, the laws of stress and strain work a certain way. When one drops a human body, the very laws of the universe work the same way. One does not get rid of the problems of evil in any simplistic fashion.

Although we cannot assign a cause to it, evil has one intelligible purpose in the psychological structure of human beings and that is knowledge. Basically, pain is a warning. Pain is an urgent insistence that there is something wrong, which had better be rectified. It has to be a knowledge of such a nature that we will go to work immediately — so that we will move as if at the urgent warning of a fire gong. When one sits on a red-hot stove he must be told immediately for his own good that there is something wrong. Consider the medical history of the man whose tooth went dead. The nerve died and he did not realize there was anything wrong with him until the infection moved almost up to the brain. It took three weeks of draining and his life hung in the balance before he was finally well — just because he did not feel pain. Pain in this sense is part of the intelligible structure of the universe. It is the extension of our ordinary sensations, for which reason it must beat with the urgency of a fire alarm.

Second, there is something perfective about pain. It seems to do something to people. If we consider the best people we know, we are likely to find a great deal of suffering in their lives. No one escapes it. If we could look into the life and heart of the man sitting next to us, we would find some sort of skeleton in his closet so that we would not be willing to trade places with him. Whether it is family, friends, love, money, health, or something else, no one escapes it. But it does something important to human beings. No one is as sympathetic as the man who has suffered himself. No one is as just as the man who has experienced injustice. It develops a sensitivity. Suffering — unless it is excessive, when it can embitter and destroy — molds character. Like fire, it tempers and forges a personality and no man reaches the perfection of a human being without it.

§ 7. SUPERNATURAL END AND MERIT

The real reason for suffering lies, however, in the very structure of human beings and in the *generosity* of the God who made them. Why is suffering necessary? Why is it that God has placed it squarely into the middle of the design for the universe? For this reason: if God had made us with lungs and no air, that would be unjust; if he had made us with a stomach and no such thing as food, that would be sadistic. We have a right to those things because our nature demands them. But there is something which God has in store for man to which we have no right, which is above nature, which is supernatural, namely the gift of his own self, an embrace which will be, for human beings, all the good and beautiful things that will satisfy the yearnings and the hunger of human hearts, that restlessness which everyone feels. This is what religious thinkers call heaven, the beatific vision, beatitude. The laws of justice in the universe are just as fundamental, are just as basic in man's life as the laws of physics, as the laws of thermodynamics. If man is to attain this which is above his nature, he must merit it, at least in an incipient inclination, an obediential potency. Without pain, there would be no merit; without suffering, without anguish, especially mental anguish, there would be no deserving, however disproportionate of the greatest good that a creature can possibly obtain, the divine goodness himself.[3] This is the proper structure,

---

[3] "Human suffering is the suffering of a person endowed with an immortal soul, which can bear the permanent mark of having experienced temporal suffering. To this can be applied the words of Léon Bloy: 'Suffering passes, having suffered does not.'

"Animal suffering is a suffering in which there is no thought of the future, because it is the suffering of beings whose souls entertain no thought of the future. It is the matter and form of the mineral, the body and soul of the plant, which is the subsistent being, and not just the form of the mineral or the soul of the plant. Likewise it is the whole animal, body and soul, which is the subsistent being, not just the soul. It is metaphysically impossible for the form of a mineral — hydrogen, chlorine or iron — to subsist without the matter which it informs; or for the plant or animal soul to subsist without the body it animates. The forms of perishable beings disappear to make room for other forms which will also disappear; the destruction of one being ensures the generation of another; in this way is explained the recurrence of species. Only the human soul, being spiritual, can subsist on its own and survive the dissolution of the body.

"Human suffering can be touched by grace, can be borne in faith and love, and bear some slight resemblance to the sufferings of Christ. Then, because of the charity which lights it, it is blessed and merits the reward inseparable from the beatitudes in the Gospel: 'Rejoice and be glad, for your reward will be great in heaven' (Matt. 5, 12). And St. Paul writes: 'I consider that the sufferings of this present time are not worth comparing with the glory that is to be revealed in us' (Rom. 8, 18).

"Animal suffering does not rise above time, but remains immersed in the constant flux of things which are made and unmade each day. It is part of the domain of the merely transient and perishable. As seen by philosophy, it shares the fate of

this is a locale into which we can fit suffering in the universe. This doesn't get rid of suffering, this doesn't eliminate it, but it does enable us to *understand* it, it enables us to use it and master it. When we know its purpose we can use suffering for our own moral perfection — which is after all the supreme development of a human being. You can really become a man with all that that signifies. Suffering is one of those stark elemental facts of reality that looms so large on the horizon of human experience that no one can ignore it, no one can avoid it. Therefore, what we should do is to take the harsh blows of life, not like a mongrel cur cringing before the heavy hand of fate, but like the soldier standing erect to receive the accolade of his king.[4]

---

astronomical phenomena and has no *Christian look* about it. The delusion and mistake would be to want to impose a Christian meaning on it" (*ibid.*, pp. 140–141).

[4] "Only a few aspects of the evil of punishment have been touched on, but they are enough to depict the life of men on earth as a long trial. How could it be otherwise? This is the *status viatoris,* not the *status termini,* our exile, not our fatherland, the time for questions, not for answers. The sufferings of the exodus into the desert had no meaning without its hope of the promised land; those of the present life are only explained by expectation of the second coming.

"It belongs to time to build in order to destroy and then to build again. It allows bonds of closest affection to be forged because it is sure of its power to pull them apart. Each individual note must be done away with to merge into 'cet ardent sanglot qui roule d'âge en âge.' 'For everything there is a season, and a time for every matter under heaven: a time to be born, and a time to die; a time to plant, and a time to pluck up what is planted; a time to kill, and a time to heal; a time to break down, and a time to build up; a time to weep, a time to laugh' (Eccles. 3, 1–4). Nothing is spared, things just or unjust, pure or impure, the reflected beauty of heaven or the ugly and deformed. The Son of Man was bruised and covered in blood. In Michelangelo's great *Deposition from the Cross,* constructed spirally, which is to be seen in Santa Maria del Fior, it is first of all the majestic peace of death spread over the Saviour's abandoned body which moves us; but if we come closer and look straight upwards at the group, the shock of the clashing, broken lines suddenly makes us grasp that violence has here struck heedlessly and has blunted itself so that it could lay low the most beautiful of the children of men.

"Yet something is made out of these ruins: two cities arise, God's and the Devil's, through the assent or refusal of creatures who appear and then disappear in order to be replaced by others.

"The momentary passage of humanity on a short-lived planet could be nothing other than a futile, absurd and cruel adventure if we did not know that, visited once by the Word made flesh and Risen from the dead, this same humanity is drawn along behind him, with the whole visible creation as his train. The discord which has come between man and the material universe since the fall will not be resolved until the end of this painful travail: 'I consider that the sufferings of this present time are not worth comparing with the glory that is to be revealed to us. For the creation waits with eager longing for the revealing of the sons of God; for the creation was subjected to futility, not of its own will but by the will of him who subjected it in hope; because the creation itself will be set free from its bondage to decay and obtain the glorious liberty of the children of God. We know that the whole creation has been groaning in travail together until now' (Rom. 8, 18–22)" (*ibid.*, pp. 249–251).

CHAPTER XIII. / PHILOSOPHY
OF ART

THERE is another type of knowledge which we have not discussed so far. Speculative knowledge gains its dignity from the fulfillment of the intellectual appetite. But it treats of universal and general concepts and somehow does not capture the profound supposital privacy, the basic core of reality in things.

Although science is the most perfect achievement of theoretical knowledge, it is not the only valid type of human knowing, as positivism would have it. There are entire areas of human experience untouched by science. We saw in the inexact or quasi-sciences of economics, psychology, and sociology a vast sphere of intelligible realities unamenable to the methods of science because of the role played in their proper objects by the phenomenon of human freedom.

But the inadequacies of scientific understanding go further than this instance. Science is always concerned with the type, the generality. It is concerned with that which *all* members of the class have in common. What the scientific mind finds significant is that *all* water boils at one hundred degrees centigrade under standard conditions; *all* horned animals have cloven hooves; *all* bodies attract each other as the squares of their masses; the square of the hypotenuse of *all* right triangles is equal to the sum of the squares of the other two sides. It is only because *all* water behaves in this way that the scientist is concerned. If only *some* specimens of water demonstrated this type of behavior while other specimens acted in different fashion, the scientist would be completely indifferent. He is interested only in what happens to *all* members of the class.

On the other hand, what is most important to concrete human beings is the *individual differences of concrete individual things*. A mother is proud that her son has curly hair, while the boy next door has straight hair. To the lover the beloved is *different* from all other girls. A whole science of psychology, as paradoxical as it may seem, has sprung up around the individual differences of things — individual or differential psychology.

Generality is after all an abstraction. It is the individual which is concrete. This is the area of a kind of knowledge very different from science or even the quasi-sciences, but one which is very valid in itself, that kind of knowledge which is found most intensely in the poet or the artist. It is practical knowledge which puts us in contact with the concrete and the individual. The airy reaches of scientific or metaphysical knowledge are too rarified for concrete, material existents. Science does not satisfy the whole man. Theoretical knowledge eventually must be supplemented by another kind of knowledge. It is what Jacques Maritain calls the problem of Faust. Either the soul will move from abstract metaphysics to the concrete practical knowledge of mystical experience, tasting God as a concrete thing to be embraced, or, as Maritain puts it, the soul will relapse upon Marguerite, using the opposite sex as a symbol of the profoundest immersion in the concrete and the individual.

§ 1. FASHION AND PHILOSOPHY

It takes a great deal of courage for a man to trespass upon the jealously guarded feminine prerogative of dress and fashion. The human male by nature is ill equipped for such a task.

The topic we would like to discuss, however, does not concern the latest creation from Paris, nor are we interested in the precise length that the hem of a dress must reach for modesty's sake. About such mysterious matters we are profoundly ignorant. The problem to which we would like your reaction was brought to our attention by a prominent British biologist. In a now famous essay, he raised the question of feminine adornment. He pointed out that man, alone of all animals, finds the female adorned. The reverse is true of all other animals. The good sense of nature is demonstrated, he claims, by the fact that the male is adorned while the female is Cinderella after midnight. An overwhelming amount of evidence can be gleaned from zoological literature and everyday information. The lion has the mane, not the lioness. The peacock sports his plumage, while in comparison the peahen is drab. The rooster has the comb and the stag the antlers. A trip to any zoo will verify this observation.

Huxley concludes that a prudent nature has traced the course her creatures should follow and it is common knowledge that certain disaster follows upon those who rebel against the laws of nature. It is the male who should be bedecked and bespangled rather than the female. Only in the human species is the female bejeweled and beribboned.

Eric Gill, the Christian artist (I am sure that some of you have heard of him, and have perhaps read his famous autobiography) takes these data and states in very vehement fashion that it is actually unnatural for woman to adorn herself. The psychological differences between the sexes is the basis for this judgment. The male is much more inflammable than the female, and she has an effect on the male that the male does not have on her. Therefore, Mr. Gill asserts that it is positively immoral to emphasize the attractiveness of the female which does not need emphasis because of the peculiar psychological structure of the man. Such a custom simply makes it more difficult, almost impossible, for boys and men to be chaste in a world where even a can of tomatoes is advertised by feminine beauty. We should like to quote a passage from Eric Gill.

> I believe the time has come to make a stand against this inversion of the natural order. I believe that vanity and personal conceit are as much the right and proper accompaniment of the male among human beings as among animals. Among women, I maintain, vanity is ipso facto vicious — a sign of degradation, a proof of departure from the divine plane, the fruit of irreligion and sexual abnormality and abandon.
>
> It is time the thing were unmasked. It is no use saying things have gone too far, women should be more careful, girls should be more modest, and so on. That is not the line to take in this business. The truth of the matter is that vanity in dress is not a female concern. Nuns, nurses and servant-maids are the only decently dressed women. Women should dress in uniforms and be thoroughly covered up. All mirrors should be taken away from them and they should learn to wear their hats upon their heads instead of upon their faces. Being good is more important than fashionable appearance, and no one will be able to stop them from learning the Penny Catechism and the rules of modesty.

Women are by the grace of God our mothers. They have everything to gain and nothing to lose by modesty. By display and vanity they have gained nothing and have come near to losing man's respect. The lovableness of women does not need the enhancement of frippery.[1]

Now, although there is some reason to this, I am afraid that Mr. Gill is suffering from an overdose of puritan morality, whereby the natural is evil.

We see the same type of reasoning in the England of the Enlightenment whereby a man could divorce his wife on the charge of witchcraft if she deceived him into marriage by means of wigs, false hips, high-heeled shoes, cosmetics, and bustles. This type of reasoning is not absent today, although the pendulum of morality has swung the other way, from rigor to laxity; but we are not going to cure laxity in morals by a rigor in morals — in fact, I am convinced that the ordinary result of an over-zealous rigor is laxity — as a rebellion.

Let us take as an example a young lady who is a member of a minor religious denomination. According to its religious teaching, smoking, dancing, and cosmetics are immoral and a devout church member who persists in such sinful acts is certain of damnation. She is absolutely positive that lipstick is sinful. She believes it on faith and nothing can change her mind. But the stark tragedy of the situation is that she is going to use lipstick even though she is damned for it! You can imagine her inner conflict, the daily horror, the very stupid viciousness of one good natural desire in perverse war against another good natural inclination.

A medieval monk, seven hundred years ago, expressed the Christian ideal of moderation. Intemperance even in virtue is a vice. Thomas Aquinas tells us that a woman should use cosmetics and adorn herself. Since her salvation was so intimately bound up with the man she marries (the one you marry can help you to the heights of moral nobility or degrade you), she has a moral obligation to get the finest man she can. To this end she should adorn and beautify herself as best she can. Not only that, but married women also should adorn themselves in order to keep their husbands once they have them.

§ 2. DRESS AND ART

What about this problem? Is it natural for women to adorn themselves when nature seems to be in opposition to it?

---

[1] Eric Gill, *Art, Nonsense, and Other Essays,* p. 17.

Thomas Aquinas, of course, would answer in the affirmative. It is not only natural for woman to adorn herself, but right and proper. Among human beings it is her prerogative, not man's, to beautify herself. How can this be explained according to the principles of St. Thomas?

The first question to answer is that of the proper nature and function of clothing. It is a way in which man perfects himself through the use of his intellect. Only man, never the brute, has the *power* to clothe or adorn himself. Man is born the weakest of the animals with no determined weapons or physical powers, no claws, horns, or fangs with which to defend himself, yet through his intellect he is the strongest of all the animals. What deer can run like a train or a Cadillac, what eagle can fly like a jet plane? A puny man with a high-powered rifle is more than a match for an elephant. Man's body is not the weakest in the animal kingdom, it is the body best suited and adapted to serve the demands of an intellectual soul. A mere glance at an infant's thumb is sufficient to show that he is an intellectual being.

So it is with clothing. Man has neither furs nor feathers, because through *that type of intellectual knowledge* called *art,* he can supply the warmest type of protection; because man has an artistic intellect he is born naked. If he did have a protective covering it would be an actual disadvantage. He would not have the climatic mobility and freedom he now has. The skin of a polar bear would be a definite handicap at the equator.

The ability to dress comes from the artistic intellect and animals cannot clothe themselves precisely because they do not have this spiritual intellect. Therefore clothing, the product of an intellect, expresses the rich and variegated personality of an intellectual being with its many facets and moods. One type of dress would be inadequate, for clothing tells us many things. Human society, which is the product of man's mind, has different offices, and clothes express these different ideas. The policeman's uniform stands for law and order. The sailor's uniform has all kinds of intelligible connotations — nobility, courage, a dedicated patriotism — ask any woman. The different kinds of dress of man and woman express something. The religious habit expresses the personality of its wearer in an idea, namely, dedication to God. Therefore adornment is natural to human beings because they are intellectual beings, they have an intellect and will.

Animals, not having an intellect, perceive things only as good and bad, which is the reason for the plumage of animals, to compensate for the psychological differences between the sexes by its power and attraction. But man has an intellect. He not only wants things as good, he sees them as beautiful. You cannot wear every coat, live in every mansion, drive every Cadillac, marry every man or woman. You are limited by your finite material nature. But there is a way in which you can possess these things. They are yours; you can delight in them as beautiful. When you look at a picture in a museum, you do not necessarily want to take it home with you. You are satisfied in looking at it — in contemplation lies the delight of beauty. You cannot put a sunset in your pocket, but you do not want to! That is the secret of leading a balanced existence and soothing the terrible itches of appetite. You never really satisfy appetites by giving them all they want. Treat things which you cannot possess as beautiful. That is what art should bring into our lives, this beauty which can have such a soothing effect on the personality and nurse the wounds that appetite digs in the soul.

§ 3. LOVE AND THE GOOD

I find myself in the unenviable position of talking about something which is not meant to be talked about. Love is something terribly intimate and private. It is meant to be experienced and not talked about. There has always been something despicable and shallow about those who kiss and tell.

Ever since the garden of Eden when God decided it was not good for man to live alone, man has spoken words of love, listened to words of love, and most futile performance of them all, spoken about love. All the different kinds of love have come in for their share.

First we have the type of love which Ovid speaks about so knowingly and from such a fullness of experience in his *De Arte Amatoria* — very practical advice which Renaissance men read, copied, and imitated. We are not going to talk about this kind of love.

Second, we have the so-called platonic love which resulted in the courtly love of the troubadours, a love which flowered only in the striving and considered fruition a contradiction. The troubadour who could die with milady's glove clapsed to his breast, or his lips to the impress of her slipper on the grass, had reached the heights of ecstatic consummation of which such love was capable. We are not going to talk about this kind of love. The troubadours have already talked it to death.

A much more practical and down-to-earth type of love was the complete doctrine of Christian love, sung by such impassioned lovers as St. Augustine, St. Bernard, Hugh and Richard of St. Victor, the great mystics of the twelfth century. They speak of man's search for God in terms of Ulysses' quest for his homeland and in terms of Isaac's love for Rachel, his beloved, for whom he labored so long.

We are not going to speak of any particular kind of love but of love in its basic nature, what it is in itself. For the roots of love spread throughout the entire universe of being, and love is as fundamental a constituent of this reality as being itself. This may not be nearly so interesting, but it is basic, and from this examination we should learn something of the different kinds of love in their own proper movements.

There are two ways in which an intelligent being may be related to other beings in the universe. One way, of course, is by knowledge. Here, as we have seen, we take the essence of the thing within us and make it a part of ourselves, thereby growing and perfecting ourselves. The other way is by love, where being as good is pursued by desire, attracting and drawing the lover to itself. A thing is good insofar as it attracts. The good is, as it were, a metaphysical center of gravity drawing things to itself. That is why St. Augustine could speak of love as a kind of weight. *"Amor meus, pondus meum."* In love you go out of yourself and become absorbed in the beloved.

When we call a thing good, we are pointing to a certain aspect of being which is not expressed in the concept of being but is found wherever anything is. Every being insofar as it is *being* is in *act* and is therefore to some extent perfect *(per factum,* thoroughly or completely made), since every act is a perfection. But insofar as it is *perfect,* a thing is desirable and therefore good. Hence every being, insofar as it is being, is good. But the concept good adds something over and above being. What is this which formally constitutes the good? The good is being in relation to appetite. The formal constituent of the good, therefore, is not the perfection of being in itself, but being as *perfective of another* insofar as it attracts and draws the other as an end. By the fact that a thing is, it has some perfection. We can say that a wine is good because it is perfect wine; it is all that a wine should be or we can say that wine is good, meaning simply that it is not vinegar. A woman can love a man because he is a perfect man, all that a man should be, or she can love a man because he meets the minimum requirements of being a man. When you call something good, you mean that it is not only perfect, but also capable of perfecting you. Love, then, is the fulfilling of our own potentialities, our own proper development in whatever order our loves happens to be. When we love we perfect ourselves.

Thus there is something essentially egoistic about love. You can call it selfish if you understand by it that one uses other things for his own perfection. But because man is an immaterial being for whom space and time do not exist, the natural ecstatic nature of love — whereby it goes out of itself and is lost in the thing loved, can be exalted to a *spiritual identity;* a man can be more profoundly and intimately united to the object of love.

Thus love is a process by which we go out of ourselves in ecstasy, love ourselves in the beloved, and in this self-renunciation, this oblation of self, we actually achieve our own perfection. Such is the refining power of love — we actually become better persons for having loved.

In conclusion, then, we should remember love as an intuitive drive for our own realization, our own perfection. When we love someone we are happy when he is happy; and we are sad when he is sad.

§ 4. KNOWLEDGE OF CONNATURALITY

Practical knowledge alone, were it a bare knowledge of making or doing, would not be adequate to supply this special kind of knowledge of the world, if it were not in some way reinforced and deepened by *love.* The reciprocal relations between knowledge and love are well known. There is a sense in which it is true to say that you do not really love a person unless you know what size shoe he wears. Obviously the trivial item of information, the simple fact in itself, is unimportant. But there is a profound truth to be explicated. To the lover, everything about the beloved is fascinating, of unquenchable interest. The lover will want to know everything about the beloved, and all of it, no matter how trivial, becomes of prime importance under the impulse of life.

It is certainly true that love begets knowledge, is eager to know everything, is inexhaustible in its capacity to absorb the most trivial detail; but the relation is in fact reciprocal: there is a way in which knowledge begets love. We usually like the courses in college in which we do best, which we know best. Likewise the courses or subjects we know best are usually the ones we like. Motivation and interest are often definitive in studies.

These reciprocal relations of love and knowledge are evident. For example, a boy dislikes swimming. His father insists that he take swimming lessons. By the end of the summer he is in the pool all day. Another example is the girl who dislikes tennis. Her father signs her up for lessons. Again, by the end of the summer she spends so much time on the court that she misses meals. Our everyday experience is witness to the fact of the effect of knowledge on love and the reciprocal relations of knowledge and love.

A basic example of the effect of love on knowledge is that of the young mother who holds her own baby in her arms. She knows a lot more about babies than when she studied genetics and embryology in college. She does not have one whit more of scientific knowledge, but she does have *a concrete knowledge of an individual thing under the incentive of her love for her baby.*

What is the philosophical foundation for such a phenomenon? We can explain this concrete knowledge of individual things by the addition of love to practical knowledge resulting in what Thomas Aquinas called the *knowledge of connaturality* and Gabriel Marcel calls *intersubjectivity.*

PRACTICAL KNOWLEDGE + LOVE ———→ KNOWLEDGE OF CONNATURALITY

As we have seen in our earlier discussions of the ontology of knowledge, when we know, we take things within us, make them part of ourselves, and we grow and expand in the process and become more perfect. Now the movement of love is just the opposite. In love we go out of ourselves and become identified with the beloved.

KNOWER ←——————— KNOWN
LOVER ———————→ BELOVED

This is so much so that whatever happens to the beloved, if it is good, makes the lover happier than if it happened to him. Whatever happens to the beloved, if it is sad, makes him sadder than if it happened to him. A father would rather undergo an operation himself, than see his child undergo it. This is evident to anyone who has witnessed the joy of parents at the graduation of their son or daughter. In love, the lover goes out of himself in love and becomes identified with the beloved in an immaterial union, similar to the immaterial union of knowledge, so that whatever happens to the beloved happens in a way to the lover. This kind of union cannot happen between bodies. Their dimensions get in the way. Only immaterial beings are capable of such an immaterial or spiritual union so that whatever happens to the one happens in a way to the other: a man will give his life for his mother or his wife. A number of years ago a poor woman in Louisiana, as the newspapers reported, contracted leprosy and refused to have her two little daughters visit her when she entered the leprosarium. As much as she missed them she wanted to spare them the sight of her affliction. And in the decision she was happier because she felt it was for their happiness.

Another name for knowledge of connaturality is *knowledge by way of inclination*. When you love something you go out of yourself and become identified with it. St. Thomas takes this into consideration when he says we should know things that are below us and love things that are above us. For when we know something we bring it up to our level, but when we love something we go out to it, *become* it in a way, and so rise or sink to its level.

As a synthesis, then, we can say that in knowledge of connaturality we have a knowledge of the concrete which escapes conceptualization, which comes from experience, which satisfies the whole man, which supplements practical knowledge, which penetrates the profound suppositional privacy of things by allowing us to become them in a way, and which is perhaps the most human type of knowledge.

It is this phenomenon which St. Bernard in his *De Consideratione* calls love of benevolence or *love of friendship (amor amicitiae, or amor benevolentiae)*, distinguishing it from *love of concupiscence (amor concupiscentiae)*. In love of concupiscence, you love something for what it does for you. You love it because it makes you happy. In love of friendship — which can only take place between human persons — you love someone because you make him happy: a woman can love a man because she makes *him* happy. One way for a man to grapple a woman to him with bands of steel is to let her know how much he needs her. Few women are proof against such a compliment. The power of the appeal of the helpless child is in his very *need* of love.

We are indebted to Martin Heidegger and Gabriel Marcel for pointing up in our time for serious philosophers that poetic knowledge and artistic knowledge, forms of the knowledge of connaturality, are not merely sensuous and emotional but are a veritable mode of knowledge, neglected to some extent in the history of western metaphysics and philosophy — the authentic knowledge of connaturality, the knowledge of the poet, the mystic, the literateur, the policeman, and the artist.

§ 5. ADORNMENT, A FEMININE PREROGATIVE

We see the perfection that follows upon love even in knowledge, the knowledge of connaturality, whereby you know individuals better and more profoundly because you love them.

In recent years books, magazine articles, and newspaper columns have given a great deal of space to the discussion of the feminine personality. There have been intriguing reviews of the mysteries of woman's nature, her thought processes and her love life. Apparently, women are interested in these discussions and of course men are always interested in women. The most remarkable thing about this rash of literary effort is its condescending attitude toward women. At times it becomes actually insulting. I suspect that women do resent being told that they do not reason; that their actions are based on emotion rather than thought; that their customary mental operation is "intuition," a sort of knowledge bound up with sensation. In other words, that she is more sensuous and animal-like than men are. It is her husband who is rational, who thinks clearly, who possesses the scientific capacity for abstract thought. The custom has been to bestow an affectionate pat on the empty feminine head and expect to be rewarded by a grateful female sex. I do not mean that there is nothing to this business of intuition, or that there is no difference, psychological or otherwise, between the sexes. The French have already expressed appreciation of that difference. But what I do mean is that a fair intelligent appraisal of the differences between the sexes redounds more to women's credit than the widely publicized insults which masquerade as authoritative evaluations.

One interesting fact, the significance of which can easily escape us, is that although there are girls who would like to be boys, there are few boys who would like to be girls, barring abnormalities of course. I do not mean that girls do not want to be girls — they know when they have a good thing.

An incident from a little French story read years ago (even the author is forgotten) illustrates this point aptly and has become identified with it in my mind. The tale is that of a small French town assaulted and taken by one of the straggling remnants of the great army of the Emperor on its way home. In those days a victorious army could be a Frankenstein monster. It could not simply be disbanded without staggering political, social, and economic repercussions. It broke up into sections which roamed homeward, living on the land and looked upon by the citizens it originally protected as a worse plague than the enemy. The tale begins at dawn with the mayor of the town standing before the gates of the city so recently lost. The citizens have drawn reinforcements from the neighboring communities and local gendarmerie and are to make a supreme effort in their new strength to regain their homes. On the morning of the attack the mayor stands silent and alone before the walls of the town watching his wife, basket in arm, coming down the road to him. She has been a ministering angel to the wounded. It is his musings on this occasion which so aptly express the thoughts of the whole male sex. "Here comes that which is most precious to me in life, for whom I would gladly give my own life. But I would consider it an indignity to be her."

Women are, in general, capable of a profounder love than men. We do not mean that there are not women who use men. Nor that men are not capable of the profoundest movements of an *amor amicitiae,* but speaking generally and with qualification, when a man loves a woman, he loves her because she makes him happy. Whereas when a woman loves a man, so often she loves him *because she makes him happy,* as we have seen above. Perhaps this power of loving is given to women as compensation for their lack of physical strength. That men are superior intellectually to women is doubtful in this day and age. The evidence seems to be against it. However, men are superior physically to the extent that they are stronger, and this may be the basis of their pride.

Herein lies the power of woman — the difference between the loves of man and woman. Woman has a nature that is more capable of losing itself in the beloved. The characteristics of the profoundest identification of love are precisely the characteristics usually applied to feminine love — passivity, surrender, sacrifice, the giving of self, a self-lessness which reaches the intensest moments of an *amor amicitiae* — the small change of sacrifice for the gold coin of love.

It is not merely accidental that the great mystics were women, or the nearest thing in temperament to the feminine, the Latin temperament. Every soul must in a way become feminine before God. The soul traditionally has been considered feminine and called "she." St. John of the Cross and the Canticle of Canticles speak like a bride of her beloved when describing the soul's relationship with God in mystical union.

In her relations with her fellowman, woman, through this power so peculiarly hers, has the mission of bringing love and beauty to man. She is literally God's angel (angelus or messenger). In the throbbings of woman's soul beats the divine heart in great generous pulsations. Woman is for man the very symbol of love, the symbol of divine charity.

And this is the proper role of clothing as a product of that human knowledge called art, to bring beauty into our lives. And that is one of the functions of woman flowing from her specific dignity as a lover capable of perfecting herself through love more easily than men. Women are in a way the vehicles of beauty to men. They bring beauty and poetry into his life.

As in any other prerogative, there is danger here, but it should be regulated by temperance, and that part of temperance called modesty.

Ornamentation through dress is a prerogative of intelligence. Clothing reveals a spiritual soul, sometimes its state. Dress then so as to express the beauty of a spiritual soul that fashions your body and leaves its impress on every part of you. Dress like an intelligent being. Fine feathers may not make fine birds, but fine birds deserve fine feathers.

CONCLUSION

TOO many metaphysicians in our day have philosophized in reaction to the positivistic worship of science. We need a balanced perspective and a tempered appreciation of science, not the idolatry of positivism, the neglect of theologism, nor the hostility of existentialism. After all, science, including the philosophical sciences, is still the supreme achievement of the human intellect in the natural order.

We do not ask anyone to bolt this entire intellectual structure in one swallow. It is enough if he chews awhile on this or that, but we do demand that he recognize the unity of our thought. What we have to say is not a collection of chance conclusions and random recollections centered about one topic — a problematic. These conclusions are drawn from principles synthesized into a total view of reality, judgments that include within themselves a perspective of the problems under consideration from all aspects. We do not amputate the arm in order to examine, in scientific isolation, a broken finger. We observe the movements of the finger as the culminative articulation of the whole body, as if beckoning. And it is for this reason that our analysis of knowledge is of prime importance, because we do not sacrifice one knowledge while pursuing another, because we see all the articulations of knowledge in one grand, intelligible pattern, wherein even their conflicts, when not resolved, are reconciled, the first step to resolution in practice.

Philosophy should have as its primary function the understanding of reality in some ultimate fashion. This ultimate perspective can then serve to integrate all the other knowledges. Philosophy then serves as a principle of unification for all the other knowledges and provides a unitary synthesis of a curriculum of separate and disparate disciplines. To spell this out has been one of the primary purposes of this volume.

APPENDIX: LOGIC

LOGIC is both science and art. It is the science of right thinking. It is also the art which directs the very act of reason, that is, it enables us to advance with order, ease, and correctness in the act of reason itself. There are three operations of the mind and a verbal expression corresponding to each:

1) The *concept,* whose verbal expression is the *term* or word.
2) The *judgment,* whose verbal expression is the *proposition.*
3) *Reasoning,* whose verbal expression is the *syllogism.*

These acts of the mind and particularly their verbal expressions, the *term,* the *proposition,* and the *syllogism,* constitute the subject matter of logic.

The Term

We have discussed the nature and generation of conceptual knowledge in general and the concept in particular. The concept expresses primarily a certain meaning, made explicit by the comprehension, and it stands for an indefinite multitude of singulars, its extension, which possess this meaning. The simple definition at which we arrive is *the possession of the form of the thing.* The concept as a pure meaning would not make sense without the principle of form as a real constituent of reality accounting for its structure and intelligibility.

The Properties of the Concept

The properties of the concept are *comprehension* and *extension,* also commonly named connotation and denotation. The comprehension is the sum of the intelligible notes of the concept. The extension is that property of the concept by which it is applicable to all the members of a class.

The basic *classification of things* is found in Aristotle's ten categories, substance and the nine accidents. Everything that can be said about anything can be located in one or another of these categories or predicaments.

Substance

1) Quantity
2) Quality
3) Time
4) Place
5) Position

6) Action
7) Passion
8) Relation
9) Ornamentation (habit)

Substance means that whose nature it is to exist in itself and not in another. It also serves as the substratum for accidents. *Accident* is that whose nature it is to exist in another as in a subject. It may be defined metaphysically as that which *contributes to the being* of a thing but does not make it *be what it is.*

Definition

The basic *classification of our knowledge of things* is found in the structure of definition: genus plus difference gives species. The *Porphyrian tree* is a schematic diagram of the classification of our knowledge of things.

THE PORPHYRIAN TREE

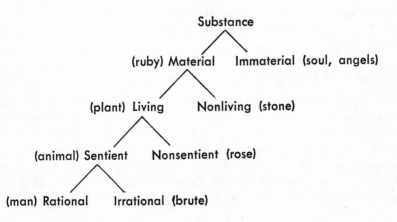

In terms of the diagram of the Porphyrian tree, the comprehension of a concept includes all the notes above it. The extension of a concept includes all the species beneath it.

Comprehension of Concepts

By means of simple apprehension, the mind knows the essence or meaning or nature of a certain object. But most objects that we consider do not have a perfectly simple meaning or nature. You cannot, for example, say in a single word what "man" is. What "man" is, his *quiddity*, or whatness, or meaning, is something complex. In logic, the parts or elements of that complex meaning are called the notes of the concept, and the sum total of these notes is called the comprehension. In short, the comprehension is the sum of the intelligible aspects, or elements, or notes of a concept.

The definition of man is *rational animal*. This definition, however, or any other definition does not make explicit all the notes in the essence "man" — because the concept "animal" is itself not simple, but is capable of being resolved into several simpler notes. "Animal" means a material substance of a certain kind, namely living; but more than this, an animal is sentient or conscious. Therefore the comprehension of the concept "animal" is: *substance — material — living — sentient*. By the same token the comprehension of the concept "man" would be: *substance — material — living — sentient — rational*.

The note *rational* is said to be the *specific difference* of "man." It is the note which distinguishes the species "man" from any other species. The other notes are said to constitute the genus of man. Therefore, the genus plus the specific difference equals the species.

The comprehension of a concept makes explicit all that the definition or species leaves implicit. When we explicate the definition *rational animal,* we derive the comprehension: rational, substance, material, living, sentient.

Extension of Concepts

Of equal importance to the comprehension of concepts is the reciprocal property of extension. Comprehension refers to the sum total of notes that constitutes the essence; extension to the sum of real things (both actual and possible) to which this essence can be applied. The comprehension of "man" is rational, substance, material, living, sentient. So the extension of the concept "man" is its reference to *all possible men,* those that are, were, and will be. So too, the extension of "animal" is *all possible animals,* of the past, present, and future, rational as well as irrational.

It is easy to see that the extension of the concept "animal" is greater than that of the concept "man," because "animal" refers to both men and irrational animals. Furthermore, even if man were the only kind of animal living, the extension of "animal" would still be greater than that of "man" because it would include all actual men and all other possible animals as well.

It is easily seen that if you increase the comprehension, you decrease the extension, and vice versa.

You add to the comprehension of a concept by specifying a more specific characteristic of the object — apple tree — but at the same time you decrease the extension of the concept by increasing its comprehension. A note is anything intelligible about a thing which you can know. In the proposition, "Man is a rational animal" rational and animal are intelligible notes or determinations. The more general your concepts are, the greater or larger picture they give you of the world, because a general concept like "plant" includes all trees, plants, shrubs, etc. Concepts are accordian-like in that one single concept may include in itself many other concepts. In a single concept can be grasped a tremendous amount of things or beings — it provides the command of a huge panorama of reality. The power and the economy of knowledge lie in the fact that in one concept you can capture in an instant all things of the same type. After all, the function of a concept is to communicate reality.

Terms

A *term* is a word or a group of words which expresses verbally a concept or a simple apprehension. Three properties of terms are: opposition, signification, and supposition.

Opposition

1. Contrary terms are opposites within the same general class (thus they also have something in common). They have an alternative between them and so they do not exhaust all reality. The opposition is merely a mental existence. For example: hot and cold (in the class of temperature).

2. Contradictories are pure opposites of each other, having absolutely nothing in common. Between themselves they exhaust all reality of a given kind. For example: animate — inanimate

finite — infinite

vertebrate — invertebrate

Signification

Signification is the ability of a term to stand for more than one unrelated concepts. A word as a word has very little existence; its prime purpose is to convey a concept. A *sign* is that which stands for something else. Words stand for the concepts of things. There are two kinds of signs: Natural signs and Arbitrary or Conventional signs. A natural sign is best described by an example — smoke signifies fire, lightning makes us wait expectantly for the peals of thunder that follow it. For an arbitrary sign, however, there is no natural connection between the word and the concept or the object except that man decides in his mind that this sign will stand for this object or this concept. It is a matter of convenience.

Division of Terms — Signification of Terms

1. Univocal terms are terms which always have exactly the same meaning. They stand for one thing only. For example: gold, sulphur, etc. Scientific terms are ideally univocal; mathematical terms are invariably univocal.

2. Equivocal terms are terms which though spelled and pronounced alike have radically different and unrelated meanings. For example: a "pen" for writing and a "pen" for the caging of animals.

3. Analogous terms are terms the meanings of which are partly the same and partly different. Although these terms are applied to different things they have related or partly similar meanings. For example: the "foot" of a mountain and a human foot.

Supposition

Supposition of terms is the mode of existence for which the term stands.

1. Material supposition — verbal. The supposition of the term is verbal. For example: "Man" is a three-lettered word.

2. Logical supposition — concept. The supposition of the term is conceptual. For example: "Man" is immaterial.

3. Real supposition — thing. The supposition of the term is a thing. For example: "Man" is a two-legged animal.

The Proposition

The *judgment* is the inner act of the mind which unites two concepts by affirmation or separates them by negation. The parts of the judgment are the subject and the predicate. The judgment unites two objective concepts, for example: *The nation is guilty.* The two concepts united are *nation* and *guilty.* The proposition, which is the verbal expression of the judgment, is divided into *subject, predicate,* and *copula.* The copula is the form or soul of the proposition because it expresses verbally the affirmation or negation which is the essence of the judgment.

Types of Categorical Propositions

There are two types of propositions: *categorical* and *hypothetical.* (We shall see later, p. 232, how hypothetical or compound propositions are analyzed in contemporary notation.) We shall be concerned principally with the categorical proposition. Categorical propositions are divided according to quantity, the possible extension of their subject terms, and according to quality, that is, as they are affirmative or negative. Accordingly, we designate the four main types of propositions: universal-affirmative or *A* propositions; universal-negative or *E* propositions; particular-affirmative or *I* propositions; and particular-negative or *O* propositions.

Square of Opposition

After the arrangement of the propositions according to quantity and quality, we come to the opposition of the proposition which is clearly shown in the *square of opposition.* In this square we have contradictories which differ in quantity, and subcontraries which are two particular opposites.

SQUARE OF OPPOSITION

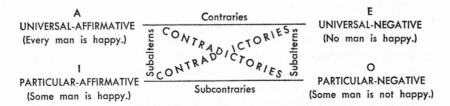

A		E
UNIVERSAL-AFFIRMATIVE	Contraries	UNIVERSAL-NEGATIVE
(Every man is happy.)		(No man is happy.)
I		O
PARTICULAR-AFFIRMATIVE		PARTICULAR-NEGATIVE
(Some man is happy.)	Subcontraries	(Some man is not happy.)

1) *A* and *O, E* and *I* are contradictories. Contradictories cannot at the same time be true nor at the same time be false. If *A* is true, *O* is false. If *E* is true, *I* is false. If *A* is false, *O* is true.

2) Contraries (*A* and *E*) cannot be true at the same time, but they can be false at the same time. If *A* is true, *E* is false. If *A* is false, *E* may be either true or false.

3) Subcontraries (*I* and *O*) can be true at the same time, but they cannot be false at the same time. If *I* is true, *O* is either true or false. If *I* is false, *O* is true.

4) Subalterns (*A* and *I*, *E* and *O*), since they are opposites, may be both true or both false. If *A* is true, *I* must be true. If *I* is false, *A* must be false.

Distribution of the Predicate Term

The distribution of the predicate term is one of the most important principles in logic. The law which states this principle is: *In affirmative propositions the predicate is always taken particularly. In negative propositions, the predicate is always taken universally.*

We come now to the properties of the propositions. Through the properties of obversion, conversion, and contraposition we find different ways of expressing the same truth.

Conversion

By conversion we interchange the predicate and the subject, keeping the quantity of the terms intact.

I *Some books are interesting* converts to
Some interesting things are books.

E propositions convert to *E*, *I* to *I*, *A* to *I*, and *O* propositions cannot be converted.

Obversion

(See below for contemporary notation.)

To obvert a proposition we state negatively what an original proposition stated affirmatively. To obvert a proposition we contradict the copula and the predicate.

I *Some books are interesting* obverts to
O *Some books are not noninteresting.*

The scheme of obversion is: *A* obverts to *E*, *E* to *A*, *I* to *O*, and *O* to *I*.

Contraposition

To contrapose a proposition partially we obvert the original and convert the obverse. To obtain full contraposition, we convert the partial contraposition.

A *All plants are green* obverts to
E *All plants are not nongreen* converts to
E *No nongreen things are plants* converts to
A *All nongreen things are nonplants.*

The Syllogism

(See below for contemporary notation.)

Reasoning, as we already know, is the third operation of the mind. It may be defined as an act of the mind in which, from the relation of two terms to a third term, we infer their relation to each other. When two propositions are so related that from them we form a third, we have a syllogism or the verbal expression of reasoning. The first two propositions are called premises, the third is the conclusion. The major premise is the one which contains the predicate of the conclusion. The minor premise is the one which contains the subject of the conclusion. The middle term is that term which is used in both premises.

DERIVATION OF THE LAWS OF THE FIGURES FROM THE MOODS OF THE SYLLOGISM

THE RULES FOR THE CATEGORICAL SYLLOGISM

1) There must be three and only three terms.

2) No term may have a greater distribution or extension in the conclusion than it had in the premises.

APPLY TO TERMS
OR FIGURES OF
THE SYLLOGISM

3) The middle term must not appear in the conclusion.

4) The middle term must be taken universally at least once.

5) Two negative premises yield no conclusion.

6) Two affirmative premises yield an affirmative conclusion.

APPLY TO
PROPOSITIONS OR
MOODS OF THE
SYLLOGISM

7) The conclusion follows the weaker premise.

   a) If one premise is particular the conclusion is particular.

   b) If one premise is negative the conclusion is negative.

8) Two particular premises yield no conclusion.

THE VALID MOODS OF THE SYLLOGISM FOR THE FIGURES

Moods are the arrangement of propositions according to the quantity and the quality (as *A, E, I,* or *O*).

There are sixteen possible combinations of premises since there are four types of categorical propositions:

⟨ Major premise: A A A A   I I I I   E E E E   O O O O
᠊ᢧ Minor premise: A E I O   A E I O   A E I O   A E I O

These, then, are the overall possibilities. It is evident that certain of these sixteen possible combinations of premises would violate one or more of the rules of the syllogism. Thus eight of the possible moods are *invalid,* as *involving either two negatives or two particular premises:*

$\dfrac{A}{A}$ Valid $\dfrac{A}{E}$ Valid

$\dfrac{E}{A}$ Valid $\dfrac{E}{E}$ Two negative premises
                                         yield no conclusion.

$\dfrac{I}{A}$ Valid $\dfrac{O}{E}$ Two negative premises
                                         yield no conclusion.

$\dfrac{O}{A}$ Valid $\dfrac{A}{I}$ Valid

$\dfrac{E}{I}$ Valid $\dfrac{E}{O}$ Two negative premises
                                         yield no conclusion.

$\dfrac{I}{I}$ Two particular premises $\dfrac{I}{O}$ Two particular premises
        yield no conclusion.   yield no conclusion.

$\dfrac{O}{I}$ Two particular premises $\dfrac{O}{O}$ Two negative premises
        yield no conclusion.   yield no conclusion.

$\dfrac{A}{O}$ Valid $\dfrac{I}{E}$ Illicit major

The mood *IE* is invalid: since when the major premise is an *I* proposition, the major term is undistributed in the premises; and since the conclusion of *IE* must be negative, the major term must be distributed in the conclusion. The mood *IE,* therefore, always involves an *illicit major.*

Therefore, the eight valid moods of the syllogism for the derivation of the laws of the figures are:

$$\dfrac{A}{A} \quad \dfrac{A}{E} \quad \dfrac{A}{I} \quad \dfrac{A}{O} \quad \dfrac{E}{A} \quad \dfrac{E}{I} \quad \dfrac{I}{A} \quad \dfrac{O}{A}$$

The Figures of the Syllogism

The figure of a categorical syllogism is determined by the position of the middle term in the major and minor premises. Here there are just four possible combinations:

1) *M* (middle term) is the subject of the major premise and the predicate of the minor premise.
2) *M* is the predicate of both major and minor premises.
3) *M* is the subject of both major and minor premises.
4) *M* is the predicate of the major premise and the subject of the minor premise.

1		2		3		4	
M	P	P	M	M	P	P	M
S	M	S	M	M	S	M	S
S	P	S	P	S	P	S	P

Terms of the syllogisms: The predicate of the conclusion is called the major term, signified by the letter *P*. The subject of the conclusion is called the minor term, designated by the letter *S*. The predicate of the conclusion is called the *major* term because a predicate is ordinarily of greater extension than its subject (which, being of lesser extension, is called the *minor*). The third term, which occurs only in the premises and is the medium of comparison between the major and minor terms, is called the *middle term,* or simply the *middle*. It is designated by the letter *M*.

The First Figure

A breakdown of the four figures using all of the eight possible moods:

$$M^{u*} \qquad P^{p}$$

A   All birds have wings.

$$S^{u} \qquad M$$

A   All sparrows are birds.

A   Therefore, all sparrows^{u} have wings.^{p}

$$M^{u} \quad P^{p}$$
$$S^{u} \quad M$$
$$S^{u} \quad P^{p}$$

This is an example of *the first figure.*

We must always check for the illicit major. That occurs when the major term in the major premise is the predicate of an affirmative proposition and is taken particularly, but in the conclusion the major term is the predicate of a negative proposition and is taken universally.

The major term in the major premise is taken particularly.

The major of the conclusion is taken particularly because it is the predicate of an affirmative proposition.

---

*Superior "u's" and "p's" indicate terms taken universally and particular, respectively.

The minor term in the major premise is taken universally because it is the subject of an affirmative proposition.

The minor term in the middle is universal.

A	M	P^p	INVALID — Illicit major
E	S	M	
E	S	P^u	

A	M^u	P^p	VALID
I	S^p	M	
I	S^p	P^p	

If one premise is negative, the conclusion is negative.

If one premise is particular, the conclusion is the same.

A	M	P^p	INVALID — Illicit minor
O	S	M	
O	S	P^u	

E	M^u	P^u	VALID
A	S^u	M	
E	S^u	P^u	

E	M^u	P^u	VALID
I	S^p	M	
O	S^p	P^u	

I	M^p	P^p	INVALID — Undistributed middle
A	S^u	M^p	
I	S^p	P^p	

O	M^p	P^u	INVALID — Undistributed middle
A	S^u	M^p	
O	S^p	P^u	

Therefore, the valid moods under the first figure are:

M	P	Major:	A A E E	(All are universal.)
S	M	Minor:	A I A I	(All are affirmative.)
S	P			

The Second Figure

A	P^u	M^p	INVALID — Undistributed middle
A	S^u	M^p	
A	S^u	P^p	

A P^u M   VALID
E S^u M^u
E $\overline{S^u\quad P^u}$

A P^u M^p INVALID — Undistributed middle
I S^p M^p
I $\overline{S^p\quad P^p}$

A P^u M   VALID
O S^p M^u
O $\overline{S^p\quad P^u}$

E P^u M^u VALID
A S^u M
E $\overline{S^u\quad P^u}$

E P^u M^u VALID
I S^p M
O $\overline{S^p\quad P^u}$

I P^p M^p INVALID — Undistributed middle
A S^u M^p
I $\overline{S^p\quad P^p}$

O P^p M   INVALID — Illicit major
A   S   M
O $\overline{S\quad P^u}$

Therefore, the valid moods under the second figure are:

P   M   Major: A A E E   (All are universal.)
S   M   Minor: E O A I   (One must be negative.)
$\overline{S\quad P}$

The Third Figure

A M^u P^p INVALID — Illicit major
A M^u S^p
A $\overline{S^u\quad P^p}$

A   All men are rational.   INVALID   (An illicit minor term.)
A   All men are animals.
A   All animals are rational.

Although the premises are *true,* the conclusion is *false.* For example, if we deduce an *I* proposition: *Some animals are rational,* then the mood is valid in the third figure.

From the *AA* and the *EA* moods, you get only particular conclusions.

A	M	P^p	INVALID – Illicit major
E	M	S	
E	S	P^u	

A	M^u	P^p	VALID
I	M^p	S^p	
I	S^p	P^p	

A	M	P^p	INVALID – Illicit major
O	M	S	
O	S	P^u	

E	M^u	P^u	VALID
A	M^u	S^p	
O	S^p	P^u	

E	M^u	P^u	VALID
I	M^p	S^p	
O	S^p	P^u	

I	M^p	P^p	VALID
A	M^u	S^p	
I	S^p	P^p	

O	M^u	P^u	VALID
A	M^u	S^p	
O	S^p	P^u	

Therefore, the valid moods under the third figure are:

M	P	Major:	A	A	E	E	I	O	Minor premise must be af-
M	S	Minor:	A	I	A	I	A	A	firmative while the conclu-
S	P		I	I	O	O	I	O	sion must be particular.

The Fourth Figure

A	P	M	VALID
A	M	S	
I	S	P	

A	P	M	VALID
E	M	S	
E	S	P	

A	P	M	INVALID — Undistributed middle
I	M	S	
I	S	P	

A	P	M	INVALID — Undistributed middle
O	M	S	
O	S	P	

E	P	M	VALID
A	M	S	
O	S	P	

E	P	M	VALID
I	M	S	
O	S	P	

I	P	M	VALID
A	M	S	
I	S	P	

O	P	M	INVALID — Illicit major
A	M	S	
O	S	P	

Therefore, the valid moods under the fourth figure are:

Major: A A E E I

Minor: A E A I A

1) If the major is affirmative, the minor is universal.
2) If the minor is affirmative, the conclusion is particular.
3) If one premise is negative, the major is universal.

P	M	Affirmative (universal)
M	S	Universal (affirmative); 1 negative
S	P	Particular

	I			II				III		
Universal	M	P	One negative	P	M				M	P
Affirmative	S	M		S	M	Affirmative	M	S
						Particular			S	P

IV

Affirmative (universal)	P	M
Universal (affirmative); negative	M	S
Particular	S	P

It becomes evident that not all of the eight valid moods are valid in every figure.

In dealing with each of the four figures, we will arrive at different sets of rules which determine the validity or invalidity of the syllogisms. Offhand, these are:

First figure: M P   1) The minor premise must be affirmative.
                 S M   2) The major must be universal.
                 S P

The minor must be affirmative, for if it is negative, the major premise must be affirmative and the conclusion negative. In the major premise, then, the major term is the predicate of an affirmative proposition and is taken particularly, but in the conclusion, the major term is the predicate of a negative proposition and is taken universally. This constitutes an illicit major.

The major must be universal. Since the minor premise is affirmative, the middle term is not distributed in the minor. Thus the middle term, which is the subject of the major premise, must be distributed there, making the major premise universal.

Of the eight possible valid moods (*AA, AE, AI, AO, EA, IA, OA, EI*), only four (*AA, EA, AI, EI*) satisfy the rules of the first figure.

Second figure: P M   1) One premise must be negative.
                S M   2) The major premise must be universal.
                 S P

One premise must be negative. Otherwise, the middle term is twice predicate of an affirmative proposition, and twice undistributed. It is in the second figure that the fallacy of the undistributed middle is most likely to occur.

The major must be universal. Since one premise is negative, the conclusion is negative. The major term is therefore distributed in the conclusion. It must also be distributed in the major premise, of which it is the subject, if we are to avoid the fallacy of the illicit major.

Of the eight possible valid moods (*AA, AE, AI, AO, EA, IA, OA, EI*), only four *(EA, AE, EI, AO)* satisfy the rules of the second figure.

Third figure: M   P   1) The minor premise must be affirmative.
                 M   S   2) The conclusion must be particular.
                ———————
                 S   P

The minor must be affirmative. As in the first figure, if the minor is negative, the major is affirmative and *P* is therefore undistributed. However, if the minor is negative, the conclusion is negative and *P* is therefore distributed. A negative minor premise would thus entail the fallacy of the illicit major.

The conclusion must be particular; since the minor premise is affirmative, *S* is therefore undistributed. It follows that the conclusion must be particular, if the fallacy of the illicit minor is to be avoided.

Since there is only one of the special rules of the third figure that affects the premises, there are six valid moods in this figure *(AA, IA, AI, EA, OA, EI)*.

Fourth figure: P   M   1) If the major premise is affirmative, the
                 M   S   minor premise must be universal.
                ———————
                 S   P   2) If the minor premise is affirmative, the
                            conclusion must be particular.
                         3) If either premise is negative, the major
                            must be universal.

If the major is affirmative, the minor must be universal. If the major is affirmative, its predicate *M* is undistributed. If the minor is then particular, its subject *M* would be taken particularly a second time.

If the minor is affirmative, the conclusion must be particular. If the minor is affirmative, its predicate *S* is undistributed. A universal conclusion would cause *S* to be distributed and thus would constitute an instance of the illicit minor.

If either premise is negative, the major must be universal. If either premise is negative, the conclusion is negative and *P* is therefore distributed. If *P* as the subject of the major premise is not also distributed, we have an illicit major.

The valid moods of the fourth, or indirect figure, are five: *AA, AE, IA, EA, EI.*

In the overall comparison, in determining the validity and the invalidity of the eight possible moods with the four figures, we arrive at this definite conclusion:

Major: A   A   A   A   I   E   O   E

Minor: A   E   I   O   A   A   A   I

We see from the above that reasoning is the most complex operation of the mind. It is by reason that we go from what we know to what we do not know, that we discover, that we demonstrate, and that we make progress in knowledge. Therefore, from the formality of the workings of the mind in its basic and various operations we become aware of the modes in which the mind deals with the world about it and interprets reality.

AN ANALYSIS OF IMMEDIATE INFERENCE IN CONTEMPORARY NOTATION[1]

In contemporary terminology a "compound proposition" is a proposition which contains, and makes an assertion about the truth or falsity of, two or more other propositions. The five kinds of compound propositions are:

1) Hypothetical $p \supset q$ If p, then q; p "implies" q. If it rains the party will not be held.

2) Alternative $p \lor q$ Either p "or" q. Either the Giants or the Angels will win the pennant.

3) Conjunctive $p \cdot q$ The Giants won the pennant and the Angels did not. (Really two categorical propositions.)

4) Disjunctive $\sim (p \cdot q) \supset (\sim p) \lor (\sim q) \supset (\sim p \cdot \sim q)$
You cannot both eat your cake and have it.

5) Exclusive $p \bigvee q$

The contemporary types of the alternative and the exclusive propositions are minor variations of the common theme of the disjunctive proposition. The contemporary disjunctive is identical with the traditional conjunctive proposition, and the contemporary conjunctive proposition is equivalent to the traditional categorical proposition.

The influence of Russell's attempt to establish a presuppositionless

---

[1] The notations used here are partial modifications of the terminology and sigilla of the *Principia Mathematica* (taken from A. J. Bahm, *Logic for Beginners*, pp. 30–35). Cf. Bertrand Russell and Alfred North Whitehead, *Principia Mathematica* (Cambridge: University Press, 1910), Vol. I, preface.

logic by reducing logical necessity to the logical function or logical connection between propositions gave a primary impetus to contemporary symbolic logic under mathematical auspices.

1) *Hypothetical* or *conditional propositions* in contemporary logical terminology — Bahm calls them hypothetical propositions while Quine calls them conditional propositions in his *Mathematical Logic.*[2] The rules for the conditional proposition are as follows:

If the antecedent is true, the consequent is true $(p \supset q)$.

If the consequent is false, then the antecedent is false $(\sim q \supset \sim p)$.

We can then use a logical notation such as $(p \supset q) \supset (\sim q \supset \sim p)$ to express in some neat, precise, and technical fashion the rules for the conditional proposition which we first explained verbally. For example: *If it rains the party will be cancelled.*

This proposition does not tell us anything about whether it is rainy or not, or whether the party is being held or not. It is not concerned about matters of fact at all. All it asserts is that *if it rains,* the party will be cancelled. It says nothing about what will happen to the party if it does not rain. It does not say that the party will be held if it does not rain. Perhaps the host was taken ill or the caterer did not arrive, or a lawsuit presented the sizable expenditure that was to go into a gala occasion. In fact, both the propositions taken individually could be false while the compound proposition is true. Its truth seems to depend on the logical connection between the propositions rather than on the truth of the propositions taken individually, or by any relation to matters of fact.

If it is rainy, *the party will be cancelled* can be true even if it does not rain and even if the party is not held. This insight into the truth value of logical connection or consistency lies at the very core of the effort known as mathematical logic.

2) *Alternative propositions* have also been called "disjunctive propositions." An example is: *Either the Giants or the Dodgers will win the pennant.*

They assert that one of the propositions will be true *or* the other will be true. Some logicians claim that it is barely possible for both propositions of an alternative compound proposition to be true. For example:

"Alternative propositions" assert that at least one of two propositions is true and possibly both. For example, the proposition, "Either it will rain soon or my crops will fail," asserts that either the proposition "It will rain soon" is true or the proposition "My crops will fail" is true; but also, *since crops may fail for other reasons, it may be*

2 Quine, *Mathematical Logic*, p. 14.

that both propositions are true. This proposition may be put in logical form as "Either (it will rain soon) or (my crops will fail)," and may be symbolized by "p ∨ q," where the symbol "∨" represents the assertion that "at least one of the two, and *possibly both,* propositions, p and q, are true.[3]

When a logician interprets the alternative proposition in this way as possibly false in respect to both propositions he does not call alternative propositions "disjunctive." Rather he reformulates the alternative proposition, using the symbol of negation, and asserts that such a proposition states that one of the "true" propositions is true and one must be false. They cannot be both false. The position of some logicians that the alternative and disjunctive propositions are both reducible to the disjunctive has some weight to it, for it delimits the scope of the proposition by the terms and structure of the proposition itself. Hence, to say, as Dr. Bahm does above, that the crops could fail for another reason — namely a blight or disease which is made more virulent by rain — is within the bounds of physical possibility but outside of the range of possibility set by the proposition itself. When the proposition asserts, *Either the Giants or the Dodgers will win the pennant,* the very structure of the proposition rules out the possibility of the Cincinnati Reds' winning the pennant, although as a matter of fact this is possible.

Either the Yankees or the Giants will win the World Series ($p ∨ q$).

Possibly neither the Yankees nor the Giants will win the World Series, but the Red Sox will win $(p ∨ q) ⊃ \sim (p . q)$ or $(p ∨ q) ⊃ (\sim p . \sim q)$ implies the disjunctive.

3) *Conjunctive propositions* assert that two propositions are both true $(p . q)$.[4]

4) *Disjunctive propositions* deny that two propositions are both true, or assert that at least one of the two is false, possibly both.[5] It cannot be *both and* $(\sim [p . q] ⊃ [\sim p] ∨ [\sim q] ⊃ [\sim p . \sim q])$.

Equivalents

When two propositions imply each other, they are said to be logical equivalents $([p ⊃ q] . [q ⊃ p] ⊃ [p ≡ q])$,[6] indicated by ≡.

Hypothetical, alternative, and disjunctive propositions are related to each other in such a way that every one has an equivalent in each of the other kinds:

3 A. J. Bahm, *op. cit.,* pp. 30–31.   5 *Ibid.*
4 *Ibid.,* p. 31.   6 *Ibid.,* pp. 33–34.

1) $(p \supset q) \equiv (\sim p \vee q) \equiv \sim (p \cdot \sim q)$
2) $(p \vee q) \equiv (\sim p \supset q) \equiv \sim (\sim p \cdot \sim q)$
3) $\sim (p \cdot q) \equiv (p \supset \sim q) \equiv (\sim p \vee \sim q)$

P. F. Strawson has supplied us with a form of contemporary notation for obversion and the other forms of immediate inference:[7]

1) Universal-affirmative or A proposition   xAy
2) Universal-negative or E proposition   xEy
3) Particular-affirmative or I proposition   xIy
4) Particular-negative or O proposition   xOy

For example, conversion of E and I propositions may be written thus:

No x is y implies no y is x.

xEy $\supset$ yEx

Some x is y implies some y is x.

xIy $\supset$ yIx

This is a convenient way of expressing conversion in contemporary notation without changing the laws. The same can be done with obversion and contraposition:

All x is y.
xAy

No x is non-y.
xEy[1] obversion

No non-y is x.
y[1]Ex conversion

All non-y is non-x.
y[1]Ax[1] obversion

Categorical Syllogism in Contemporary Notation

The theory of the syllogism with its moods and figures can also be expressed in contemporary notation as well as the traditional notation we have already delineated. For example:

A	M	P	zAy
A	S	M	xAz
A	S	P	xAy

---

[7] P. F. Strawson, *Introduction to Logical Theory*, pp. 152–163.

Hypothetical Syllogism

In like fashion the hypothetical syllogism can be transliterated into contemporary propositional notation:

1) Hypothetical syllogism

$p \supset q$	If it rains the party will not be held.
p	But it is raining.
q	Therefore the party will not be held.

$p \supset q$	If it rains the party will not be held.
$\sim q$	But the party will be held.
$\sim p$	Therefore, it is not raining.

2) Alternative syllogism

$p \vee q$	Either the Giants or the Angels will win the pennant.
$\sim p$	But the Giants did not win the pennant.
q	Therefore the Angels won the pennant.

$p \vee q$	Either the Giants or the Angels will win the pennant.
p	But the Giants did win the pennant.
$\sim q$	Therefore the Angels did not win the pennant.

3) Conjunctive syllogism

$\sim (p \cdot q)$	You cannot both eat your cake and have it.
p	But you ate your cake.
q	Therefore you do not have it.

$\sim (p \cdot q)$	You cannot both eat your cake and have it.
q	But you have your cake.
p	Therefore you did not eat it.

BIBLIOGRAPHY

Acton, John, *History of Freedom* (London, 1909).

Adler, Mortimer, *The Conditions of Philosophy* (New York: Athenaeum, 1965).

Aquinas, Thomas, *De Potentia* (Rome: Marietti, 1942).

―――― *In I Ethica;* Trans. Armand Mauer (Rome: Pirotta).

―――― *In Boethium De Trinitate,* ed. A. Maurer, *The Divisions and Methods of the Sciences* (Toronto: Pontifical Mediaeval Institute, 1953).

Austin, J. L., *Philosophical Papers* (J. O. Urmson and G. J. Warnock, eds.) (Oxford: Clarendon Press, 1961).

―――― *Sense and Sensibilia* (New York: Oxford University Press, 1964).

Ayer, A. J., *The Foundations of Empirical Knowledge* (London: Macmillan and Co., 1953).

Bambrough, J. R. "Universals and Family Resemblances" *Proceedings of the Aristotelian Society,* LXI, 1960–61.

Beckner, M., *The Biological Way of Thought* (New York: Columbia University Press, 1962).

Bestor, Arthur E., *Educational Wastelands* (Urbana: The University of Illinois Press, 1953).

Black, Max, *A Companion to Wittgenstein's Tractatus* (Ithaca, N. Y.: Cornell University Press, 1964).

Bohm, David, *Causality and Chance in Modern Physics* (New York: Harper and Row, 1961).

Carlo, William, *The Ultimate Reducibility of Essence to Existence in Existential Metaphysics* (The Hague: Martinus Nijhoff, 1966).

―――― "Freedom and Human Knowledge," *The Concept of Freedom.* (Carl Grindel, G.M., ed.) (Chicago: Regnery, 1955).

―――― "The Ontological Status of Matter: Matter as a Mode of *Esse*" *Proceedings of the American Catholic Philosophical Association,* XXXVIII Washington, 1964.

Cassiodorus, *Institutions* (Mynors Ed.).

Caws, P., *The Philosophy of Science* (Princeton, N. J.: Van Nostrand Co., 1965).

Charlesworth, M. J., *Philosophy and Linguistic Analysis* (Pittsburgh: Duquesne University, Philosophical Series, 1959).

Crocker, Bruce F., "A Biochemist Looks at Evolution," in *Evolution* (T. W. Cameron, ed.) (Toronto: University of Toronto Press, 1960).

Crombie, A. C., *Grosseteste and Experimental Science,* (Oxford: Oxford University Press, 1943).

Dampier, Sir William Cecil, *A History of Science* (New York: Harcourt, 1949).
Descartes, René, *Discourse on Method* (Adam-Tannery Trans.).
—— *Meditationes* (Adam-Tannery Trans.).
De Chardin, Pierre Teilhard, *The Phenomenon of Man*, Trans. Bernard Wall (New York: Harper and Row, 1959).
De Konnick, Charles, *De La Primauté Du Bien Commun*, (Quebec, 1943).
Dewey, John, *Reconstruction in Philosophy* (New York: Holt, 1926).
Driesch, H., *The History and Theory of Vitalism* (London: Macmillan, 1914).

Eschmann, Ignatius, O.P., "Studies on the Notion of Society in St. Thomas Aquinas" *Mediaeval Studies*, Toronto, 1946.
Etkin, W., "Science and Creation," *Judaism*, IV, 2, Spring 1965.
Ewing, J. Franklin, "Precis on Evolution" *Thought*, XXV, 1950.

Feyerabend, Paul K. "Problems of Empiricism" in *Beyond the Edge of Certainty: Essays in Contemporary Science and Philosophy* (ed., Robert G. Colodny) (Englewood Cliffs, N. J.: Prentice Hall, 1965).
Field, Guy, *Plato and His Contemporaries* (London: 1948).
Fitzgerald, John S., "Maritain's Critical Realism," *Jacques Maritain* (J. W. Evans, ed.) (New York: Sheed and Ward, 1963).
Foldy, L. L. "The Structure of Nucleons," *Physics Today*, Vol. 18, September, 1965.
Foley, Leo, *Cosmology* (Milwaukee: The Bruce Publishing Co., 1963).
Fothergill, P. G., *Evolution and Christians* (London: Longman, 1960).

Gilson, Étienne, *Being and Some Philosophers* (Toronto: Pontifical Institute of Mediaeval Studies, 1952).
—— *The Unity of Philosophical Experience* (New York: Scribner's, 1939).
Goudge, T., *The Thought of C. S. Pierce*, (Toronto: Toronto University Press, 1941).
Grunberg, B. C., *Science and the Public Mind* (New York, 1953).

Harris, E. E., *The Foundations of Metaphysics in Science* (H. D. Lewis ed.) (New York: Humanities Press, 1965).
Hegel, G. W. F., *The Phenomenology of Mind*, Trans. James Baillie (London: George Allen and Unwin, 1964).
Heidegger, Martin, *Being and Time*, Trans. John Macquarrie and Edward Robinson (New York: Harper and Row, 1962).
Hobbes, Thomas, *Leviathan* (Cambridge, 1904).
Hoyle, "The Steady State Universe," *The Universe* (New York, 1957).
Hume, David, *Enquiry Concerning Human Understanding* (Selby-Bigge ed., 1748).
—— *Treatise on Human Understanding* (Selby-Bigge ed., 1748).
Husserl, Edmund, *Cartesian Meditations*, Trans. Dorien Cairns (The Hague: Martinus Nijhoff, 1960).

James, William, *Essays in Pragmatism*, Alburey Castell ed. (New York: Hafner Pub. Co., 1948).

Journet, Charles, *Exigences Chrétiennes en Politique* (Paris, 1944).

―― *The Church of the Word Incarnate: An Essay in Speculative Theology*, Trans. A. H. C. Downes (New York: Sheed and Ward, 1955).

―― *The Meaning of Evil*, Trans. Michael Barry (New York: P. J. Kenedy and Sons, 1963).

Kierkegaard, Søren, *Concluding Unscientific Postscript* (Princeton, N. J.: Princeton University Press, 1941).

Kneale, William, *Probability and Induction* (Oxford: Oxford University Press, 1952).

Laski, Harold, *Grammar of Politics* (London, 1930).

Lauer, Quentin, *Phenomenology: Its Genesis and Prospect* (New York: Harper Torchbooks, 1958).

Lemaitre, Canon Georges, *The Primeval Atom* (New York, 1950).

Lewis, C. S., *The World's Last Night* (New York, 1960).

Mach, Arthur and Freeman, Ira, A., *The New World of Physics* (New York: Vintage Books, 1963).

Marcel, Gabriel, *The Mystery of Being*, (Chicago: Henry Regnery Co., 1950).

Maritain, J., *The Degrees of Knowledge* (New York: Scribners, 1959).

―― *Man and the State* (Chicago: University of Chicago Press, 1948).

Martin, W. O., *Order and Integration of Knowledge* (Ann Arbor: University of Michigan Press, 1957).

Marx, Karl, *Capital*, Vol. I (London: 1889).

―― *Economic and Philosophical Manuscripts of 1844* (Moscow, 1959).

Mascall, E. L., *Science and Theology* (Oxford, 1955).

McKeon, R., *The Basic Works of Aristotle*, (New York: Random House, 1941).

Merleau-Ponty, M., *The Structure of Behavior*, Trans. A. Fischer (Boston: Beacon Press, 1963).

Munitz, Milton, *The Mystery of Existence* (New York: Appleton-Century Crofts, 1965).

Nagel, E., *The Structure of Science* (New York: Harcourt, Brace and World, 1961).

Oppenheimer, Jane M., "Embryological Concepts in the Twentieth Century," *Survey of Biological Progress*, III, 1957.

Passmore, John, *A Hundred Years of Philosophy* (London: Duckworth, 1957).

Phelan, G. B., "The Being of Creatures," *Proceedings of the American Catholic Philosophical Association*, Vol. XXXI, 1957.

Pitcher, D., *The Philosophy of Wittgenstein* (Englewood Cliffs, N. J.: Prentice Hall, 1965).

Poincaré, *Science and Hypothesis,* Trans. G. B. Halstead (New York: The Science Press, 1905).

Postan, M., "Why Was Science Backward in the Middle Ages," in *The History of Science* (Glencoe: Free Press, 1951).

Quine, W., *Methods of Logic* (New York: Holt, Rinehart, and Winston, 1961).

Reichenbach, Hans, *The Rise of Scientific Philosophy* (Berkeley: University of California Press, 1961).

Reik, T., *Listening With the Third Ear* (New York: Grove Press, 1948).

Royce, Josiah, *The Spirit of Modern Philosophy,* (New York: Houghton Mifflin and Co., 1892).

Russell, Bertrand, and Whitehead, A. N., *Principia Mathematica* (Cambridge: at the University Press, 1910).

——— "Mathematical Logic as Based on the Theory of Types," *American Journal of Mathematics,* Vol. 30, 1908.

Ryle, Gilbert, *The Concept of Mind,* (London: Hutchinson, 1949).

Santayana, G., *Skepticism and Animal Faith* (New York: Dover, 1955).

Sartre, J. P., *Being and Nothingness,* Trans. A. Barnes (New York: Philosophical Library, 1956).

Scharrer, Ernst, "The Concept of Analogy," *Pubbl. Staz. Zool. Napoli,* 1956.

Schlick, M. "Philosophy of Organic Life," *Readings in the Philosophy of Science* (Feigl and Brodbeck eds.) (New York, 1953).

Schulbert-Soldern, R., *Mechanism and Vitalism* (P. G. Fothergill ed.) (Notre Dame, Ind.: Notre Dame University Press, 1959).

Simpson, G. G., *The Major Features of Evolution* (New York: Harcourt, 1955).

Swanson, Carl P., *The Cell* (Englewood Cliffs, N. J.: Prentice Hall, 1960).

Thompson, W. R., *Science and Common Sense* (Albany: Magi Books, 1965).

Thorndike, Lynn, *The Herbal of Rufinus* (Chicago, 1946).

Waddington, C. H., *The Scientific Attitude* (Cambridge: Cambridge University Press, 1948).

Wallace, William A., *The Scientific Methodology of Theodoric of Freiburg* (Fribourg, 1959).

Wendt, *In Search of Adam* (Cambridge, 1956).

Wetter, Gustav, *Dialectical Materialism,* Trans. Peter Heath (New York: Frederick A. Praeger Inc., 1963).

White, Morton, *The Age of Analysis* (New York: New American Library, 1958).

Whitehead, A. N., *Science and the Modern World* (New York: Mentor, 1948).

Wild, J., *The Challenge of Existentialism* (Bloomington, Ind.: Indiana University Press, 1959).

Wittgenstein, L., *Tractatus Logico-Philosophicus* (London: Routledge and Kegan Paul, 1958).

INDEX

Abstraction, 64; degrees of, 61
Accident, 217
Acton, Lord, 179
Adelard of Bath, approach to study of nature, 108 f
Adler, Mortimer, 2
Adornment, a feminine prerogative, 211 ff; a prerogative of intelligence, 214
Agent intellect, 11
Albert of Saxony, 112; on trajectory of projectiles, 111
Alfred of Sareshal, 138
Alternative propositions, 233 ff; a compound proposition, 232
Alternative syllogism, 236
Analogous terms, 220
Anaxagoras, 151
Anaximander, 151
Anaximenes, 151
Antimatter, concept of, 153 ff; and problem of reductionism, 140
Aptitude tests, 3
Aquinas, Thomas, St., 11, 89, 92, 98, 152, 188, 205, 206, 211; causes of society, 182; on change, 62; concept vs. idea, 88; evolution and his metaphysics, 126; and knowledge of connaturality, 210; man's natural desire for knowledge, 23; on political order, 183; provisional character of scientific reasoning, 102; on society, 180; on state, 181; theology as science, 94, 95
Aristotle, 11, 47, 111 n, 137, 151, 183, 189, 217; on causes 31, 180; embryology, 127; essences, 44; explanation of motion, 124; on hierarchy of knowledges, 37; on hierarchy of sciences, 112; and induction, 109, 167; introduction into West, 108; man's natural desire for knowledge, 23; man's social nature, 184; metaphysics, 75; metaphysics vs. dialectic, 71; soul as entelechy, 129; soul as form, 133; soul and living organism, 141; theory of matter and form, 61
Art, and dress, 205 ff; and freedom, 82 f; and immaterial intellect, 17; and philosophy, 202 ff; type of practical knowledge, 173
Arthus, Maurice, physiology, 158
Atomic theory, 140; and philosophic theory of indefinite divisibility of bodies, 153 ff

Augustine, 11, 97, 99, 149 n, 152, 188, 208; and Christian love, 207; evolution, 115; and neo-Platonic philosophy, 95; object of theology, 94
Averroës, 11; substitutional theory of modern science, 104
Avicenna, 11
Axial gradient theory, 133; as theory of total organization, 129 ff
Axioms, as arbitrary assumptions, 172

Bacon, Roger, classification of sciences, 55 ff; experimental method, 167; and induction, 40; unified method, 167
Baer, Karl von, embryological work of, 116, 127
Bahm, A. J., 233, 234
Beckner, W., 142
Being, additions to, 72 f; of common sense, 152; description of, 152; as first and adequate object of knowledge, 89; the origin of, 152
Bell jar experiment, 12
Bentley, natural theology, 94, 96
Bergson, 19 n
Berkeley, 11
Bernard, St., 207, 211
"Big-bang" theory, 148 f, 151
Body-soul relationship, 66 ff
Boethius, person, 183
Bohm, David, 142; and "modes of being," 142 n
Bridgman, science as art, 113
Buffon, 147
Buridan, John, 112; theory of impetus, 111

Cajetan, and concrete being of sensible quiddity, 77
Carlo, William E., 14 n, 138 n, 143, 180 n
Categorical syllogism, in contemporary notation, 235 f; rules applying to propositions or moods of syllogism, 223; rules applying to terms or figures of syllogism, 223; rules of, 223
Category, 217
Causes, kinds of, 31 ff, 180; meaning of, 31
Cell death, 134 ff
Cell theory, 128 f
Child, on axial gradient theory, 129 f

241